MACMILLAN

Caribbean Certificate Atlas

THIRD EDITION

Editorial Adviser: Neil Sealey

MACMILLAN
CARIBBEAN

CONTENTS

GENERAL

NATURAL SYSTEMS

GEOMORPHIC

CLIMATIC

BIOTIC

MAN MADE SYSTEMS

AGRICULTURE AND INDUSTRY

SETTLEMENT

MAN MADE SYSTEMS (cont.)

CARIBBEAN

First published 2001 by
MACMILLAN EDUCATION LTD
London and Oxford
Companies and representatives throughout the world

www.macmillan-caribbean.com

ISBN 0-333-92410-X
10 9 8 7 6 5 4 3 2 1
10 09 08 07 06 05 04 03 02 01

This book is printed on paper suitable for recycling and made from fully managed and sustained forest sources.

Printed in Hong Kong

A catalogue record for this book is available from the British Library.

Cartography, computer graphics and page layout by MAPgraphics Pty Ltd, Brisbane, Queensland, Australia

CENTRAL AMERICA

NORTH AMERICA

SOUTH AMERICA

EUROPE

AFRICA

ASIA

AUSTRALASIA

THE POLES

CXC CASE STUDIES

INDEX

3

How this atlas is organised

This is a user-friendly atlas that provides a detailed, comprehensive and integrated view of the world. Special features include:
- a layout and content that meets the needs of the CXC Geography syllabus
- case studies to illustrate man-made systems around the world
- large Caribbean section with detailed information on individual territories
- integration of maps with other geographical data such as fact files, cross-sections, graphs, tables, photos, satellite images, topographic maps and historical data
- a double-page spread or broadsheet approach, with interrelated data focusing on a particular region or theme
- colour bands that link the contents to regions and global statistics
- a cross-section for the Caribbean and each continent to show the nature and shape of the land surface
- each continent is introduced in a double-page spread with the political map on the left and the physical on the right, integrated with a fact file of important data and a cross-section
- maps and graphs for each continent provide a basis for global comparison
- climatic graphs for more than 70 different locations
- global statistics consolidated in one section
- a metric line scale, representative fraction and map projection indicated on each map
- a settlement key on all political maps and a relief key on all physical maps
- the symbols used throughout are explained on page 4
- the index provides a comprehensive alphabetical list of place names using both latitude and longitude and the alpha-numeric coordinates

Addendum

- In 1975 Indonesia occupied the former Portuguese colony of East Timor. On 30 August 1999, the people of East Timor voted to begin a process leading towards independence. The United Nations Transitional Administration in East Timor (UNTAET) was established to administer the territory during the transition period.

HOW TO USE THIS ATLAS

READING THE KEY

A key or legend on a map uses colours or symbols to identify features such as rivers, lakes, roads, railways, towns and cities. The different heights above sea level are shown on physical maps by variations of colours and shadings, ranging through green for lowlands, to browns for highlands. Spot heights (black triangles) show the exact height above sea level in metres.

Settlement on the Caribbean maps

Location	Name	Status
■	**Bridgetown**	Capital city
●	Montego Bay	Important town
●	West End	Other settlement

Settlement on the World maps

Location	Name	Population
■	**Havana**	Over 1 000 000
●	**Mendoza**	500 000 to 1 000 000
●	Jackson	100 000 to 500 000
●	Stavanger	50 000 to 100 000
○	Kabarole	Under 50 000
●	**Asunción**	Capital city

Linear representation

Style	Feature
——————	Latitude and longitude
– – – – –	Tropics and circles
——————	Coastline
——————	Rivers
┼┼┼┼┼	Canals
——————	Major roads
——————	Minor roads/tracks
┼─┼─┼─┼	Railways

International boundaries
- on Political maps
- on Physical maps

Internal administrative boundaries
- on Caribbean maps
- when shown with International boundaries

Point representation

Location	Feature
▲ *Pico Duarte 3175 m*	Mountain with name and height in metres
⛴	Major port
⛴	Cruiseship port
✈	Major international airport
✈	Regional airport
✈	Airport/airfield

Area representation

Coral reef

Swamp

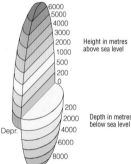

Colours for the height of the land and the depth of the sea

6000
5000
4000
3000
2000
1000
500
200
0
Height in metres above sea level

200
2000
4000
6000
8000
Depth in metres below sea level

Depr.

FINDING PLACES

We can find places in an atlas by using direction, alpha-numeric grids, and latitude and longitude.
Direction can be shown by: *compass reading* – on the map opposite, Annotto Bay is north of Kingston, and Harbour View is east-southeast of Kingston; *bearing* – the angle measured in degrees clockwise from north to a direction line. A bearing of 90° is due east and a bearing of 180° is due south. Bearings are used in air and sea navigation. The **alpha-numeric grid** shows letters of the alphabet across the top and bottom, and numbers at the sides. Kingston is in square F1 and Annotto Bay is in square F2.

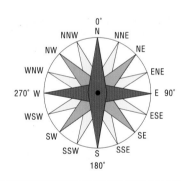

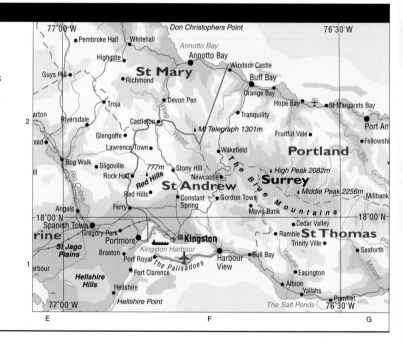

LATITUDE and LONGITUDE

A more accurate method of finding places is to use a geographical grid consisting of imaginary lines of latitude and longitude. Lines which run from east to west are *parallels of latitude* and are measured in degrees north or south of the Equator at 0 degrees (°). The North Pole has a latitude of 90°N and the South Pole is 90°S. *Meridians of longitude* run from north to south, and are measured in degrees east or west of the prime meridian (0°) which runs through Greenwich, London.

Meridians of longitude measure up to 180° east or west.
Any place in the world can be located accurately at the point where its latitude and longitude intersect. On the map above, the location of Kingston is 17°N 76°W. For more accuracy, each degree can be further divided into 60 minutes, then 60 seconds. A more accurate location for Kingston is 17° 58'N 76° 48'W.

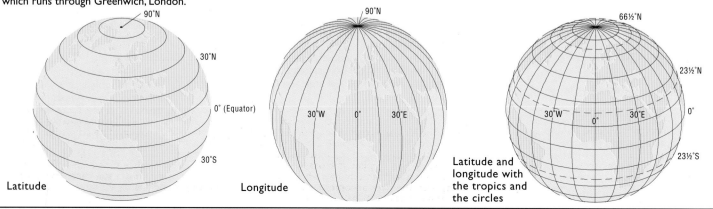

Latitude

Longitude

Latitude and longitude with the tropics and the circles

USING SCALE

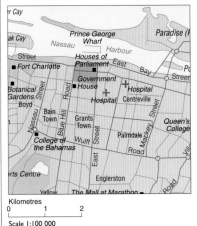

Kilometres
0   1   2
Scale 1:100 000

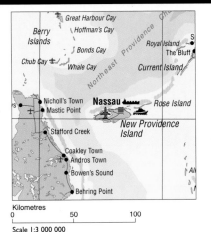

Kilometres
0   50   100
Scale 1:3 000 000

Kilometres
0   300   600
Scale 1:11 000 000

Kilometres
0   500   1000
Scale 1:40 000 000

To draw a map of any area it must be reduced, or scaled down, to fit on a map sheet or atlas page. Scale is the ratio between distance on a map and the corresponding true distance on the ground. Scale can be expressed in three ways: a *linear scale* – a horizontal line divided into sections that represent units of measurement on the ground expressed in metric (kilometres) or imperial (miles) form; a *statement* such as 1 cm to 1 km (1 centimetre on the map represents 1 kilometre on the ground); and a *representative fraction (RF)* that can be a ratio such as 1:50 000 or a fraction such as 1/50 000. Any unit can be used in an RF provided the same unit is used to link distances on the map with true distances on the ground. A scale of 1:100 000 means that 1 cm on the map is represented by 100 000 centimetres (1000 metres or 1 kilometre) on the ground. The smaller the map scale, the larger the area that can be covered; the larger the scale, the more detail that can be shown.

This is illustrated by the four maps of Nassau at different scales (opposite).

Measuring distances – To find the straight-line distance between two points, use a straight-edged piece of paper and mark the two points. Place this against the linear scale and read the distance. Distances that are not straight lines can be measured by twisting the edge of the paper to mark intermediate distances. Alternatively, a piece of string can be used.

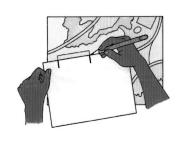
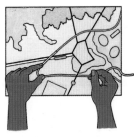

5

TIME ZONES

Scale 1:220 000 000
Modified Times Projection

+2h	Number of hours ahead or behind Greenwich Mean Time (GMT)
	Time zones that differ from Greenwich time by an even number of hours
	Time zones that differ from standard by half an hour
	Time zones that differ from Greenwich time by an odd number of hours
	Time zones that differ from standard by other than half an hour

The world is divided into 24 time zones, each 15° longitude wide, which is the longitudinal distance the sun appears to travel every hour. The Greenwich meridian 0° longitude is the starting point and the mid-meridian of each zone fixes the time for that zone. Since the earth rotates towards the east, time zones to the west of Greenwich are earlier and to the east are later. Local standard time can be determined for any area by adding one hour for each time zone going east and subtracting one hour for each time zone going west. The International Date Line (at the 180° meridian of longitude) is used to separate one day from the next. When this line is crossed going west, the date is advanced one day; when crossed going east, the date becomes a day earlier. The time of day remains the same on both sides of the line. The standard time zone system has been fixed by international agreement, however some countries establish time zones based on political boundaries or adopt the time zone of a neighbour. China, for example, covers five time zones but all of China is based on the standard time zone of the capital, Beijing.

SOLAR SYSTEM

Our solar system includes a sun, the nine major planets (Mercury, Venus, Earth, Mars, Jupiter, Saturn, Uranus, Neptune and Pluto), their satellites and an immense number of minor planets, comets and meteoroids. At an average distance of 149.6 million km, the sun is our closest star and lies at the centre of our solar system. The sun is a giant, spinning ball of very hot gas and is fuelled by nuclear fusion reactions in its central core. Heat and light is radiated from its surface and makes life possible on Earth.

THE SOLAR SYSTEM

Planet	Distance from the Sun (million km)		Period of revolution around the Sun (Earth days)	Equatorial diameter (km)	No. of satellites
	Aphelion (Max.)	Perihelion (Min.)			
Pluto	7 304.3	4 435.0	90 588.0	2 390.0	1
Neptune	4 545.7	4 444.5	59 799.9	49 528.0	8
Uranus	3 003.6	2 741.3	30 588.7	51 118.0	18
Saturn	1 514.5	1 352.6	10 746.9	120 536.0	18
Jupiter	816.6	740.5	4 330.6	142 984.0	16
Mars	249.2	206.6	687.0	6 794.0	2
Earth	152.1	147.1	365.3	12 756.2	1
Venus	108.9	107.5	224.7	12 103.6	0
Mercury	69.8	46.0	88.0	4 879.4	0
Sun				1 390 176.0	

RELATIVE SIZES OF THE PLANETS

Sun

Jupiter

Saturn

Mercury Venus Earth Mars

Uranus Neptune Pluto

Satellite: The Moon

Satellites: Phobos Deimos

Satellites:
Adrastia Europa Metis
Amalthea Ganymede Pasiphae
Ananke Himalia Sinope
Callisto Io Thebe
Carme Leda
Elara Lysithia

Satellites:
Atlas Hyperion Phoebe
Calypso Iapetus Prometheus
Dione Janus Rhea
Enceladus Mimas Telestro
Epimetheus Pan Tethys
Helene Pandora Titan

Satellites:
Ariel Miranda
Belinda Oberon
Bianca Ophelia
Caliban Portia
Cordelia Puck
Cressida Rosalind
Desdemona Sycorax
Juliet Titania
1986 U10 (awaiting certification) Umbriel

Satellites:
Despina
Galatea
Larissa
Naiad
Nereid
Proteus
Thalassa
Triton

Satellite:
Charon

MERCURY

Global mosaic from Mariner 10

VENUS

Ultraviolet image of Venus' clouds from the Pioneer Venus Orbiter

EARTH

Photograph from Apollo 17

MARS

Late spring on Mars - Hubble Space Telescope

THE SOLAR SYSTEM

Pluto
Jupiter
Neptune
Earth Sun
Mercury Venus Asteroid belt
Saturn
Mars
Uranus

There is no detailed image of Pluto available.

JUPITER

Image from Voyager 1 showing the Great Red Spot

NEPTUNE

Colour image showing its Great Dark Spot

URANUS

Colour image from Voyager 2

SATURN

Infrared image - Hubble Space Telescope

6

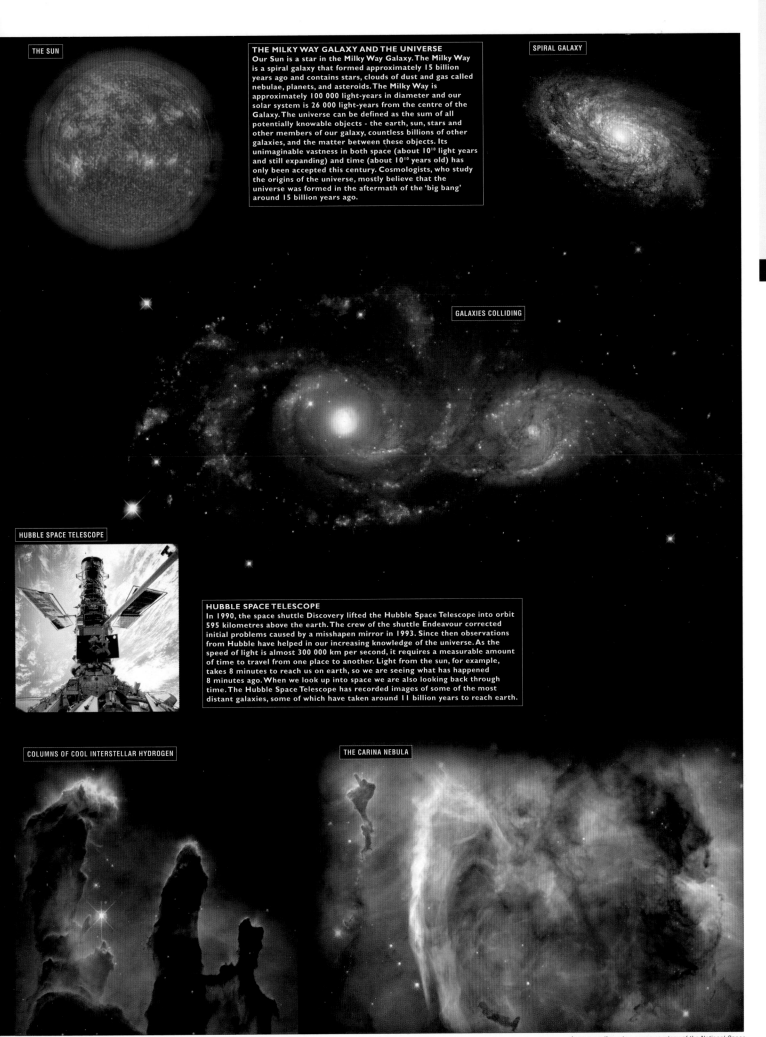

THE SUN

SPIRAL GALAXY

THE MILKY WAY GALAXY AND THE UNIVERSE
Our Sun is a star in the Milky Way Galaxy. The Milky Way is a spiral galaxy that formed approximately 15 billion years ago and contains stars, clouds of dust and gas called nebulae, planets, and asteroids. The Milky Way is approximately 100 000 light-years in diameter and our solar system is 26 000 light-years from the centre of the Galaxy. The universe can be defined as the sum of all potentially knowable objects - the earth, sun, stars and other members of our galaxy, countless billions of other galaxies, and the matter between these objects. Its unimaginable vastness in both space (about 10^{10} light years and still expanding) and time (about 10^{10} years old) has only been accepted this century. Cosmologists, who study the origins of the universe, mostly believe that the universe was formed in the aftermath of the 'big bang' around 15 billion years ago.

GALAXIES COLLIDING

HUBBLE SPACE TELESCOPE

HUBBLE SPACE TELESCOPE
In 1990, the space shuttle Discovery lifted the Hubble Space Telescope into orbit 595 kilometres above the earth. The crew of the shuttle Endeavour corrected initial problems caused by a misshapen mirror in 1993. Since then observations from Hubble have helped in our increasing knowledge of the universe. As the speed of light is almost 300 000 km per second, it requires a measurable amount of time to travel from one place to another. Light from the sun, for example, takes 8 minutes to reach us on earth, so we are seeing what has happened 8 minutes ago. When we look up into space we are also looking back through time. The Hubble Space Telescope has recorded images of some of the most distant galaxies, some of which have taken around 11 billion years to reach earth.

COLUMNS OF COOL INTERSTELLAR HYDROGEN

THE CARINA NEBULA

Images on these two pages courtesy of the National Space Science Data Center/NASA Goddard Space Flight Center

7

STRUCTURE OF THE EARTH

THE EARTH

A Section through the Earth's Crust

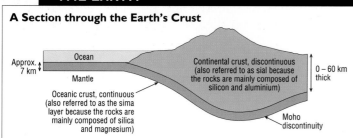

Approx. 7 km — Ocean

Mantle

Continental crust, discontinuous (also referred to as sial because the rocks are mainly composed of silicon and aluminium)

0 – 60 km thick

Oceanic crust, continuous (also referred to as the sima layer because the rocks are mainly composed of silica and magnesium)

Moho discontinuity

Most of our knowledge about the earth is indirectly obtained from the study of earthquake waves. For this reason there are a variety of possible explanations, but in general all of them consider the earth to have three main components, namely a crust, which is relatively very thin, a mantle, and a core.

The crust is known from direct observation and consists of a thin oceanic shell on which the continents rest. The continental crust is therefore limited to the continental and nearby areas.

The oceanic crust on which it rests is broken up into a number of plates as shown on the map on the opposite page, and these plates are moved by convection currents in the mantle, and in turn carry the continents with them. This is what is meant by 'plate tectonics'.

The mantle forms the largest part of the earth. Its upper part is somewhat complex, but divided quite sharply from the crust by the Mohorovičić discontinuity (Moho), a boundary zone between rocks of different density. Although it is not liquid, the mantle is subject to plastic flow, as heat rises towards the crust, and these slow currents are the driving force for the movement of the crustal plates.

At the Moho the mantle rocks can melt if pressure is reduced by fracturing, and magma is ejected into and onto the crust in the form of lava flows and volcanic eruptions.

The core is the least known zone, but earthquake waves pass through it quite differently from the Mantle, indicating that it is solid at the centre and molten on the outside.

Temperatures increase towards the centre of the earth, reaching 1200°C at the Moho, 3500°C at the Gutenberg Discontinuity, and 5500°C at the centre of the earth.

The Main Subdivisions of the Earth

	Approximate depth in kilometres	State	Estimated temperature in °C
Continental crust / Oceanic crust	50	Solid	400
Upper mantle	100		1 000
Lower mantle		Semi-solid	
	2 900		3 500
Outer core		Liquid	
	5 180		3 700
Inner core	6 400	Solid	4 000 - 5 500

A Cross-section through the Earth

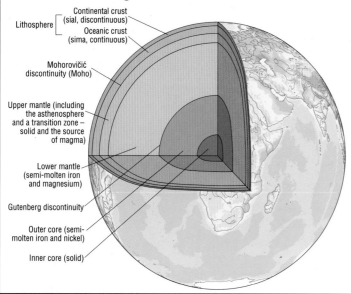

Lithosphere { Continental crust (sial, discontinuous) / Oceanic crust (sima, continuous)

Mohorovičić discontinuity (Moho)

Upper mantle (including the asthenosphere and a transition zone – solid and the source of magma)

Lower mantle (semi-molten iron and magnesium)

Gutenberg discontinuity

Outer core (semi-molten iron and nickel)

Inner core (solid)

THE ATMOSPHERE

The earth is surrounded by a thin layer of gases which form the atmosphere. The atmosphere protects the earth from temperatures which would otherwise reach such extremes between day and night that life on earth would be destroyed. The lower part of the atmosphere, known as the troposphere, extends to about 8 kilometres over the poles and to about 18 kilometres over the equator. The temperature falls by 6°C for every kilometre in height until it stabilises at the tropopause, or at the top of the troposphere.

The next section of the atmosphere is the stratosphere, which extends to about 50 kilometres. Within the stratosphere temperatures rise again from -55°C to 10°C until the ozone layer is reached, which filters out the sun's harmful ultraviolet rays.

Above the stratosphere is the mesosphere where cooling takes place again. Temperatures of about -100°C are reached at the top of the mesosphere at a height of 80 to 100 kilometres.

Beyond the mesosphere are the thermosphere and exosphere, where temperatures increase again. The exosphere eventually merges into space. The region of the atmosphere between 50 and 500 kilometres is known as the ionosphere. It contains layers of ions, or electrically charged particles, which reflect radio waves around the earth, making long distance communications possible.

A section through the Atmosphere

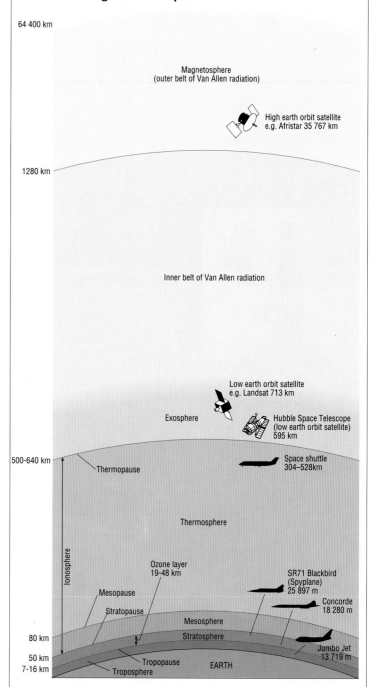

64 400 km

Magnetosphere (outer belt of Van Allen radiation)

High earth orbit satellite e.g. Afristar 35 767 km

1280 km

Inner belt of Van Allen radiation

Low earth orbit satellite e.g. Landsat 713 km

Exosphere

Hubble Space Telescope (low earth orbit satellite) 595 km

500-640 km — Thermopause

Space shuttle 304–528km

Thermosphere

Ionosphere

Ozone layer 19-48 km

SR71 Blackbird (Spyplane) 25 897 m

Concorde 18 280 m

Mesopause

Stratopause

Mesosphere

80 km — Stratosphere

50 km — Tropopause

7-16 km — Troposphere

EARTH

Jumbo Jet 13 719 m

EVOLUTION OF THE CONTINENTS

180 million years ago

The original single landmass of Pangaea split into two continental blocks; Laurasia, which drifted northwards and Gondwanaland which began to break up. India separated, and the South American/African block moved away from Antarctica-Australia.

135 million years ago

Gondwanaland and Laurasia continued to drift northwards and the Tethy's Sea between Africa and Eurasia started to close up in the east. The North Atlantic and Indian Oceans opened up further as the South Atlantic began to form. India continued to move north towards Asia.

65 million years ago

Madagascar broke from Africa while Australia remained connected to Antarctica. South America separated from Africa and, as it moved north and west, the South Atlantic Ocean opened up behind it. The Mediterranean Sea was now recognisable as the Tethy's Sea finally closed.

TECTONIC FORCES

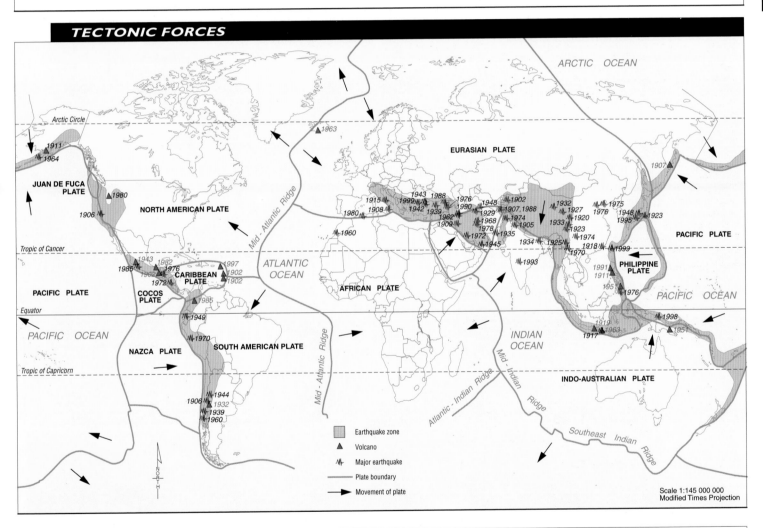

Scale 1:145 000 000
Modified Times Projection

Legend:
- Earthquake zone
- ▲ Volcano
- ⋀⋀⋀ Major earthquake
- Plate boundary
- → Movement of plate

Major earthquakes of the 20th Century

Date	Location	No of Deaths	Magnitude	Date	Location	No of Deaths	Magnitude	Date	Location	No of Deaths	Magnitude
1902	Turkestan	4 500	6.4	1939	Chillan, Chile	28 000	8.3	1976	Tangshan, China	>255 000	8.0
1905	Kangra, India	19 000	8.6	1939	Erzincan, Turkey	30 000	8.0	1976	Mindanao, Philippines	8 000	7.9
1906	Santiago, Chile	20 000	8.6	1942	Turkey	4 000	7.6	1976	northwest border region, Iran	5 000	7.3
1906	San Francisco, USA	700	8.3	1943	Turkey	4 000	7.6				
1907	Central Asia	12 000	8.1	1944	San Juan, Argentina	5 000	7.8	1978	Iran	15 000	7.8
1908	Messina, Italy	>70 000	7.5	1945	Iran	4 000	8.2	1980	El Asnam, Algeria	3 500	7.7
1909	Iran	5 500	7.3	1948	Fukui, Japan	5 390	7.3	1985	Michoacan, Mexico	>9 500	8.1
1915	Avezzano, Italy	29 980	7.5	1948	Ashgabat, Turkmenistan	110 000	7.3	1988	northeast border region, Turkey	25 000	7.0
1917	Bali, Indonesia	15 000		1949	Ambato, Ecuador	6 000	6.8				
1918	Kwantung, China	10 000	7.3	1960	Agadir, Morocco	>10 000	5.9	1990	western Iran	>40 000	7.7
1920	Gansu, China	200 000	8.6	1960	Chile	>4 000	8.5	1993	southern India	9 748	6.3
1923	China	5 000	7.3	1962	Qazvin, Iran	12 230	7.3	1995	Kobe, Japan	5 502	6.9
1923	Kwanto & Tokyo-Yokohama, Japan	143 000	8.3	1964	Alaska	131	8.6	1998	border region, Afghanistan - Tajikistan	4 000	6.9
				1968	Iran	>12 000	7.3				
1925	Yunnan, China	5 000	7.1	1970	Yunnan Province, China	10 000	7.5	1998	north coast, Papua New Guinea	2 183	7.1
1927	near Xining, China	200 000	8.3	1970	Peru	66 000	7.8				
1929	Iran	3 300	7.4	1972	southern Iran	5 054	7.1	1999	Turkey	15 657	7.4
1932	Gansu, China	70 000	7.6	1972	Managua, Nicaragua	6 000	6.5	1999	central Taiwan	2 400	7.6
1933	China	10 000	7.4	1974	China	20 000	6.8				
1934	Bihar-Nepal, India	10 700	8.4	1974	Pakistan	5 300	6.2				
1935	Formosa	3 200	7.1	1975	China	10 000	7.4				
1935	Quetta, Pakistan	>30 000	7.5	1976	Guatemala	27 000	7.6				

Major volcanic eruptions of the 20th Century

Date	Volcano	Location	No of Deaths (if known)
1902	Mt Pelée	Martinique	29 025
1902	Santa Maria	Guatemala	
1902	Soufrière	St Vincent	1 680
1907	Ksudach	Russia	
1911	Katmai	USA	
1911	Taal	Philippines	1 335
1919	Kelut	Indonesia	5 110
1932	Cerro Azul	Chile	
1943	Paricutín	Mexico	
1951	Lamington	Papua New Guinea	2 942
1951	Hibok-Hibok	Philippines	500
1956	Bezymianny	Russia	
1963	Agung	Indonesia	1 184
1963	Surtsey	Iceland	
1980	Mt St Helens	USA	61
1982	El Chichón	Mexico	2 000
1985	Nevada del Ruiz	Colombia	25 000
1991	Pinatubo	Philippines	800
1997	Soufrière Hills	Montserrat	20

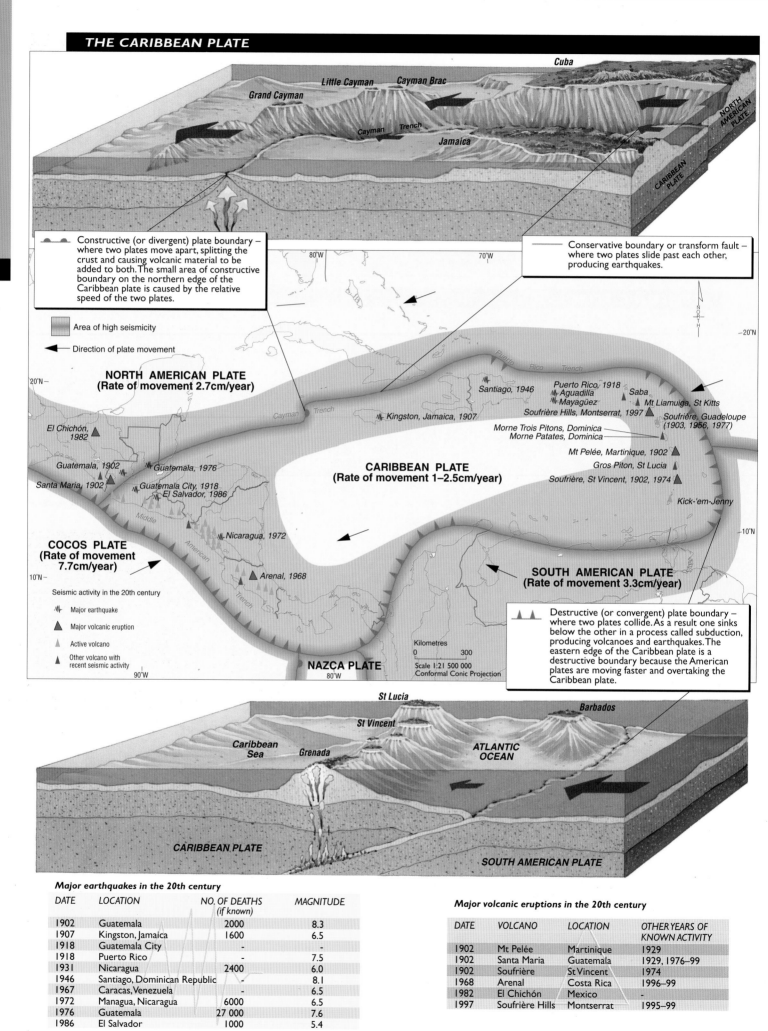

THE CARIBBEAN PLATE

Constructive (or divergent) plate boundary – where two plates move apart, splitting the crust and causing volcanic material to be added to both. The small area of constructive boundary on the northern edge of the Caribbean plate is caused by the relative speed of the two plates.

Area of high seismicity

Direction of plate movement

Conservative boundary or transform fault – where two plates slide past each other, producing earthquakes.

NORTH AMERICAN PLATE
(Rate of movement 2.7cm/year)

CARIBBEAN PLATE
(Rate of movement 1–2.5cm/year)

COCOS PLATE
(Rate of movement 7.7cm/year)

SOUTH AMERICAN PLATE
(Rate of movement 3.3cm/year)

NAZCA PLATE

Seismic activity in the 20th century

- Major earthquake
- Major volcanic eruption
- Active volcano
- Other volcano with recent seismic activity

Kilometres
0   300
Scale 1:21 500 000
Conformal Conic Projection

Destructive (or convergent) plate boundary – where two plates collide. As a result one sinks below the other in a process called subduction, producing volcanoes and earthquakes. The eastern edge of the Caribbean plate is a destructive boundary because the American plates are moving faster and overtaking the Caribbean plate.

El Chichón, 1982
Guatemala, 1902
Santa Maria, 1902
Guatemala, 1976
Guatemala City, 1918
El Salvador, 1986
Nicaragua, 1972
Arenal, 1968
Santiago, 1946
Kingston, Jamaica, 1907
Puerto Rico, 1918
Aguadilla
Mayagüez
Soufrière Hills, Montserrat, 1997
Morne Trois Pitons, Dominica
Morne Patates, Dominica
Saba
Mt Liamuiga, St Kitts
Soufrière, Guadeloupe (1903, 1956, 1977)
Mt Pelée, Martinique, 1902
Gros Piton, St Lucia
Soufrière, St Vincent, 1902, 1974
Kick-'em-Jenny

Grand Cayman, Little Cayman, Cayman Brac, Cuba, Cayman Trench, Jamaica, NORTH AMERICAN PLATE, CARIBBEAN PLATE

St Lucia, St Vincent, Barbados, Grenada, Caribbean Sea, ATLANTIC OCEAN, CARIBBEAN PLATE, SOUTH AMERICAN PLATE

Major earthquakes in the 20th century

DATE	LOCATION	NO. OF DEATHS (if known)	MAGNITUDE
1902	Guatemala	2000	8.3
1907	Kingston, Jamaica	1600	6.5
1918	Guatemala City	-	-
1918	Puerto Rico	-	7.5
1931	Nicaragua	2400	6.0
1946	Santiago, Dominican Republic	-	8.1
1967	Caracas, Venezuela	-	6.5
1972	Managua, Nicaragua	6000	6.5
1976	Guatemala	27 000	7.6
1986	El Salvador	1000	5.4

Major volcanic eruptions in the 20th century

DATE	VOLCANO	LOCATION	OTHER YEARS OF KNOWN ACTIVITY
1902	Mt Pelée	Martinique	1929
1902	Santa Maria	Guatemala	1929, 1976–99
1902	Soufrière	St Vincent	1974
1968	Arenal	Costa Rica	1996–99
1982	El Chichón	Mexico	-
1997	Soufrière Hills	Montserrat	1995–99

THE SOUFRIÈRE HILLS VOLCANIC ERUPTIONS ON MONTSERRAT, 1995-97

Areas affected by eruptions and population zones

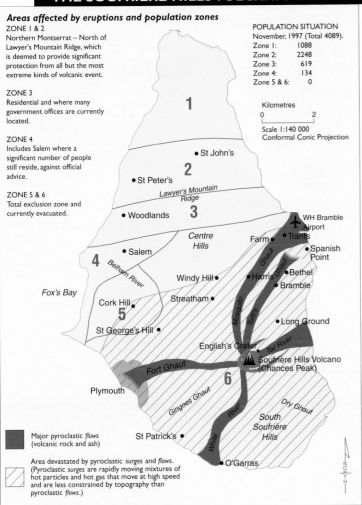

ZONE 1 & 2
Northern Montserrat – North of Lawyer's Mountain Ridge, which is deemed to provide significant protection from all but the most extreme kinds of volcanic event.

ZONE 3
Residential and where many government offices are currently located.

ZONE 4
Includes Salem where a significant number of people still reside, against official advice.

ZONE 5 & 6
Total exclusion zone and currently evacuated.

POPULATION SITUATION
November, 1997 (Total 4089).

Zone	Population
Zone 1:	1088
Zone 2:	2248
Zone 3:	619
Zone 4:	134
Zone 5 & 6:	0

Kilometres
0   2

Scale 1:140 000
Conformal Conic Projection

Major pyroclastic *flows* (volcanic rock and ash)

Area devastated by pyroclastic *surges* and *flows*. (Pyroclastic *surges* are rapidly moving mixtures of hot particles and hot gas that move at high speed and are less constrained by topography than pyroclastic *flows*.)

Chronology of eruptions at Soufrière Hills volcano

1995
18th July. Eruption begins within English's Crater, causing vigorous steam explosions.
21st August. Eruption of ash blankets Plymouth and causes darkness for fifteen minutes. First evacuation of southern Montserrat initiated.
September-December. Magma rises up and forms a lava dome.
1st-2nd December. Evacuation of southern Montserrat until 1st January, 1996.

1996
3rd April. First pyroclastic flow travels 2.4 kilometres down the Tar River valley to the east of the volcano. Third evacuation started.
12th May. Pyroclastic flow reaches the sea. Followed by large flows from July to September.
17th September. First explosive eruption occurs. Major ash plume rises to about fourteen kilometres; six hundred thousand tonnes of ash deposited in southern Montserrat; rocks and pumice fall in the south of the island (including one metre diameter blocks being deposited two kilometres away); houses destroyed at Long Ground.

1997
30th March-11th April. First flow to the south travels down the White River to within five hundred metres of the sea at O'Garras.
May-June. First pyroclastic flows in northern ghauts.
25th June. Major flows travel down Mosquito Ghaut to within fifty metres of the airport. About eight million cubic metres of the dome avalanched in twenty minutes devastating Streatham, Riley, Harris, Windy Hill, Bramble, Bethel, Spanish Point, Trants and Farm. Seven are confirmed dead with nineteen missing, presumed dead.
July. Pyroclastic flows travel west, along Fort Ghaut and reach the edge of Plymouth.
3rd-4th August. Major pyroclastic flows cause partial destruction of Plymouth.
21st September. Largest pyroclastic flow to date destroys airport terminal and reaches the sea.
22nd September-21st October. Seventy-six explosions occurred, sending ash clouds up to fourteen kilometres and depositing pumice fragments across the whole island.
6th November. A large pyroclastic flow reaches the sea at O'Garras.
26th December. Major collapse of the old volcano edifice represents the highest magnitude and most intensive volcanic activity yet.

Since then volcanic activity has continued to a lesser degree, but despite that the volcano is very dangerous and further explosions and pyroclastic flows are still possible.

Environmental impact of the Soufrière Hills eruption

Before the eruption, Chances Peak had some of the finest cloud forest in the Caribbean region and was home to the endemic Montserrat Oriole. The ongoing eruption has had a massive effect on the vegetation, wildlife and coral reefs of southern Montserrat.
- Vegetation and wildlife destroyed by pyroclastic flows and surges.
- Vegetation destroyed by acid rain – sulphuric volcanic gases combine with rain to produce sulphuric acid droplets, which cause the characteristic browning that can be seen in southern Montserrat.
- With the loss of so much vegetation, wildlife is affected as its habitat and food supply is drastically reduced.
- Total loss of vegetation near the crater has resulted in severe soil erosion, with the soil being washed into the rivers and ghauts.
- Soil and other volcanic debris in the rivers is carried out to sea forming plumes of sediment especially at the mouths of the Tar River, White River, Belham River, Gingoes Ghaut and Fort Ghaut.
- Coral reefs in the south of the island are suffering badly as a result of the volcanic activity: reefs are being buried under volcanic ash falling from the air or volcanic debris and soil sediment washed out to sea in the rivers; there is also coral bleaching, increased disease and the disintegration of large sponges. Sediment in the sea reduces the light reaching the coral causing problems with photosynthesis.

The Future of Montserrat

The recent volcanic activity has devastated Montserrat, virtually destroying the capital city, much of the airport and the port and making sixty six square kilometres of the land mass uninhabitable (equivalent to 65% of the island's surface). The destruction of the southern part of the island is substantial with damage to buildings estimated to be over EC$ 125 million. As there is a substantial risk of further volcanic activity over the next thirty years, only the area to the north of Lawyer's Mountain ridge is suitable for all forms of development. The area between Lawyer's Mountain and the Belham River valley will be acceptable to live in (although further public development will not be considered) and the area to the south of Belham River has been assessed as unsafe for occupation and development. With this in mind a Sustainable Development Programme has been drawn up to plan for the future of the island. This includes the following objectives:
- Complete the programme of rebuilding and rehabilitation of economic and social infrastructure in the north of the island.
- Provide a new port in order to support commercial and tourist development.
- Improve the existing road system and establish a new road system in areas being opened up for development in the north.
- Establish a location for a new airport.
- Create an economically viable and environmentally sustainable agriculture sector, the primary aim of which will be to supply the domestic market.
- Develop the tourism sector by promoting Montserrat as an adventure travel destination and create an education and science centre to study the volcano.

Volcanic ash blankets Plymouth after the eruption of 21st August 1995

Risk Map, September 1997

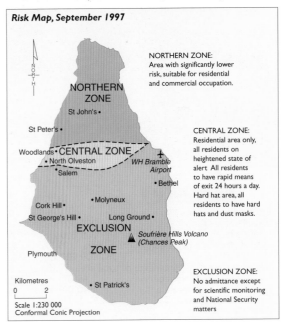

NORTHERN ZONE:
Area with significantly lower risk, suitable for residential and commercial occupation.

CENTRAL ZONE:
Residential area only, all residents on heightened state of alert All residents to have rapid means of exit 24 hours a day. Hard hat area, all residents to have hard hats and dust masks.

EXCLUSION ZONE:
No admittance except for scientific monitoring and National Security matters

Kilometres
0   2

Scale 1:230 000
Conformal Conic Projection

FACT FILE

Earth dimensions

Superficial area	510 000 000 km²
Land surface	149 000 000 km²
Land surface as a percentage of total area	29.2%
Water surface	361 000 000 km²
Water surface as a percentage of total area	70.8%
Equatorial circumference	40 077 km
Meridional circumference	40 009 km
Equatorial diameter	12 757 km
Polar diameter	12 714 km

Continents

Asia	43 608 000 km²
Africa	30 335 000 km²
North America	25 349 000 km²
South America	17 611 000 km²
Antarctica	13 340 000 km²
Europe	10 498 000 km²
Australia	7 682 000 km²

Oceans and seas

Pacific Ocean	165 384 000 km²
Atlantic Ocean	82 217 000 km²
Indian Ocean	73 481 000 km²
Arctic Ocean	14 056 000 km²
Mediterranean Sea	2 505 000 km²
South China Sea	2 318 000 km²
Bering Sea	2 269 000 km²

Highest mountains

Mt Everest, Asia
Godwin Austen (K2), Asia
Mt Kangchenjunga, Asia
Mt Makalu, Asia
Mt Dhaulagiri, Asia
Mt Nanga Parbat, Asia
Mt Annapurna, Asia
Aconcagua, South America
(highest outside Asia)

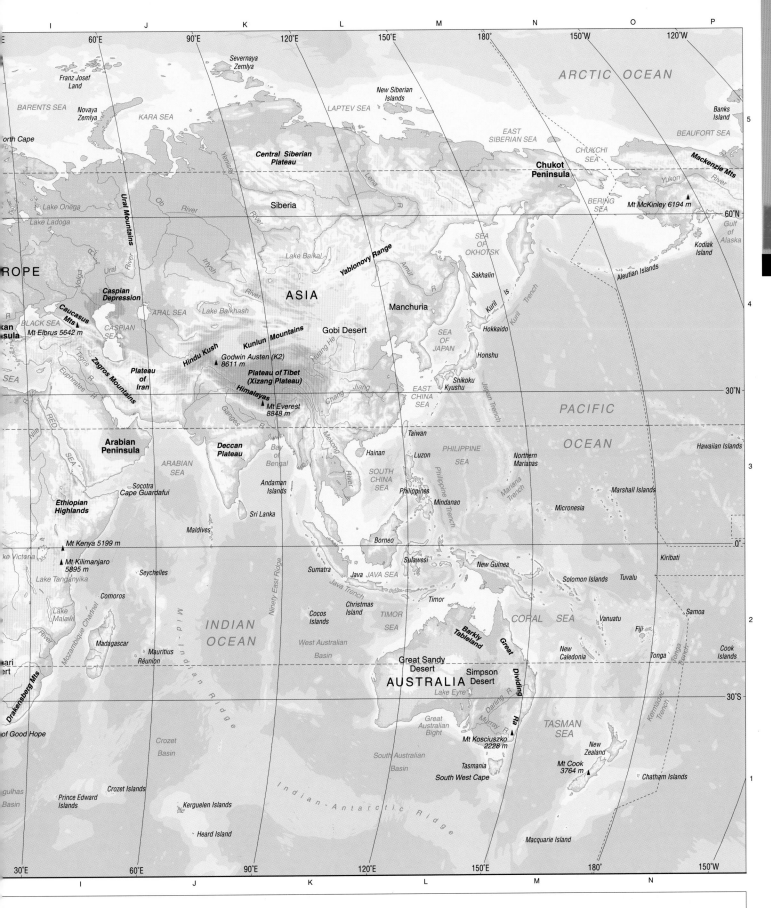

13

Deepest trenches		**Longest rivers**		**Largest inland seas and lakes**	
848 m		Nile, Africa	6695 km	Caspian Sea, Asia	372 000 km²
Mariana Trench, Pacific Ocean	11 034 m	Amazon, South America	6516 km	Lake Superior, North America	82 400 km²
611 m	Tonga Trench, Pacific Ocean	10 882 m	Chang Jiang, Asia	6380 km	Lake Victoria, Africa	67 900 km²
586 m	Japan Trench, Pacific Ocean	10 595 m	Mississippi-Missouri, North America	6019 km	Aral Sea, Asia	66 500 km²
463 m	Kuril Trench, Pacific Ocean	10 542 m	Ob-Irtysh, Asia	5570 km	Lake Huron, North America	59 600 km²
167 m	Philippine Trench, Pacific Ocean	10 497 m	Yenisey-Angara, Asia	5550 km	Lake Michigan, North America	58 020 km²
125 m	Kermadec Trench, Pacific Ocean	10 047 m	Huang He, Asia	5464 km	Lake Tanganyika, Africa	32 900 km²
091 m					
60 m					

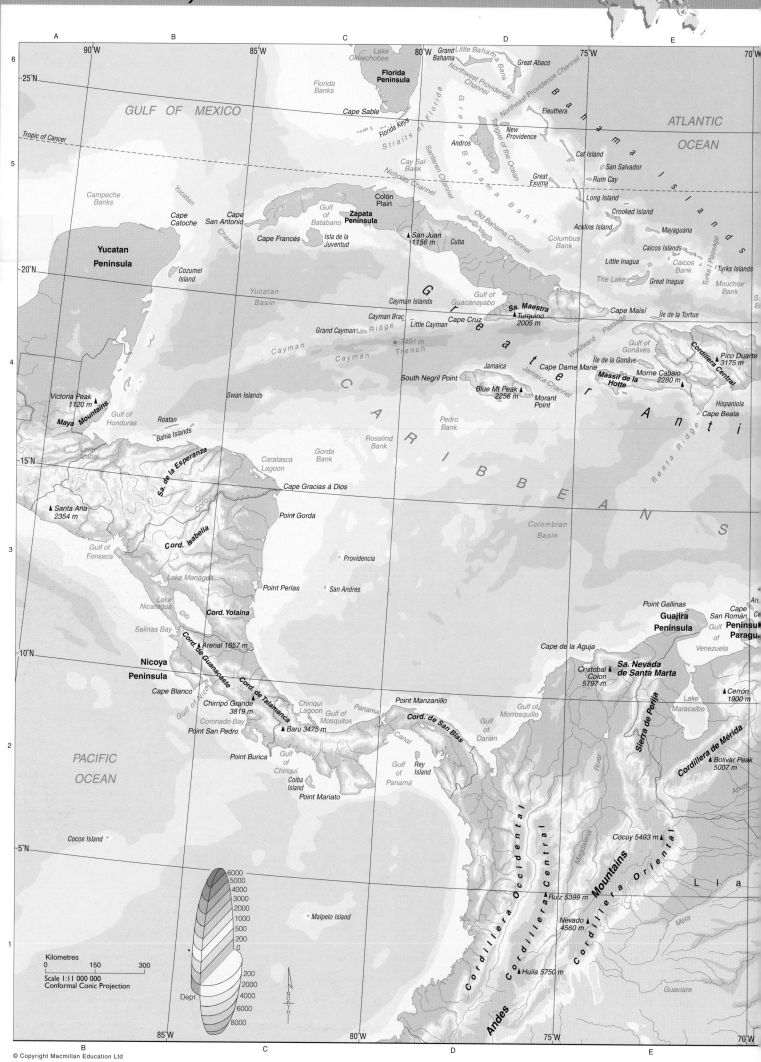

14

Labels and features

GULF OF MEXICO

Lake Okeechobee

Florida Peninsula

Grand Bahama · Little Bahama Bank

Great Abaco

Northwest Providence Channel

Cape Sable

Florida Banks

Florida Keys

Straits of Florida

Santaren Channel

Nicholas Channel

Northeast Providence Channel

Eleuthera

New Providence

Andros

ATLANTIC OCEAN

Tongue of the Ocean

Cat Island

San Salvador

Rum Cay

Great Exuma

Long Island

Crooked Island

Acklins Island

Mayaguana

Columbus Bank

Caicos Islands

Caicos Bank

Little Inagua

The Lakes

Great Inagua

Mouchoir Bank

Turks Islands

Turks I Passage

Tropic of Cancer

Campeche Banks

Yucatan Channel

Cape Catoche

Cape San Antonio

Gulf of Batabano

Colón Plain

Zapata Peninsula

Cape Francés

Isla de la Juventud

San Juan 1156 m

Cuba

Old Bahama Channel

Yucatan Peninsula

Cozumel Island

Yucatan Basin

Cayman Islands

Gulf of Guacanayabo

Sa. Maestra ▲ Turquino 2005 m

Cape Maisí

Île de la Tortue

Cayman Brac

Cape Cruz

Grand Cayman

Little Cayman

Cayman Ridge

● -7491 m Trench

Cayman Trench

Windward Passage

Île de la Gonâve

Gulf of Gonâves

Cordillera Central

Pico Duarte 3175 m

Victoria Peak 1120 m

Maya Mountains

Gulf of Honduras

Roatan

Bahia Islands

Swan Islands

Jamaica

South Negril Point

Jamaica Channel

Cape Dame Marie

Massif de la Hotte

Morne Cabaio 2280 m

Blue Mt Peak 2256 m

Morant Point

Hispaniola

Cape Beata

Lake Izabal

Sa. de la Esperanza

Caratasca Lagoon

Gorda Bank

Pedro Bank

Beata Ridge

Santa Ana 2354 m

Coco

Cape Gracias á Dios

Rosalind Bank

Colombian Basin

CARIBBEAN

Cord. Isabella

Gulf of Fonseca

Point Gorda

Providencia

Lake Managua

Point Perlas

San Andres

Point Gallinas

Cord. Yolaina

Lake Nicaragua

Guajira Peninsula

Cape San Román

Península Paragu

Salinas Bay

Cord. de Guanacaste

▲ Arenal 1657 m

Cape de la Aguja

Sa. Nevada de Santa Marta

Gulf of Venezuela

Nicoya Peninsula

Cristobal Colon 5797 m

Cape Blanco

Gulf of Nicoya

Cord. de Talamanca

Point Manzanillo

Cord. de San Blas

Cerrón 1900 m

Chirripó Grande 3819 m

Chiriquí Lagoon

Gulf of Mosquitos

Panama

Gulf of Morrosquillo

Lake Maracaibo

Sierra de Perija

Coronado Bay

Point San Pedro

Baru 3475 m

Canal

Gulf of Darién

Cordillera de Mérida

Bolivar Peak 5007 m

Point Burica

Gulf of Chiriquí

Rey Island

PACIFIC OCEAN

Coiba Island

Gulf of Panamá

Apuro

Point Mariato

Magdalena

Cocos Island

Cordillera Occidental

Cordillera Central

Andes Mountains

Cocuy 5493 m

Cordillera Oriental

Ruiz 5399 m

Malpelo Island

Nevado 4560 m

Meta

Huila 5750 m

Lia

Guaviare

Scale and legend

Kilometres
0   150   300

Scale 1:11 000 000
Conformal Conic Projection

6000
5000
4000
3000
2000
1000
500
200
0
200
2000
4000
6000
8000
Depr.

NORTH

CROSS-SECTION Through Belize, Jamaica and Hispaniola

Vertical scale 1:72 000
Horizontal scale 1:13 000 000
Vertical exaggeration 180 times

DOMINICAN REPUBLIC
Pico Duarte 3175 m

metres
2000
1000
500
200
Sea level
200

GUATEMALA
BELIZE
Swan Islands
JAMAICA
HAITI
Island of Gonâve

F   G   H

FACT FILE

Caribbean Geographical Statistics
Largest island: Cuba 110 850 km²
Smallest island state: Anguilla 96 km²
Highest peak: Pico Duarte 3175 m (Dominican Republic)
Deepest trench: Milwaukee Deep 8605 m (Puerto Rico Trench)
Area of Caribbean Sea: 2 515 900 km²

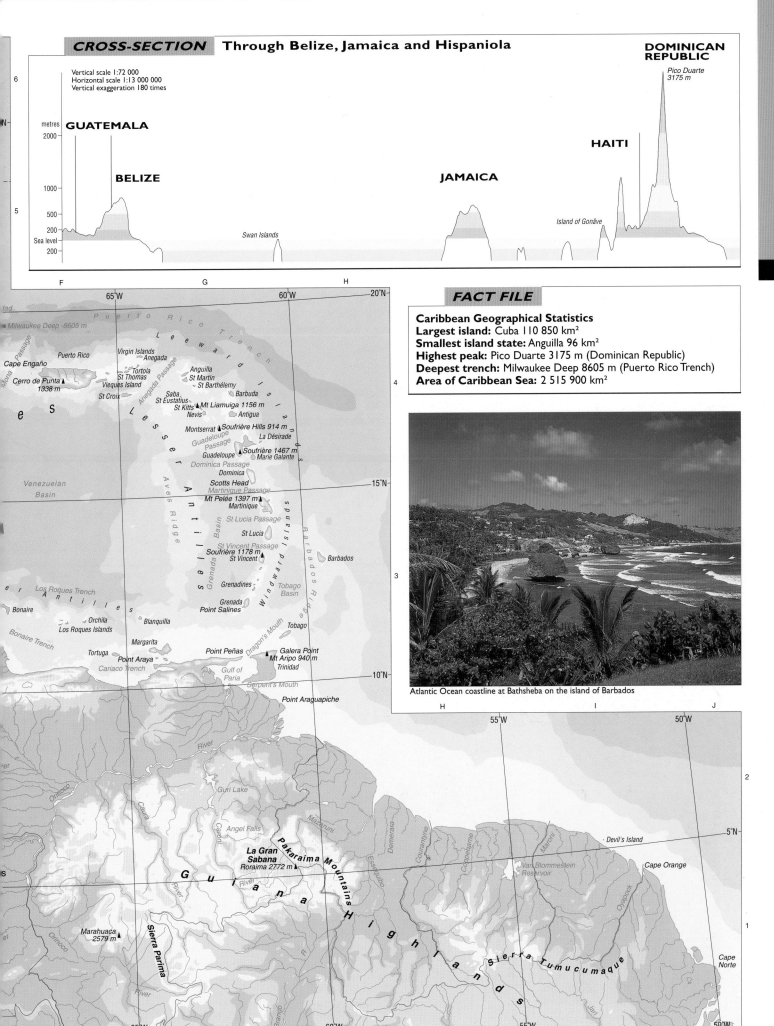

Milwaukee Deep -8605 m
Puerto Rico Trench
Puerto Rico
Cape Engaño
Cerro de Punta 1338 m
Mona Passage
St Croix
Virgin Islands
Anegada
St Thomas
Tortola
Vieques Island
Anegada Passage
Leeward Islands
Anguilla
St Martin
St Barthélemy
Saba
St Eustatius
St Kitts
Nevis
Mt Liamuiga 1156 m
Barbuda
Antigua
Montserrat ▲Soufrière Hills 914 m
Guadeloupe Passage
La Désirade
Guadeloupe ▲Soufrière 1467 m
Marie Galante
Dominica Passage
Dominica
Scotts Head
Martinique Passage
Mt Pelée 1397 m ▲
Martinique
St Lucia Passage
St Lucia
St Vincent Passage
Soufrière 1178 m ▲
St Vincent
Barbados
Grenadines
Tobago Basin
Grenada
Point Salines
Tobago
Venezuelan Basin
Aves Ridge
Grenada Basin
Windward Islands
Barbados Ridge
Los Roques Trench
Bonaire
Orchila
Los Roques Islands
Blanquilla
Margarita
Tortuga
Point Araya
Point Peñas
Galera Point
Mt Aripo 940 m
Trinidad
Dragon's Mouth
Gulf of Paria
Serpent's Mouth
Point Araguapiche
Cariaco Trench
Bonaire Trench
Lesser Antilles

Atlantic Ocean coastline at Bathsheba on the island of Barbados

Orinoco
River
Guri Lake
Caura
Caroni
Angel Falls
La Gran Sabana
Roraima 2772 m
Pakaraima Mountains
Guiana Highlands
Mazaruni
Demerara
Courantyne
Coppename
Maroni
Van Blommestein Reservoir
Devil's Island
Cape Orange
Sierra Tumucumaque
Marahuaca 2579 m
Sierra Parima
Essequibo
Brando
Cape Norte
Jari

65°W 60°W 55°W 50°W
20°N 15°N 10°N 5°N

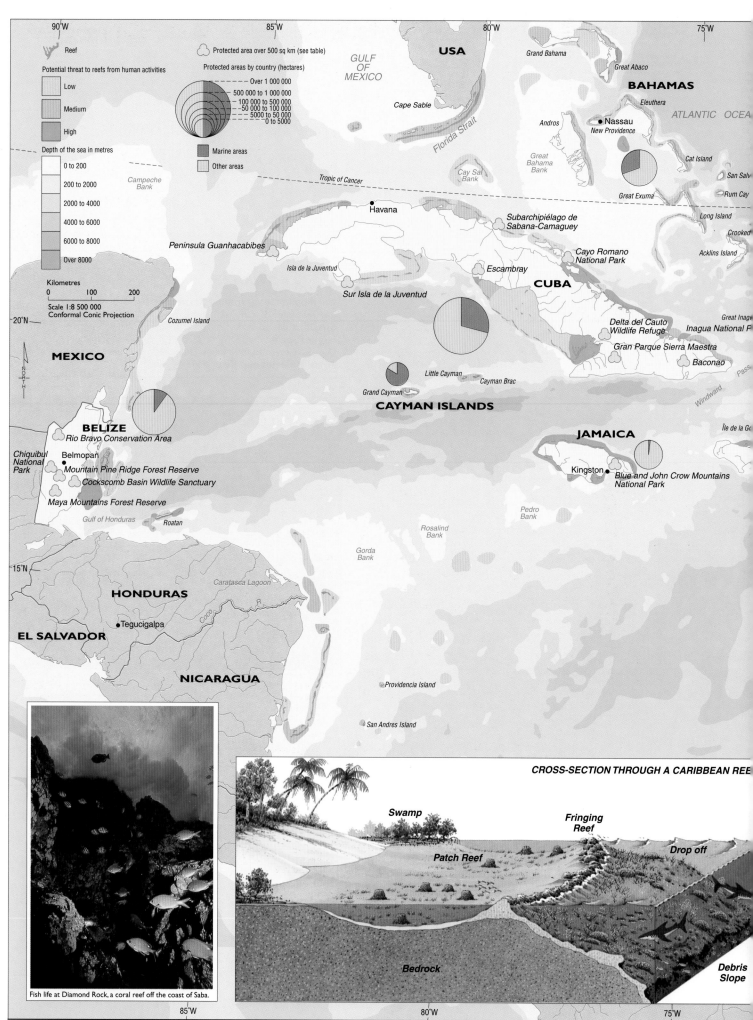

Reef

Potential threat to reefs from human activities

- Low
- Medium
- High

Depth of the sea in metres

- 0 to 200
- 200 to 2000
- 2000 to 4000
- 4000 to 6000
- 6000 to 8000
- Over 8000

Kilometres

0   100   200

Scale 1:8 500 000
Conformal Conic Projection

Protected area over 500 sq km (see table)

Protected areas by country (hectares)

- Over 1 000 000
- 500 000 to 1 000 000
- 100 000 to 500 000
- 50 000 to 100 000
- 5000 to 50 000
- 0 to 5000

Marine areas
Other areas

90°W   85°W   80°W   75°W

USA

GULF OF MEXICO

Cape Sable

Florida Strait

Grand Bahama   Great Abaco

BAHAMAS

Eleuthera

Andros   Nassau
New Providence

ATLANTIC OCEA

Cat Island   San Salv

Rum Cay

Great Exuma

Long Island

Crooked

Tropic of Cancer

Campeche Bank

Havana

Subarchipiélago de Sabana-Camaguey

Cayo Romano National Park

Acklins Island

Peninsula Guanhacabibes

Isla de la Juventud   Escambray

CUBA

Great Inag
Inagua National P

Sur Isla de la Juventud

Delta del Cauto Wildlife Refuge

Gran Parque Sierra Maestra   Baconao

20°N

Cozumel Island

Little Cayman

Cayman Brac

Windward   Pass

MEXICO

Grand Cayman

CAYMAN ISLANDS

Île de la Go

JAMAICA

Kingston   Blue and John Crow Mountains National Park

Rio Bravo Conservation Area

Chiquibul National Park   Belmopan

Mountain Pine Ridge Forest Reserve

Cockscomb Basin Wildlife Sanctuary

Maya Mountains Forest Reserve

Gulf of Honduras   Roatan

Pedro Bank

Rosalind Bank

15°N

Caratasca Lagoon

Gorda Bank

HONDURAS

Coco   Tegucigalpa

EL SALVADOR

NICARAGUA

Providencia Island

San Andres Island

Fish life at Diamond Rock, a coral reef off the coast of Saba.

CROSS-SECTION THROUGH A CARIBBEAN REE

Swamp

Fringing Reef

Patch Reef

Drop off

Bedrock

Debris Slope

85°W   80°W   75°W

BELIZE

16

FACT FILE

e first areas to be given protected status in the aribbean were forest areas, as these were viously being destroyed rapidly. In recent years e trend has been towards 'land and sea' parks d 'marine protected areas' both reflecting the eat to many marine species from over-fishing d pollution. In addition, as the economies of ost countries are now firmly dependent on urism which is essentially focussed on the sea, s essential to preserve the natural resources on hich this industry depends.

tal reef area in the Caribbean	20 000 km²
eas under threat: Low	7800 km² (39%)
Medium	6400 km² (32%)
High	5800 km² (29%)
arine protected areas	85 252 km²

PROTECTED AREAS IN THE BAHAMAS

Key:
- National park or reserve
- National park or reserve boundary
- Wild bird reserve

Kilometres
0   50   100
Scale 1:5 000 000
Conformal Conic Projection

17

Protected areas over 500 km² in size

Name	Country	Area in km²
Chiquibul National Park	Belize	1076
Cockscomb Basin Wildlife Sanctuary	Belize	1024
Blue and John Crow Mountains National Park	Jamaica	780
Inagua National Park	Bahamas	743
Rio Bravo Conservation Area	Belize	688
Parc National de la Martinique	Martinique	627
Kaieteur National Park	Guyana	586
North, Middle and East Caicos Nature Reserve	Turks and Caicos	544
Maya Mountains Forest Reserve	Belize	521
Mountain Pine Ridge Forest Reserve	Belize	513

As a result of their size, Cuba and the Dominican Republic have very large areas nominally designated as protected areas (commonly called 'Paper Parks'). In fact there is virtually no enforcement practised and therefore the individual areas have been omitted from the table.

TEMPERATURE and OCEAN CURRENTS – JANUARY

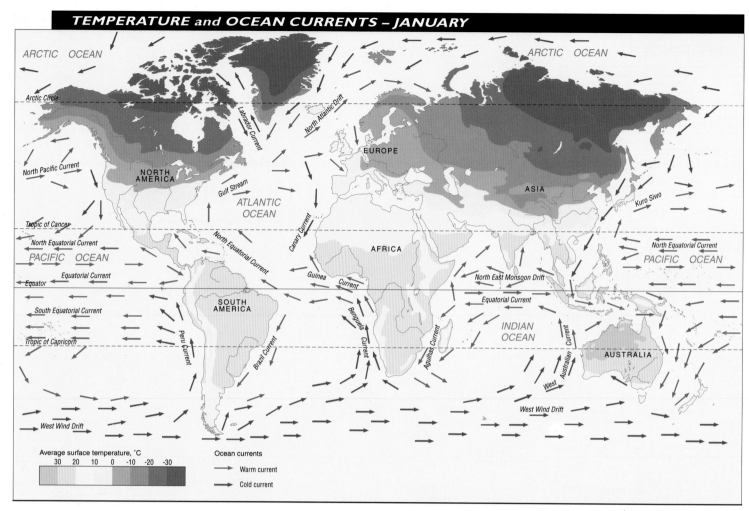

Average surface temperature, °C

30 20 10 0 -10 -20 -30

Ocean currents

→ Warm current

→ Cold current

TEMPERATURE and OCEAN CURRENTS – JULY

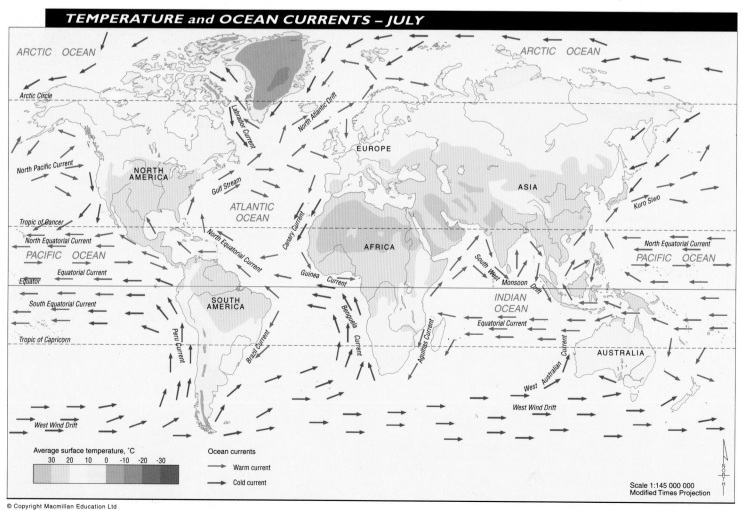

Average surface temperature, °C

30 20 10 0 -10 -20 -30

Ocean currents

→ Warm current

→ Cold current

Scale 1:145 000 000
Modified Times Projection

PRECIPITATION and WINDS

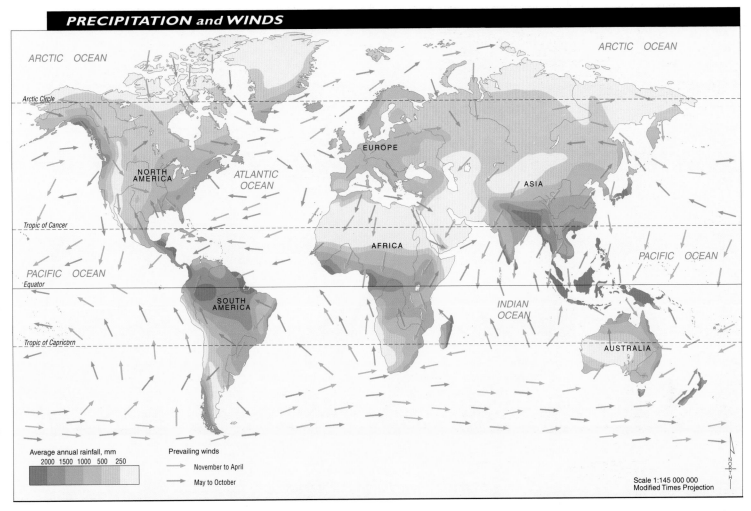

ARCTIC OCEAN

Arctic Circle

EUROPE

NORTH
AMERICA

ATLANTIC
OCEAN

ASIA

ARCTIC OCEAN

Tropic of Cancer

AFRICA

PACIFIC OCEAN

PACIFIC OCEAN

Equator

SOUTH
AMERICA

INDIAN
OCEAN

Tropic of Capricorn

AUSTRALIA

Average annual rainfall, mm

2000 1500 1000 500 250

Prevailing winds

November to April

May to October

Scale 1:145 000 000
Modified Times Projection

AIR PRESSURE

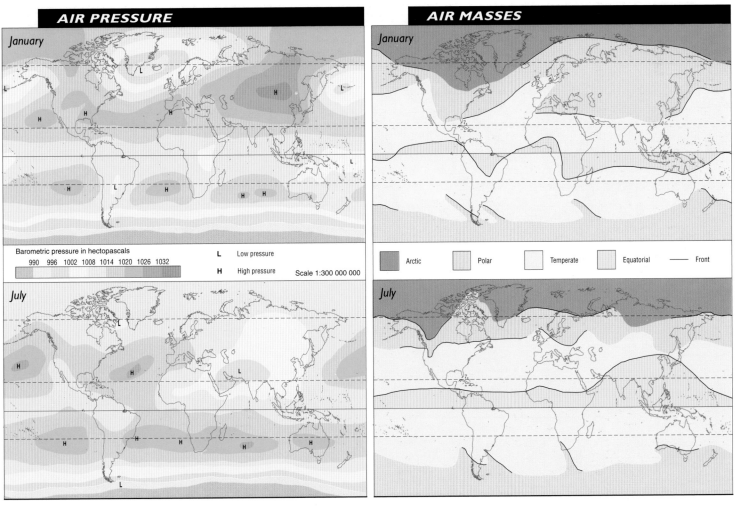

January

L

H

H

H

L

H

L

H

H

H

Barometric pressure in hectopascals

990 996 1002 1008 1014 1020 1026 1032

L   Low pressure

H   High pressure

Scale 1:300 000 000

July

L

H

H

L

H

H

H

L

AIR MASSES

January

Arctic   Polar   Temperate   Equatorial   —— Front

July

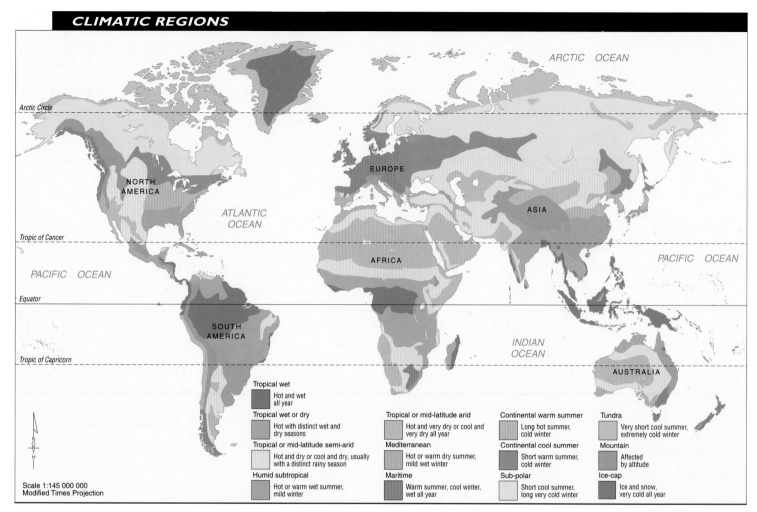

CLIMATIC REGIONS

Tropical wet
Hot and wet all year

Tropical wet or dry
Hot with distinct wet and dry seasons

Tropical or mid-latitude semi-arid
Hot and dry or cool and dry, usually with a distinct rainy season

Humid subtropical
Hot or warm wet summer, mild winter

Tropical or mid-latitude arid
Hot and very dry or cool and very dry all year

Mediterranean
Hot or warm dry summer, mild wet winter

Maritime
Warm summer, cool winter, wet all year

Continental warm summer
Long hot summer, cold winter

Continental cool summer
Short warm summer, cold winter

Sub-polar
Short cool summer, long very cold winter

Tundra
Very short cool summer, extremely cold winter

Mountain
Affected by altitude

Ice-cap
Ice and snow, very cold all year

Scale 1:145 000 000
Modified Times Projection

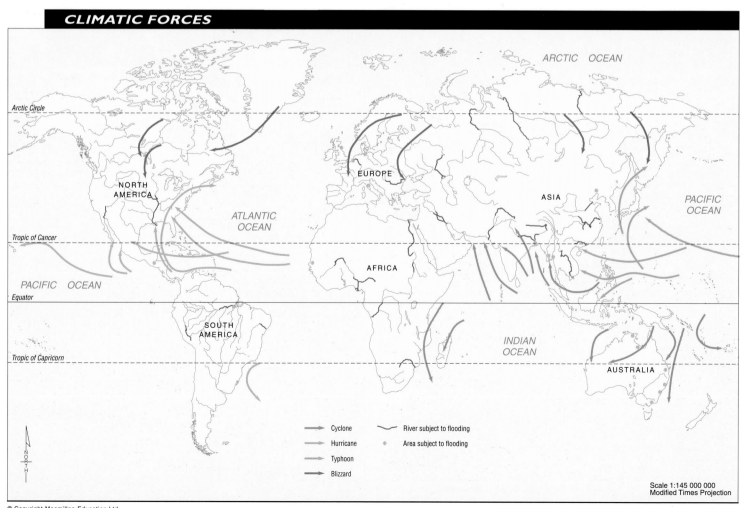

CLIMATIC FORCES

Cyclone
Hurricane
Typhoon
Blizzard
River subject to flooding
Area subject to flooding

Scale 1:145 000 000
Modified Times Projection

HURRICANE RISK AND STORM TRACKS FOR THE 1998 HURRICANE SEASON

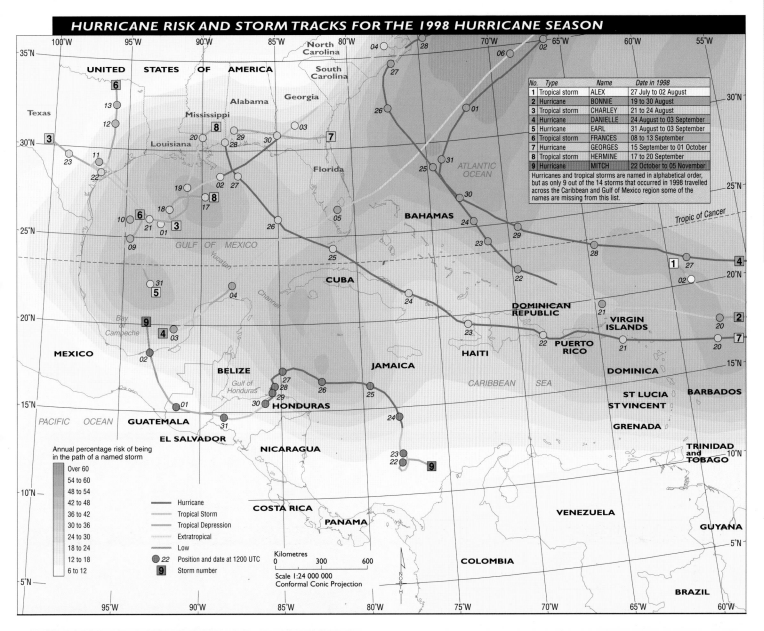

No.	Type	Name	Date in 1998
1	Tropical storm	ALEX	27 July to 02 August
2	Hurricane	BONNIE	19 to 30 August
3	Tropical storm	CHARLEY	21 to 24 August
4	Hurricane	DANIELLE	24 August to 03 September
5	Hurricane	EARL	31 August to 03 September
6	Tropical storm	FRANCES	08 to 13 September
7	Hurricane	GEORGES	15 September to 01 October
8	Tropical storm	HERMINE	17 to 20 September
9	Hurricane	MITCH	22 October to 05 November

Hurricanes and tropical storms are named in alphabetical order, but as only 9 out of the 14 storms that occurred in 1998 travelled across the Caribbean and Gulf of Mexico region some of the names are missing from this list.

Annual percentage risk of being in the path of a named storm
- Over 60
- 54 to 60
- 48 to 54
- 42 to 48
- 36 to 42
- 30 to 36
- 24 to 30
- 18 to 24
- 12 to 18
- 6 to 12

— Hurricane
— Tropical Storm
— Tropical Depression
— Extratropical
— Low
22 Position and date at 1200 UTC
9 Storm number

Kilometres 0 300 600
Scale 1:24 000 000
Conformal Conic Projection

Satellite image of Hurricane Mitch, which caused massive devastation to Central America, as it passed across the Caribbean Sea on October 26th 1998

Major Hurricanes of the Twentieth Century

Date	Name	Strength	Number of deaths	Date	Name	Strength	Number of deaths
1999	FLOYD	4	57	1979	FREDERIC	3	-
1998	GEORGES	4	602	1974	FIFI	Tropical storm	3000
1998	MITCH	5	11 000	1972	AGNES	1	120
1996	LILI	3	-	1969	CAMILLE	5	260
1996	FRAN	3	34	1966	INEZ	1	1000
1995	OPAL	4	50	1965	BETSY	3	70
1994	GORDON	1	1100	1963	FLORA	1	7000
1992	ANDREW	4	26	1955	JANET	?	600
1991	BOB	2	-	1954	HAZEL	4	500
1989	HUGO	4	50	1935	-	5	1000
1988	GILBERT	5	300	1934	-	3	2000
1985	ELENA	3	-	1932	-	4	2500
1985	JUAN	1	-	1928	-	4	3000
1983	ALICIA	3	-	1909	-	4	7000
1979	DAVID	4	2 000				

SAFFIR-SIMPSON HURRICANE SCALE

Category	Damage - Likely Effects	Pressure (millibars)	Surge (metres)	Winds (kph)
ONE	*Minimal:* No real damage to building structures. Damage primarily to unanchored mobile homes, shrubbery, and trees. Also some coastal road flooding and minor pier damage.	980	1.2 to 1.5	120 to 153
TWO	*Moderate:* Some roofing material, door, and window damage to buildings. Considerable damage to vegetation, mobile homes, and piers. Small craft in unprotected anchorages break moorings.	965 to 979	1.5 to 2.5	154 to 177
THREE	*Extensive:* Some structural damage to small residences and utility buildings with a minor amount of curtainwall failures. Mobile homes are destroyed. Flooding near the coast destroys smaller structures with larger structures damaged by floating debris. Terrain may be flooded well inland.	945 to 964	2.5 to 4.0	178 to 209
FOUR	*Extreme:* More extensive curtainwall failures with some complete roof structure failure on small residences. Major erosion on beach areas. Major damage to lower floors of structures near the shore. Terrain may be flooded well inland.	920 to 944	4.0 to 5.5	210 to 250
FIVE	*Catastrophic:* Complete roof failure on many residences and industrial buildings. Some complete building failures with small utility buildings blown over or away. Major damage to lower floors of all structures located near the shoreline. Massive evacuation of residential areas may be required.	Less than 920	Over 5.5	Over 250

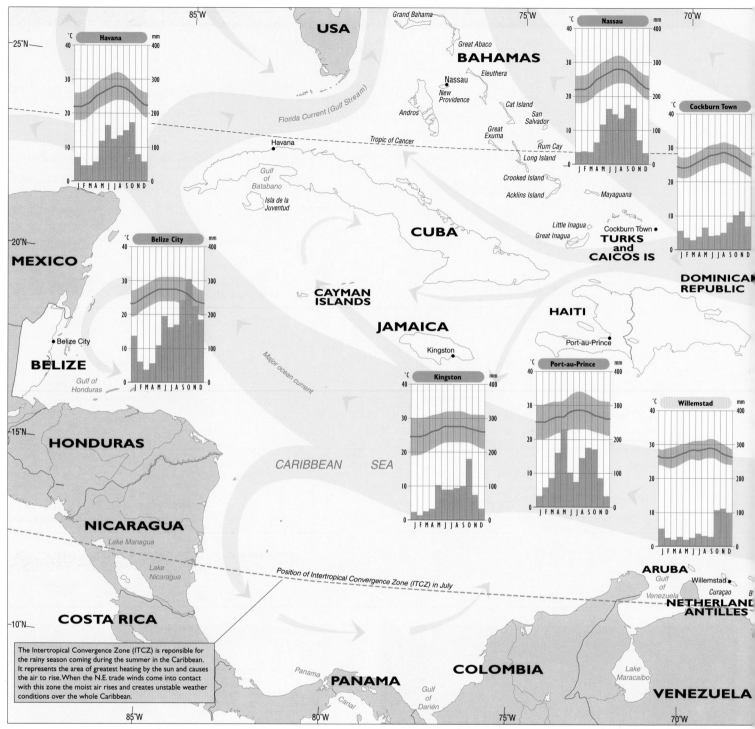

The Intertropical Convergence Zone (ITCZ) is reponsible for the rainy season coming during the summer in the Caribbean. It represents the area of greatest heating by the sun and causes the air to rise. When the N.E. trade winds come into contact with this zone the moist air rises and creates unstable weather conditions over the whole Caribbean.

FACT FILE

Climate information is collected from climatological stations throughout the region. Climate graphs are a useful way of presenting some of this information graphically to help understand the climate of a particular place and for making easy comparisons between different places. On the graph, temperature is shown as a red line and rainfall as columns. This allows you to clearly see the relationship between temperature and rainfall to analyse seasonal differences. The red line represents the mean monthly temperature. The mean monthly maximum and minium temperatures have also been plotted to show the range of the temperature possible each month (the area shaded brown). The mean monthly rainfall figures are plotted and each monthly column is then coloured. Note that the colour bands for all climate graph headings in this atlas conform to the colour of the climatic region in which each place is located.

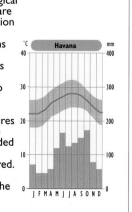

CLIMATIC REGIONS

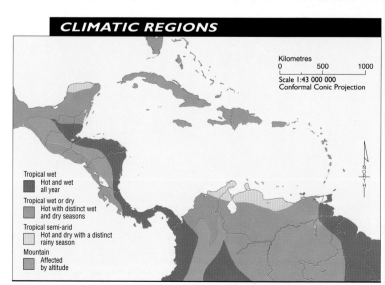

Kilometres
0   500   1000

Scale 1:43 000 000
Conformal Conic Projection

Tropical wet
Hot and wet all year

Tropical wet or dry
Hot with distinct wet and dry seasons

Tropical semi-arid
Hot and dry with a distinct rainy season

Mountain
Affected by altitude

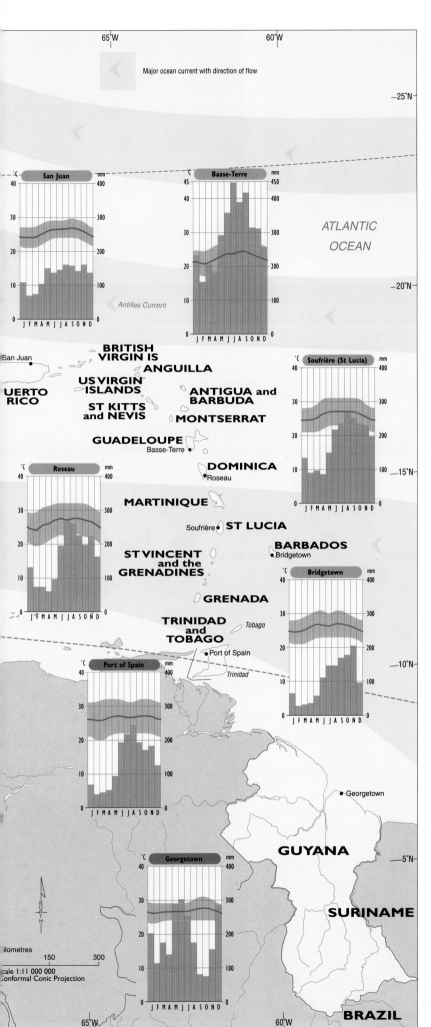

Major ocean current with direction of flow

ATLANTIC OCEAN

25°N

20°N

Antilles Current

San Juan

Basse-Terre

Soufrière (St Lucia)

Roseau

Bridgetown

Port of Spain

Georgetown

San Juan

BRITISH VIRGIN IS
ANGUILLA
US VIRGIN ISLANDS
ANTIGUA and BARBUDA
PUERTO RICO
ST KITTS and NEVIS
MONTSERRAT
GUADELOUPE
Basse-Terre
DOMINICA
Roseau
MARTINIQUE
SOUFRIÈRE ST LUCIA
ST VINCENT and the GRENADINES
BARBADOS
Bridgetown
GRENADA
TRINIDAD and TOBAGO
Tobago
Port of Spain
Trinidad

15°N

10°N

Georgetown

GUYANA

SURINAME

5°N

BRAZIL

65°W   60°W

kilometres
150   300
Scale 1:11 000 000
Conformal Conic Projection

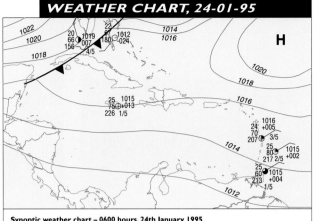

WEATHER CHART, 24-01-95

H

Synoptic weather chart – 0600 hours, 24th January 1995
A cold front extends from a low to the north-east of the Caribbean and approaches Cuba and the Bahamas, pushing out a ridge of high pressure over the eastern Caribbean and the Atlantic.

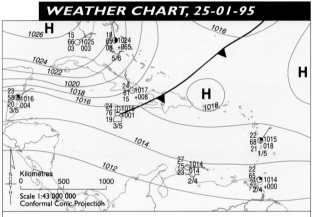

WEATHER CHART, 25-01-95

H   H   H

Kilometres
0   500   1000
Scale 1:43 000 000
Conformal Conic Projection

Synoptic weather chart – 0600 hours, 25th January 1995
24 hours later the cold front has moved south-east, pushing the ridge of high pressure further out into the Atlantic and a local 'travelling high' has developed over Puerto Rico. Note the fall in temperature at Key West and Nassau as the cold front passes through.

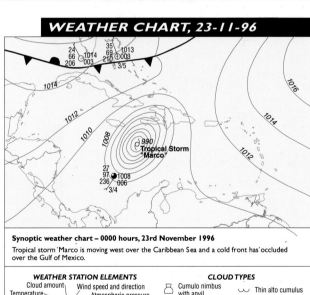

WEATHER CHART, 23-11-96

Tropical Storm "Marco"

Synoptic weather chart – 0000 hours, 23rd November 1996
Tropical storm 'Marco is moving west over the Caribbean Sea and a cold front has 'occluded over the Gulf of Mexico.

WEATHER STATION ELEMENTS

Cloud amount
Temperature — 24
Wind speed and direction
76 ○ 1015   Atmospheric pressure
Visibility — 19   +001   Pressure tendency (rise/fall in past 6 hours)
Dewpoint
Weather Station   3/5   Low cloud
Cloud ceiling

CLOUD AMOUNT

○ Clear
◔ Covered 1/8 or less
◑ 2/8 covered
◑ 3/8 covered
◑ 4/8 covered
◑ 5/8 covered
◕ 6/8 covered
◕ 7/8 covered
● Completely covered
⊗ Obscured by fog
☒ No data

CLOUD TYPES

⛁ Cumulo nimbus with anvil
⛀ Medium or large towering cumulus
⌣ Thin alto cumulus
⌣ All alto cumulus

WIND DIRECTION AND SPEED

Direction
Speed - each full tick indicates wind speed of 10 knots

VISIBILITY CODE
The figure gives the visibility in tenths of a kilometre (e.g. 20 = 2 km) Above 5 km visibilities are recorded in whole kilometres plus 50 (eg 56 = 6 km)

● ─── Warm front   ▼ ─── Cold front   1008 ─── Atmospheric pressure (hectopascals)

A synoptic weather chart is a summary of the weather conditions at a given time. The meteorological data needed to draw up these charts is obtained from a network of weather stations, which are indicated on the chart by a circle surrounded by the various weather observations. (The examples above show the current station coding used on synoptic charts in the Caribbean and North American regions.)

Mediterranean vegetation on Rhodes, Greece

Giant cacti in Central Desert National Park, Mexico

A twister or tornado in Texas, USA

NATURAL VEGETATION

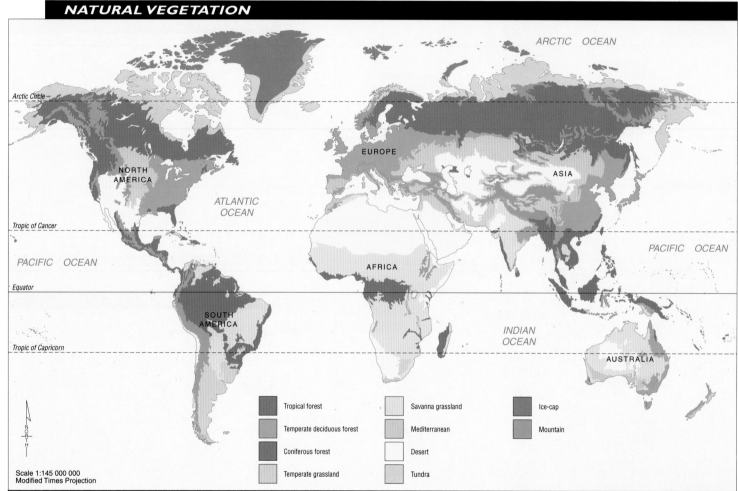

ARCTIC OCEAN

Arctic Circle

EUROPE

NORTH AMERICA

ASIA

ATLANTIC OCEAN

Tropic of Cancer

PACIFIC OCEAN

PACIFIC OCEAN

AFRICA

Equator

SOUTH AMERICA

INDIAN OCEAN

Tropic of Capricorn

AUSTRALIA

NORTH

- Tropical forest
- Temperate deciduous forest
- Coniferous forest
- Temperate grassland
- Savanna grassland
- Mediterranean
- Desert
- Tundra
- Ice-cap
- Mountain

Scale 1:145 000 000
Modified Times Projection

Tundra vegetation, Norway

Mountain vegetation, Swiss Alps

Aerial view of the edge of the ice-cap, Greenland

ENVIRONMENTAL DAMAGE

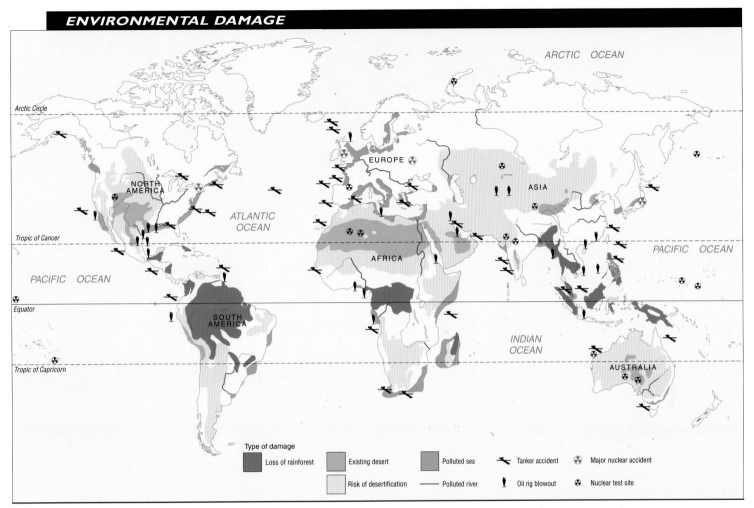

Type of damage

◼ Loss of rainforest	◼ Existing desert	◼ Polluted sea	✈ Tanker accident	☢ Major nuclear accident
◻ Risk of desertification	— Polluted river	↓ Oil rig blowout	☢ Nuclear test site

GLOBAL WARMING

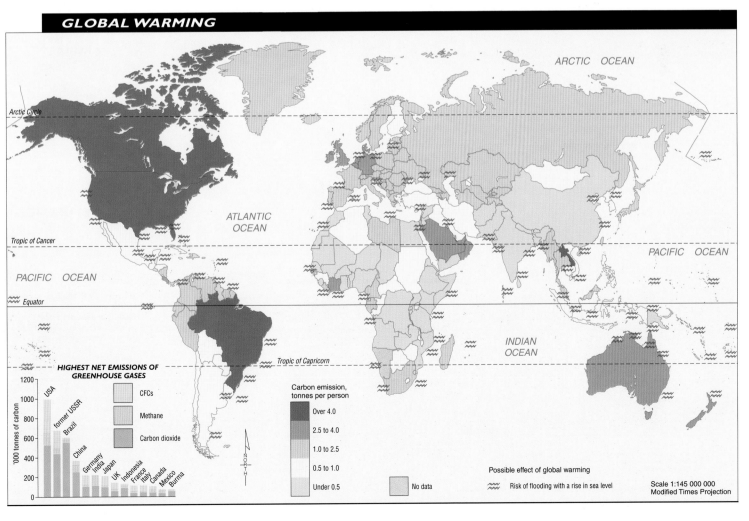

HIGHEST NET EMISSIONS OF GREENHOUSE GASES

USA, former USSR, Brazil, China, Germany, India, Japan, UK, Indonesia, France, Italy, Canada, Mexico, Burma

'000 tonnes of carbon: 0, 200, 400, 600, 800, 1000, 1200

◻ CFCs
◻ Methane
◼ Carbon dioxide

Carbon emission, tonnes per person

◼ Over 4.0
◼ 2.5 to 4.0
◼ 1.0 to 2.5
◻ 0.5 to 1.0
◻ Under 0.5

◼ No data

Possible effect of global warming

∿∿ Risk of flooding with a rise in sea level

Scale 1:145 000 000
Modified Times Projection

CARIBBEAN Environmental Issues

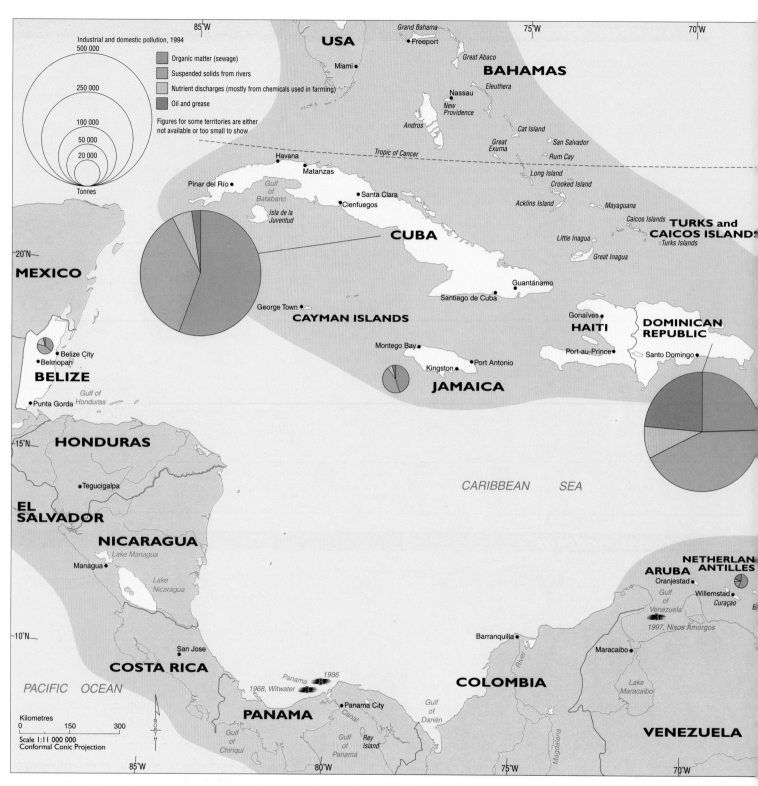

Industrial and domestic pollution, 1994

500 000
250 000
100 000
50 000
20 000
Tonnes

- Organic matter (sewage)
- Suspended solids from rivers
- Nutrient discharges (mostly from chemicals used in farming)
- Oil and grease

Figures for some territories are either not available or too small to show

USA
Miami

Grand Bahama
Freeport
Great Abaco

BAHAMAS
Eleuthera
Nassau
New Providence
Andros
Cat Island
Great Exuma
San Salvador
Rum Cay
Long Island
Crooked Island
Acklins Island
Mayaguana
Caicos Islands
TURKS and CAICOS ISLANDS
Turks Islands
Little Inagua
Great Inagua

Tropic of Cancer

20°N

MEXICO

Havana
Matanzas
Pinar del Río
Gulf of Batabano
Santa Clara
Cienfuegos
Isla de la Juventud
CUBA
Guantánamo
Santiago de Cuba

George Town
CAYMAN ISLANDS

Gonaïves
HAITI
Port-au-Prince
DOMINICAN REPUBLIC
Santo Domingo

Belize City
Belmopan
BELIZE
Punta Gorda
Gulf of Honduras

Montego Bay
Kingston
Port Antonio
JAMAICA

15°N

HONDURAS
Tegucigalpa

EL SALVADOR

NICARAGUA
Lake Managua
Managua
Lake Nicaragua

CARIBBEAN   SEA

NETHERLANDS ANTILLES
ARUBA
Oranjestad
Willemstad
Curaçao
Gulf of Venezuela
1997, Nisos Amorgos

10°N

San Jose

COSTA RICA

PACIFIC OCEAN

Barranquilla
Maracaibo
River
COLOMBIA
Lake Maracaibo

1986
Panama
1968, Witwater
Panama City
Canal
PANAMA
Gulf of Chiriquí
Gulf of Panamá
Rey Island
Gulf of Darién

VENEZUELA

Magdalena

Kilometres
0   150   300
Scale 1:11 000 000
Conformal Conic Projection

85°W   80°W   75°W   70°W

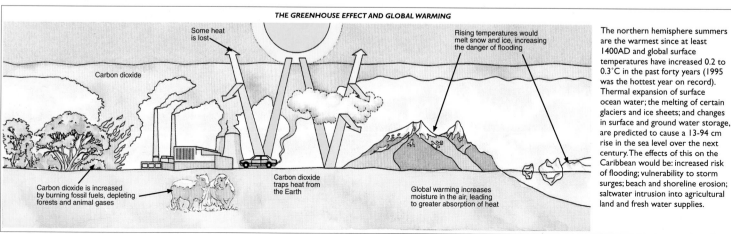

THE GREENHOUSE EFFECT AND GLOBAL WARMING

Some heat is lost

Carbon dioxide

Rising temperatures would melt snow and ice, increasing the danger of flooding

Carbon dioxide is increased by burning fossil fuels, depleting forests and animal gases

Carbon dioxide traps heat from the Earth

Global warming increases moisture in the air, leading to greater absorption of heat

The northern hemisphere summers are the warmest since at least 1400AD and global surface temperatures have increased 0.2 to 0.3°C in the past forty years (1995 was the hottest year on record). Thermal expansion of surface ocean water; the melting of certain glaciers and ice sheets; and changes in surface and ground water storage, are predicted to cause a 13-94 cm rise in the sea level over the next century. The effects of this on the Caribbean would be: increased risk of flooding; vulnerability to storm surges; beach and shoreline erosion; saltwater intrusion into agricultural land and fresh water supplies.

Oil polluted sea

Many parts of the Atlantic Ocean and Caribbean Sea are polluted with oil and tar from tankers discharging sludge, spillages and other ships pumping their bilges into the sea.

Oil and other sea pollution

Pesticides, sewage and other toxic substances, either washed into the sea from land or dumped in the sea causes pollution close to shore.

■ Major oil spills showing millions of litres

Santa Augusta Year of oil spill and name of ship

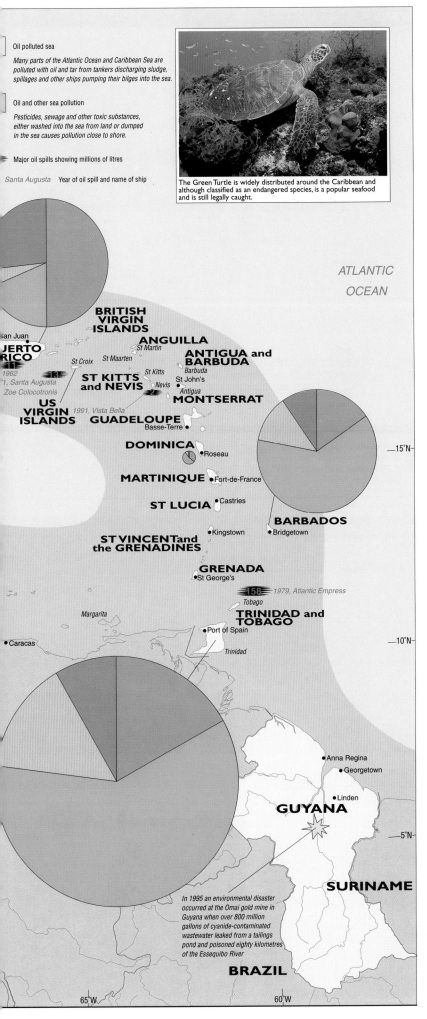

The Green Turtle is widely distributed around the Caribbean and although classified as an endangered species, is a popular seafood and is still legally caught.

ATLANTIC

OCEAN

BRITISH VIRGIN ISLANDS

ANGUILLA

San Juan
St Martin
PUERTO RICO
St Croix   St Maarten   ANTIGUA and BARBUDA
1962
St Kitts   Barbuda
1, Santa Augusta   ST KITTS and NEVIS   Nevis   St John's
Zoe Colocotronis   Antigua
US VIRGIN ISLANDS   MONTSERRAT
1991, Vista Bella   GUADELOUPE
Basse-Terre

DOMINICA
Roseau

MARTINIQUE   Fort-de-France

—15°N—

ST LUCIA   Castries

BARBADOS
Bridgetown
ST VINCENT and the GRENADINES
Kingstown

GRENADA
St George's

158   1979, Atlantic Empress
Tobago
Margarita   TRINIDAD and TOBAGO
Port of Spain
Caracas   —10°N—
Trinidad

Anna Regina
Georgetown

Linden

GUYANA   —5°N—

In 1995 an environmental disaster occurred at the Omai gold mine in Guyana when over 800 million gallons of cyanide-contaminated wastewater leaked from a tailings pond and poisoned eighty kilometres of the Essequibo River

SURINAME

BRAZIL

65°W   60°W

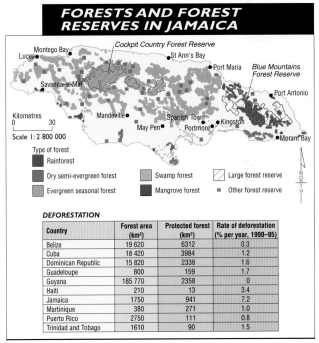

CONSERVATION IN TRINIDAD AND TOBAGO

PROTECTED AREAS

Name	Area (hectares)	Date established
Wildlife Sanctuaries:		
1 Bush Bush-Nariva Swamp	1554	1968
2 Central Range	2153	1934
3 Little Tobago	101	1928
4 Northern Range-Maracas Valley	936	1935
5 St Giles Island	29	1968
6 Saut d'Eau	10	1935
7 Soldado Rock	6	1934
8 Southern Watershed	1874	1934
9 Trinity Hills	8246	1934
Major Nature Reserve:		
10 Buccoo Reef	650	1973
Prohibited Areas:		
11 Aripo Savannas	1800	1987
12 Caroni Swamp	200	1987
13 Matura Beach	3500	1990

In addition to Wildlife Sanctuaries and Nature Reserves there are 9000 hectares of protected forests.

Tobago   5
3
10   Scarborough

• Small nature reserve

6   4
Port of Spain   Arima   11
12   13
Chaguanas   Sangre Grande
Talparo
Trinidad   2   1
Tabaquite
San Fernando   Rio Claro
Princes Town
Point Fortin
Morne l'Enfer   Penal   9
(area not available)
7   8

Kilometres
0   20

Scale 1:2 200 000

FORESTS AND FOREST RESERVES IN JAMAICA

Montego Bay   *Cockpit Country Forest Reserve*   St Ann's Bay
Lucea   Port Maria   *Blue Mountains Forest Reserve*
Savanna-la-Mar   Port Antonio
Kilometres
0   30   Mandeville   Spanish Town   Kingston
Scale 1:2 800 000   May Pen   Portmore   Morant Bay

Type of forest
■ Rainforest
■ Dry semi-evergreen forest   Swamp forest   ▨ Large forest reserve
Evergreen seasonal forest   ■ Mangrove forest   ■ Other forest reserve

DEFORESTATION

Country	Forest area (km²)	Protected forest (km²)	Rate of deforestation (% per year, 1990–95)
Belize	19 620	6312	0.3
Cuba	18 420	3984	1.2
Dominican Republic	15 820	2338	1.6
Guadeloupe	800	159	1.7
Guyana	185 770	2358	0
Haiti	210	13	3.4
Jamaica	1750	941	7.2
Martinique	380	271	1.0
Puerto Rico	2750	111	0.8
Trinidad and Tobago	1610	90	1.5

THREATENED WILDLIFE

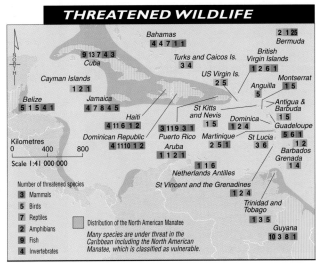

Bahamas   2 1 25
4 4 7 1 1   Bermuda
9 13 7 4 3   British Virgin Islands
Cuba   Turks and Caicos Is.
3 4   1 2 6 1
Cayman Islands   US Virgin Is.   Montserrat
1 2 1   2 5   Anguilla   1 5
Belize   5   Antigua & Barbuda
5 1 5 4 1   Jamaica   St Kitts   1 5
4 7 8 4 5   and Nevis   Dominica   Guadeloupe
Haiti   1 5   1 2 4   5 6 1
4 1 16 1 2   3 1 19 3 1   St Lucia
Dominican Republic   Puerto Rico   Martinique   3 6   Barbados
4 1 1 10 1 2   2 5 1   1 2
Aruba   Grenada
Kilometres   1 1 2 1   1 4
0   400   800
1 1 6
Scale 1:41 000 000   Netherlands Antilles
St Vincent and the Grenadines
1 2 4
Number of threatened species   Trinidad and Tobago
3 Mammals   1 3 5
5 Birds
7 Reptiles   Distribution of the North American Manatee   Guyana
2 Amphibians   *Many species are under threat in the*   10 3 8 1
9 Fish   *Caribbean including the North American*
4 Invertebrates   *Manatee, which is classified as vulnerable.*

AGRICULTURE, FORESTRY and FISHING

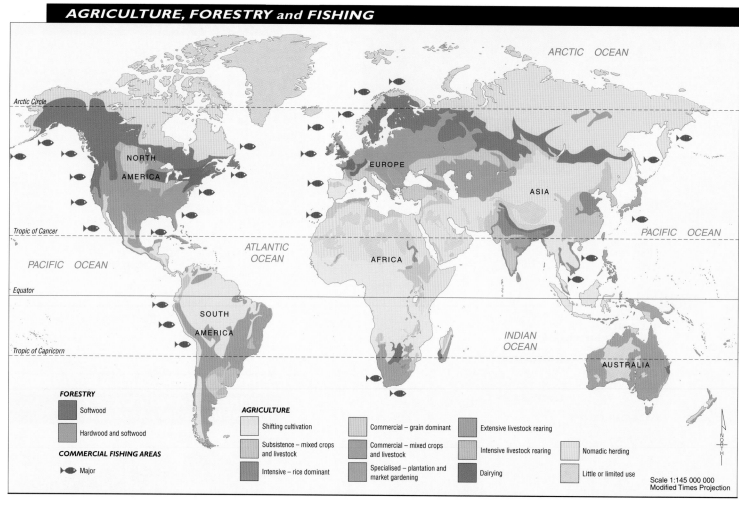

FORESTRY
- Softwood
- Hardwood and softwood

COMMERCIAL FISHING AREAS
- Major

AGRICULTURE
- Shifting cultivation
- Subsistence – mixed crops and livestock
- Intensive – rice dominant
- Commercial – grain dominant
- Commercial – mixed crops and livestock
- Specialised – plantation and market gardening
- Extensive livestock rearing
- Intensive livestock rearing
- Dairying
- Nomadic herding
- Little or limited use

Scale 1:145 000 000
Modified Times Projection

28

WORLD WHEAT PRODUCTION, 1999 (RANKED)
China
India
USA
France
Russia
Canada

= 10 million tonnes

WORLD RICE PRODUCTION, 1999 (RANKED)
China
India
Indonesia
Bangladesh
Vietnam
Thailand

= 10 million tonnes

WORLD CATTLE NUMBERS, 1999 (RANKED)
India
Brazil
USA
China
Argentina
Ethiopia

= 20 million head

WORLD SHEEP NUMBERS, 1999 (RANKED)
Australia
China
India
Iran
New Zealand
United Kingdom

= 10 million head

Fishing boats, Vietnam
© Copyright Macmillan Education Ltd

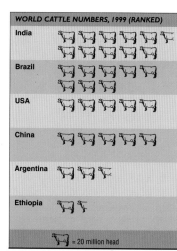

Mixed crop and livestock farming, southern England

A woman fertilising maize plants, Zimbabwe

MINERALS, ENERGY and INDUSTRY

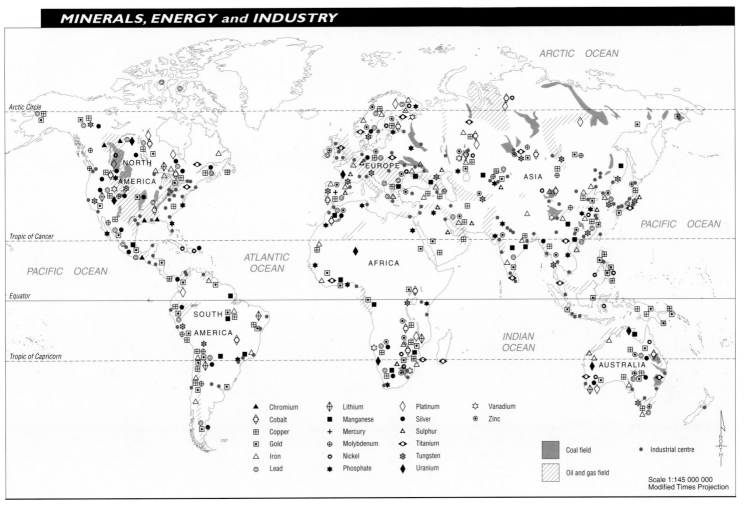

▲	Chromium	⊕	Lithium	◇ Platinum	☆ Vanadium
◇	Cobalt	■	Manganese	● Silver	◉ Zinc
⊞	Copper	+	Mercury	△ Sulphur	
▣	Gold	⊕	Molybdenum	◆ Titanium	
△	Iron	○	Nickel	✪ Tungsten	
◎	Lead	✳	Phosphate	◆ Uranium	

Coal field   ● Industrial centre

Oil and gas field

Scale 1:145 000 000
Modified Times Projection

EMPLOYMENT STRUCTURE

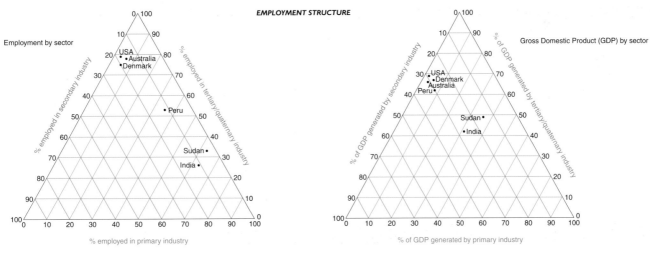

Employment by sector

% employed in secondary industry
% employed in tertiary/quaternary industry
% employed in primary industry

USA
Australia
Denmark
Peru
Sudan
India

Gross Domestic Product (GDP) by sector

% of GDP generated by secondary industry
% of GDP generated by tertiary/quaternary industry
% of GDP generated by primary industry

USA
Denmark
Australia
Peru
Sudan
India

Assembling pick-up trucks, Thailand

Chuquitamata copper mine, Chile

Oil production platform, North Sea

FUEL PRODUCTION

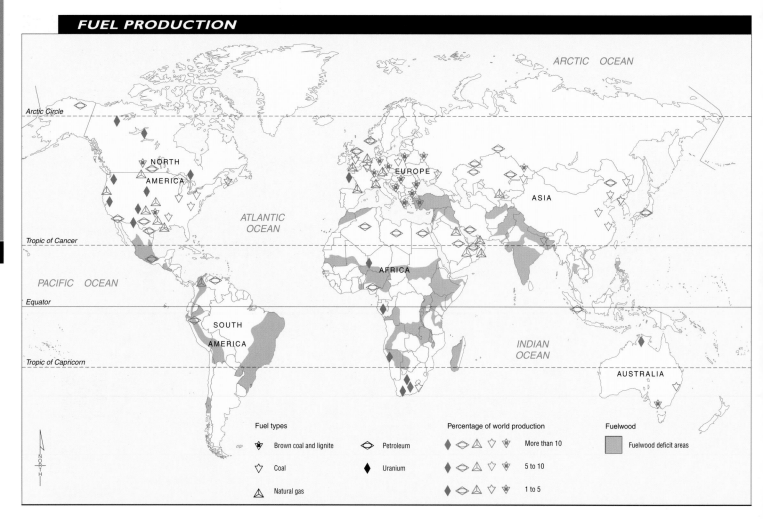

Fuel types

◈ Brown coal and lignite   ◇ Petroleum

▽ Coal   ◆ Uranium

△ Natural gas

Percentage of world production

◆ ◇ △ ▽ ⬗   More than 10

◆ ◇ △ ▽ ⬗   5 to 10

◆ ◇ △ ▽ ⬗   1 to 5

Fuelwood

▨ Fuelwood deficit areas

30

NUCLEAR ENERGY

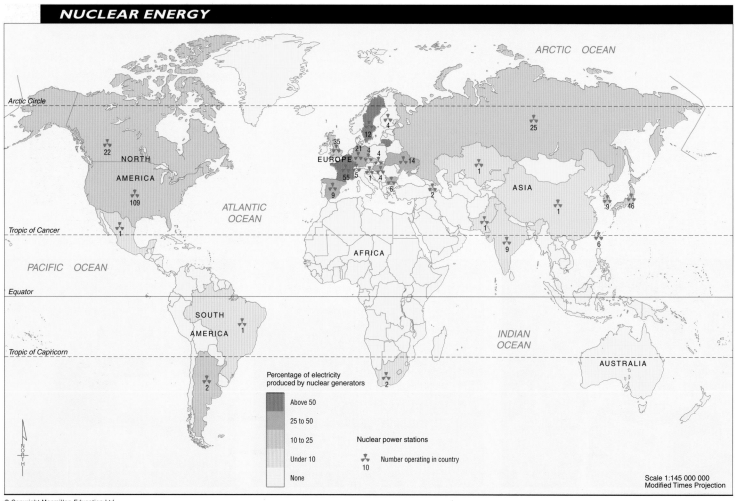

Percentage of electricity produced by nuclear generators

Above 50

25 to 50

10 to 25

Under 10

None

Nuclear power stations

☢ Number operating in country
10

Scale 1:145 000 000
Modified Times Projection

ENERGY PRODUCTION

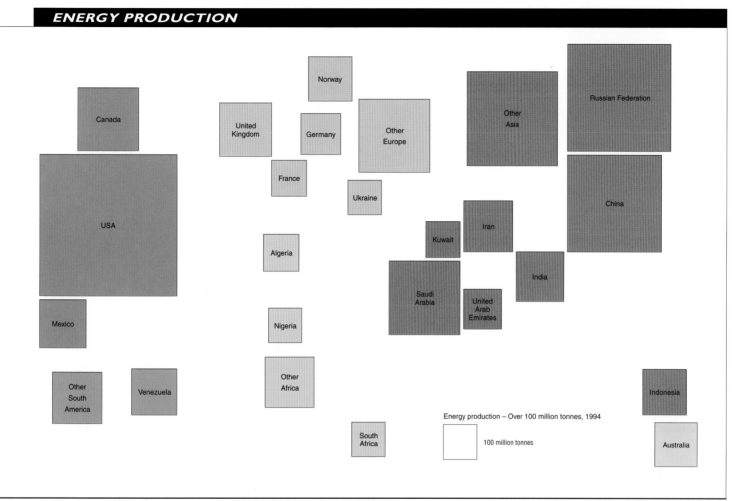

Energy production – Over 100 million tonnes, 1994

100 million tonnes

ENERGY CONSUMPTION

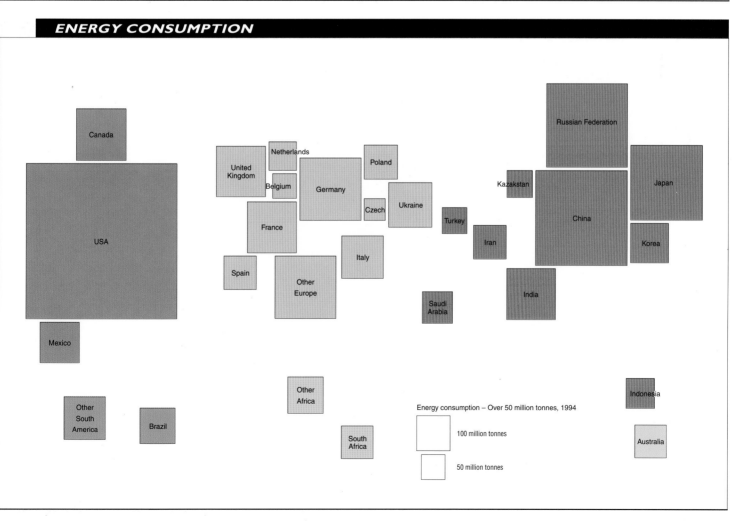

Energy consumption – Over 50 million tonnes, 1994

100 million tonnes

50 million tonnes

32

GROSS DOMESTIC PRODUCT

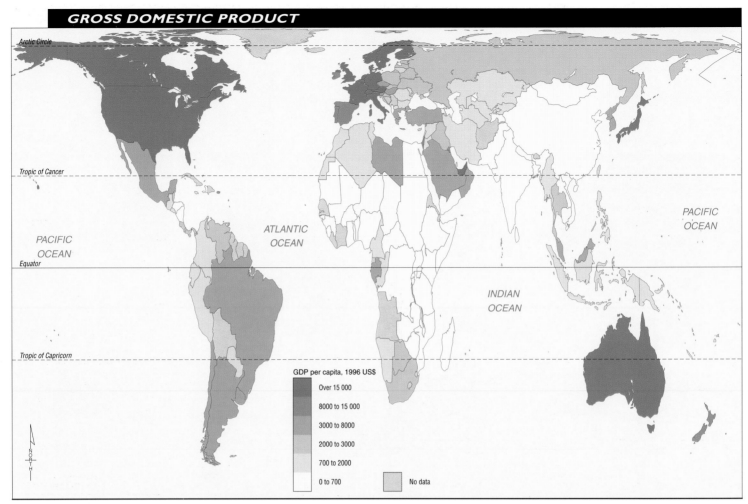

GDP per capita, 1996 US$

Over 15 000
8000 to 15 000
3000 to 8000
2000 to 3000
700 to 2000
0 to 700
No data

MANUFACTURES

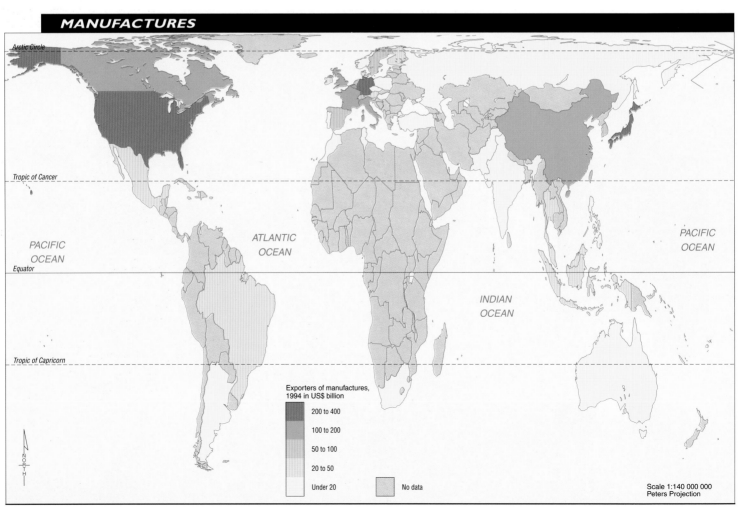

Exporters of manufactures,
1994 in US$ billion

200 to 400
100 to 200
50 to 100
20 to 50
Under 20
No data

Scale 1:140 000 000
Peters Projection

TOURIST DESTINATIONS

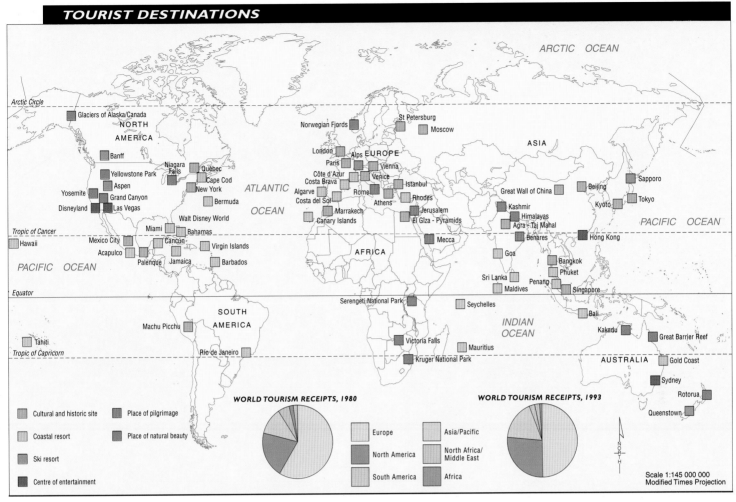

ARCTIC OCEAN

Arctic Circle

Glaciers of Alaska/Canada
NORTH
AMERICA

Norwegian Fjords
St Petersburg
Moscow

ASIA

London
Paris
Banff
Alps EUROPE
Vienna
Côte d'Azur
Venice
Costa Brava
Algarve
Rome
Costa del Sol
Athens
Marrakech
Canary Islands

Great Wall of China
Beijing
Sapporo
Tokyo
Kyoto

Niagara Falls
Québec
Cape Cod
New York

Yellowstone Park
Aspen
Yosemite
Grand Canyon
Disneyland
Las Vegas

ATLANTIC
OCEAN

Istanbul
Rhodes
Jerusalem
El Gîza - Pyramids
Mecca

Kashmir
Himalayas
Agra - Taj Mahal
Benares

PACIFIC OCEAN

Hong Kong

PACIFIC OCEAN

Bermuda

Walt Disney World

Tropic of Cancer

Hawaii

Miami
Bahamas

Mexico City
Cancún
Acapulco
Palenque
Jamaica
Barbados

Virgin Islands

AFRICA

Goa

Bangkok
Phuket
Penang
Singapore

Sri Lanka
Maldives

Equator

PACIFIC
OCEAN

SOUTH
AMERICA

Machu Picchu

Serengeti National Park

Seychelles

INDIAN
OCEAN

Bali

Kakadu

Great Barrier Reef

Tahiti

Tropic of Capricorn

Río de Janeiro

Victoria Falls

Mauritius

Kruger National Park

AUSTRALIA

Gold Coast

Sydney

Rotorua

Queenstown

Cultural and historic site
Coastal resort
Ski resort
Centre of entertainment
Place of pilgrimage
Place of natural beauty

WORLD TOURISM RECEIPTS, 1980

WORLD TOURISM RECEIPTS, 1993

Europe
North America
South America
Asia/Pacific
North Africa/Middle East
Africa

Scale 1:145 000 000
Modified Times Projection

WORLD HERITAGE SITES

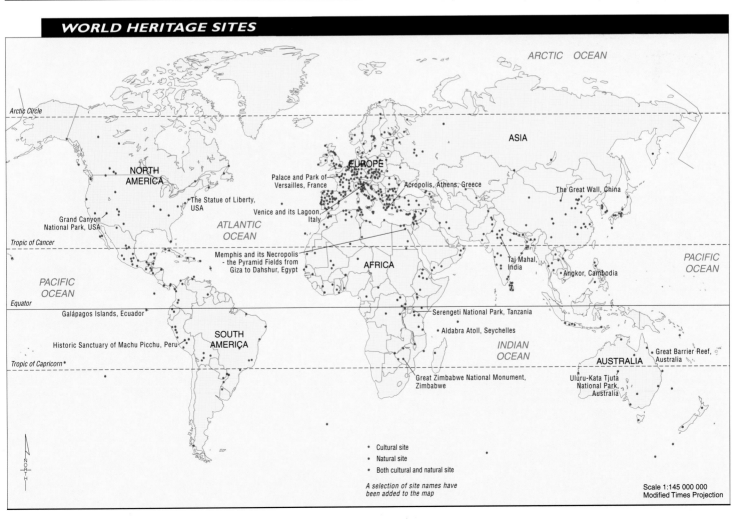

ARCTIC OCEAN

Arctic Circle

NORTH
AMERICA

ASIA

EUROPE

Palace and Park of Versailles, France

Acropolis, Athens, Greece

The Great Wall, China

The Statue of Liberty, USA

Grand Canyon National Park, USA

ATLANTIC
OCEAN

Venice and its Lagoon, Italy

Tropic of Cancer

Memphis and its Necropolis - the Pyramid Fields from Giza to Dahshur, Egypt

AFRICA

Taj Mahal, India

PACIFIC
OCEAN

Angkor, Cambodia

PACIFIC
OCEAN

Equator

Galápagos Islands, Ecuador

SOUTH
AMERICA

Serengeti National Park, Tanzania

Aldabra Atoll, Seychelles

INDIAN
OCEAN

Historic Sanctuary of Machu Picchu, Peru

Great Barrier Reef, Australia

Tropic of Capricorn *

Great Zimbabwe National Monument, Zimbabwe

Uluru-Kata Tjuta National Park, Australia

AUSTRALIA

• Cultural site
• Natural site
• Both cultural and natural site

A selection of site names have been added to the map

Scale 1:145 000 000
Modified Times Projection

EXPORTS

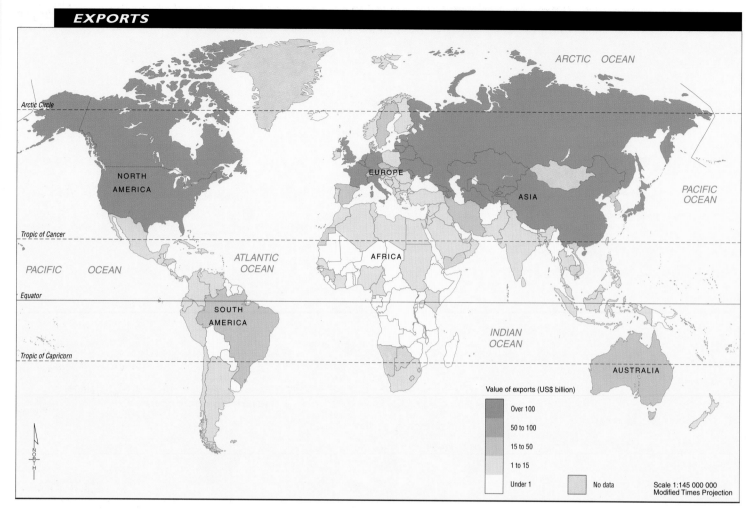

North America · Europe · Asia · Africa · South America · Australia

ARCTIC OCEAN
PACIFIC OCEAN
ATLANTIC OCEAN
INDIAN OCEAN

Arctic Circle
Tropic of Cancer
Equator
Tropic of Capricorn

NORTH

Value of exports (US$ billion)

	Over 100
	50 to 100
	15 to 50
	1 to 15
	Under 1
	No data

Scale 1:145 000 000
Modified Times Projection

CHANGE IN EXPORTS

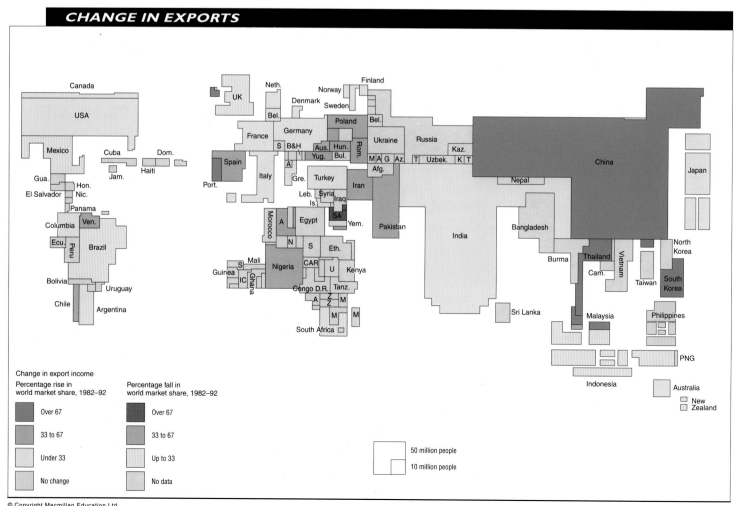

Change in export income

Percentage rise in world market share, 1982–92

	Over 67
	33 to 67
	Under 33
	No change

Percentage fall in world market share, 1982–92

	Over 67
	33 to 67
	Up to 33
	No data

50 million people
10 million people

SHIPPING ROUTES

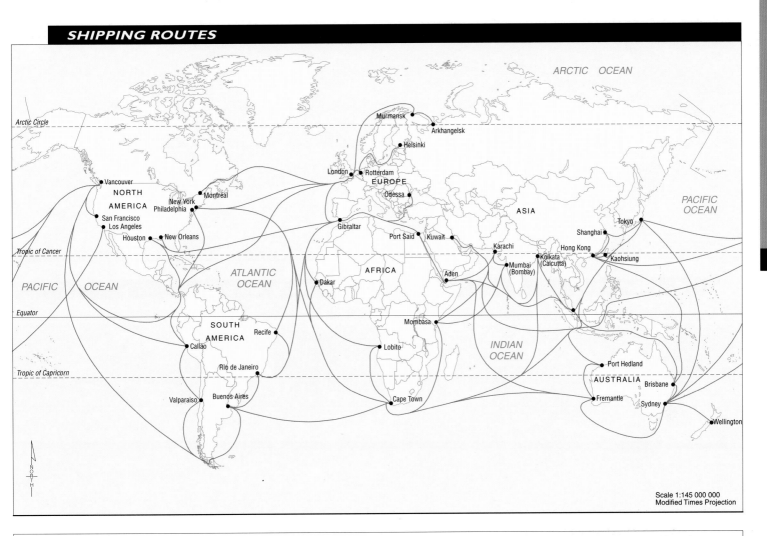

Scale 1:145 000 000
Modified Times Projection

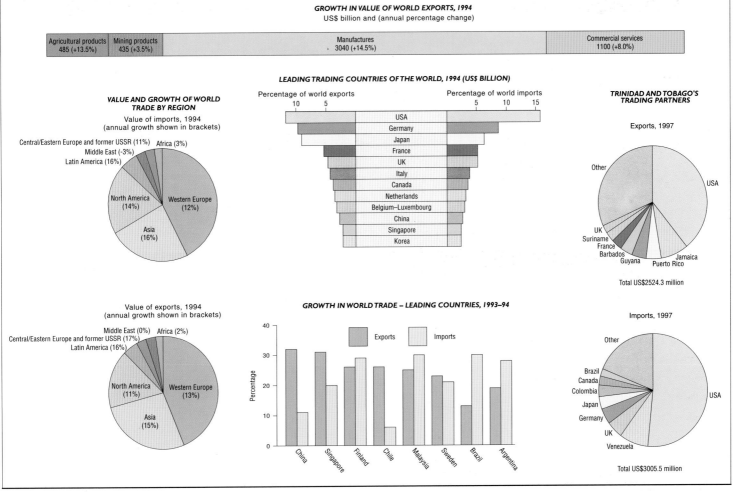

GROWTH IN VALUE OF WORLD EXPORTS, 1994
US$ billion and (annual percentage change)

Agricultural products 485 (+13.5%)	Mining products 435 (+3.5%)	Manufactures 3040 (+14.5%)	Commercial services 1100 (+8.0%)

LEADING TRADING COUNTRIES OF THE WORLD, 1994 (US$ BILLION)

Percentage of world exports — Percentage of world imports

USA
Germany
Japan
France
UK
Italy
Canada
Netherlands
Belgium–Luxembourg
China
Singapore
Korea

VALUE AND GROWTH OF WORLD TRADE BY REGION

Value of imports, 1994
(annual growth shown in brackets)

Central/Eastern Europe and former USSR (11%) Africa (3%)
Middle East (-3%)
Latin America (16%)
North America (14%)
Asia (16%)
Western Europe (12%)

Value of exports, 1994
(annual growth shown in brackets)

Middle East (0%) Africa (2%)
Central/Eastern Europe and former USSR (17%)
Latin America (16%)
North America (11%)
Asia (15%)
Western Europe (13%)

GROWTH IN WORLD TRADE – LEADING COUNTRIES, 1993–94

Exports Imports

Percentage

China, Singapore, Finland, Chile, Malaysia, Sweden, Brazil, Argentina

TRINIDAD AND TOBAGO'S TRADING PARTNERS

Exports, 1997

Other
USA
UK
Suriname
France
Barbados
Guyana
Puerto Rico
Jamaica

Total US$2524.3 million

Imports, 1997

Other
Brazil
Canada
Colombia
Japan
Germany
UK
Venezuela
USA

Total US$3005.5 million

NATO and CIS

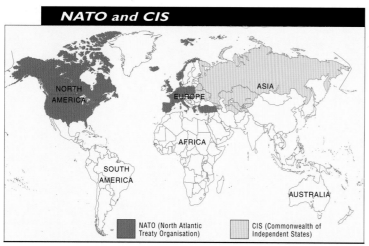

NATO (North Atlantic Treaty Organisation)

CIS (Commonwealth of Independent States)

COMMONWEALTH

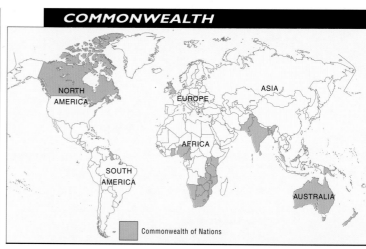

Commonwealth of Nations

OAS and OAU

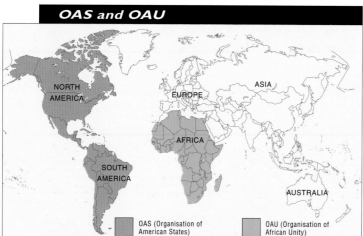

OAS (Organisation of American States)

OAU (Organisation of African Unity)

OECD and G8

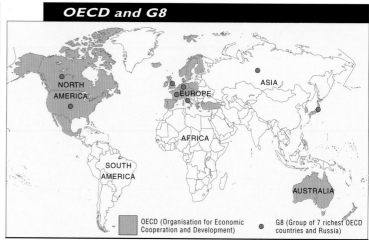

OECD (Organisation for Economic Cooperation and Development)

G8 (Group of 7 richest OECD countries and Russia)

ECCAS and NAFTA

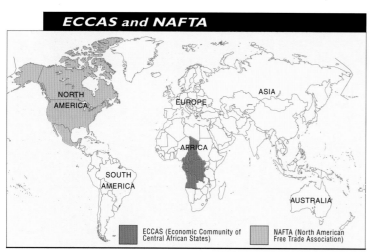

ECCAS (Economic Community of Central African States)

NAFTA (North American Free Trade Association)

APEC

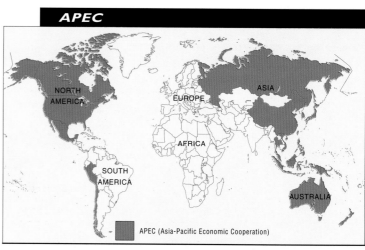

APEC (Asia-Pacific Economic Cooperation)

OPEC

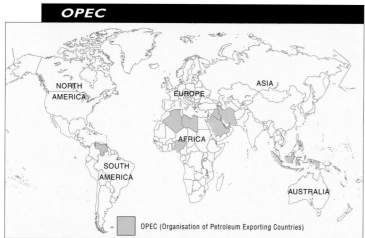

OPEC (Organisation of Petroleum Exporting Countries)

EU and ACP

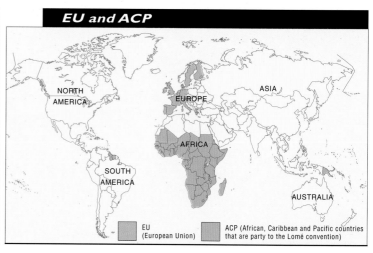

EU (European Union)

ACP (African, Caribbean and Pacific countries that are party to the Lomé convention)

ARAB LEAGUE and COLOMBO PLAN

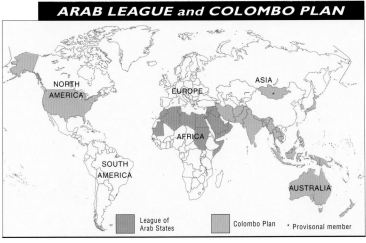

League of Arab States   Colombo Plan   * Provisional member

SADC and ECOWAS

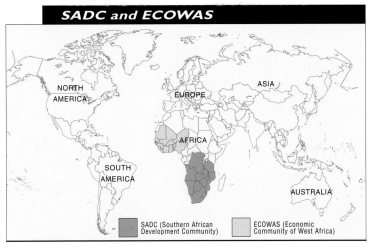

SADC (Southern African Development Community)   ECOWAS (Economic Community of West Africa)

SPF and CARICOM

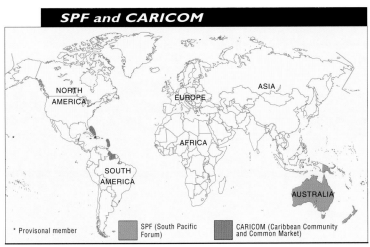

* Provisional member   SPF (South Pacific Forum)   CARICOM (Caribbean Community and Common Market)

ASEAN and LAIA

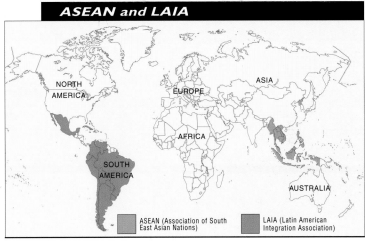

ASEAN (Association of South East Asian Nations)   LAIA (Latin American Integration Association)

FACT FILE

United Nations (UN) and NGOs

The UN aims to promote world peace and deal with humanitarian problems. It was formed in 1945 immediately after World War II. Fifty nations originally signed the UN Charter, which obliges member nations to find peaceful solutions to international disputes. Although some countries have opted not to join, there were 185 members of the UN in 1999. The UN has helped to resolve international disputes through its peace-keeping operations and has provided humanitarian assistance to many disadvantaged people throughout the world. Since 1948, some 118 countries have voluntarily provided more than 750 000 military and civilian police personnel. They have served, along with thousands of civilians, in 49 peacekeeping operations. Currently, some 12 500 military and civilian police personnel are deployed in 14 areas around the world. Many NGOs (non-governmental organisations) are working in various humanitarian projects worldwide. They include Red Cross, Red Crescent, Amnesty International, Oxfam, CARE International and Médecins sans frontières.

UN soldiers in Rwanda, 1994

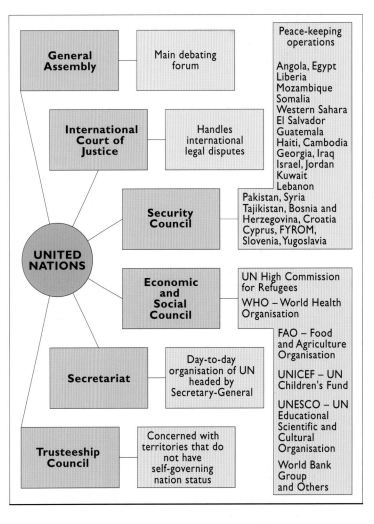

UNITED NATIONS

General Assembly — Main debating forum

International Court of Justice — Handles international legal disputes

Security Council

Economic and Social Council — UN High Commission for Refugees / WHO – World Health Organisation

Secretariat — Day-to-day organisation of UN headed by Secretary-General

Trusteeship Council — Concerned with territories that do not have self-governing nation status

Peace-keeping operations

Angola, Egypt
Liberia
Mozambique
Somalia
Western Sahara
El Salvador
Guatemala
Haiti, Cambodia
Georgia, Iraq
Israel, Jordan
Kuwait
Lebanon
Pakistan, Syria
Tajikistan, Bosnia and Herzegovina, Croatia
Cyprus, FYROM,
Slovenia, Yugoslavia

FAO – Food and Agriculture Organisation

UNICEF – UN Children's Fund

UNESCO – UN Educational Scientific and Cultural Organisation

World Bank Group and Others

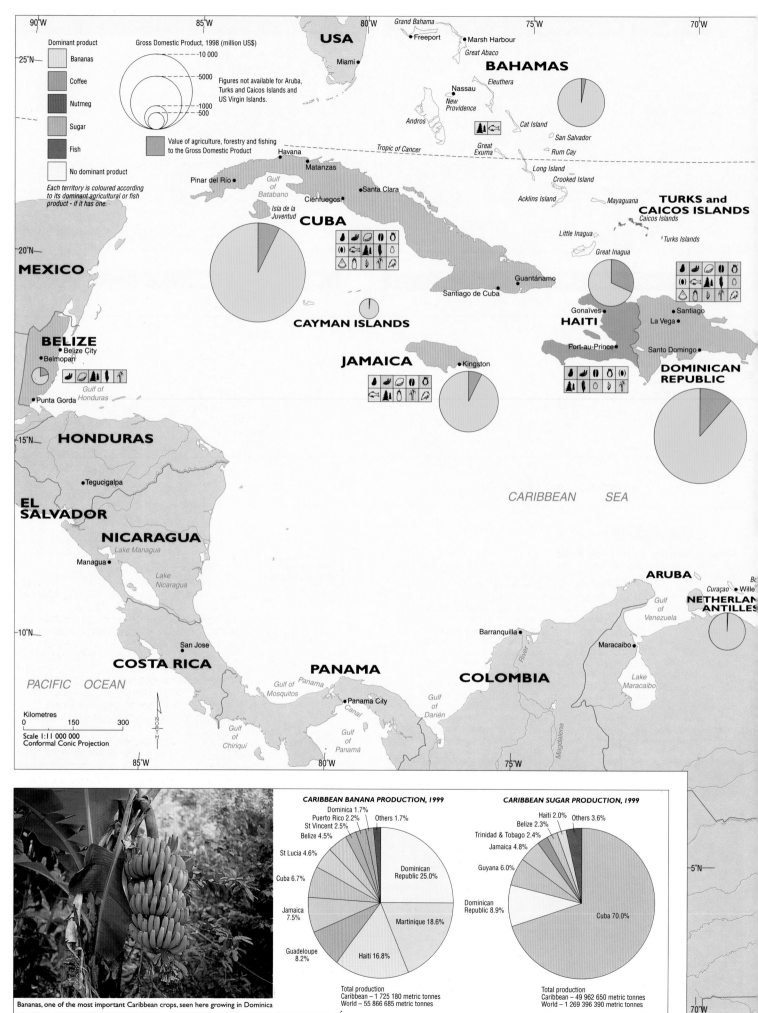

Dominant product

Bananas
Coffee
Nutmeg
Sugar
Fish
No dominant product

Each territory is coloured according to its dominant agricultural or fish product - if it has one.

Gross Domestic Product, 1998 (million US$)

—10 000
—5000
—1000
—500

Figures not available for Aruba, Turks and Caicos Islands and US Virgin Islands.

Value of agriculture, forestry and fishing to the Gross Domestic Product

USA
Miami
Grand Bahama
Freeport
Great Abaco
Marsh Harbour
BAHAMAS
Nassau
Eleuthera
New Providence
Andros
Cat Island
San Salvador
Great Exuma
Rum Cay
Tropic of Cancer
Long Island
Crooked Island
Acklins Island
Mayaguana
TURKS and CAICOS ISLANDS
Caicos Islands
Turks Islands
Little Inagua
Great Inagua

Havana
Matanzas
Pinar del Río
Gulf of Batabano
Santa Clara
Cienfuegos
Isla de la Juventud
CUBA
Guantánamo
Santiago de Cuba

CAYMAN ISLANDS

Gonaïves
HAITI
Port-au-Prince
Santiago
La Vega
Santo Domingo
DOMINICAN REPUBLIC

JAMAICA
Kingston

MEXICO

BELIZE
Belize City
Belmopan
Gulf of Honduras
Punta Gorda

HONDURAS
Tegucigalpa

EL SALVADOR

NICARAGUA
Lake Managua
Managua
Lake Nicaragua

COSTA RICA
San Jose

PACIFIC OCEAN

PANAMA
Gulf of Mosquitos
Panama Canal
Panama City
Gulf of Panamá
Gulf of Chiriquí

CARIBBEAN SEA

ARUBA
Curaçao
Wille
NETHERLANDS ANTILLES
Gulf of Venezuela

Barranquilla
Maracaibo
COLOMBIA
Lake Maracaibo
River Magdalena

Gulf of Darién

Kilometres
0   150   300
Scale 1:11 000 000
Conformal Conic Projection

NORTH

Bananas, one of the most important Caribbean crops, seen here growing in Dominica

CARIBBEAN BANANA PRODUCTION, 1999

Dominica 1.7%
Puerto Rico 2.2%   Others 1.7%
St Vincent 2.5%
Belize 4.5%
St Lucia 4.6%
Cuba 6.7%
Jamaica 7.5%
Guadeloupe 8.2%
Haiti 16.8%
Martinique 18.6%
Dominican Republic 25.0%

Total production
Caribbean – 1 725 180 metric tonnes
World – 55 866 685 metric tonnes

CARIBBEAN SUGAR PRODUCTION, 1999

Haiti 2.0%   Others 3.6%
Belize 2.3%
Trinidad & Tobago 2.4%
Jamaica 4.8%
Guyana 6.0%
Dominican Republic 8.9%
Cuba 70.0%

Total production
Caribbean – 49 962 650 metric tonnes
World – 1 269 396 390 metric tonnes

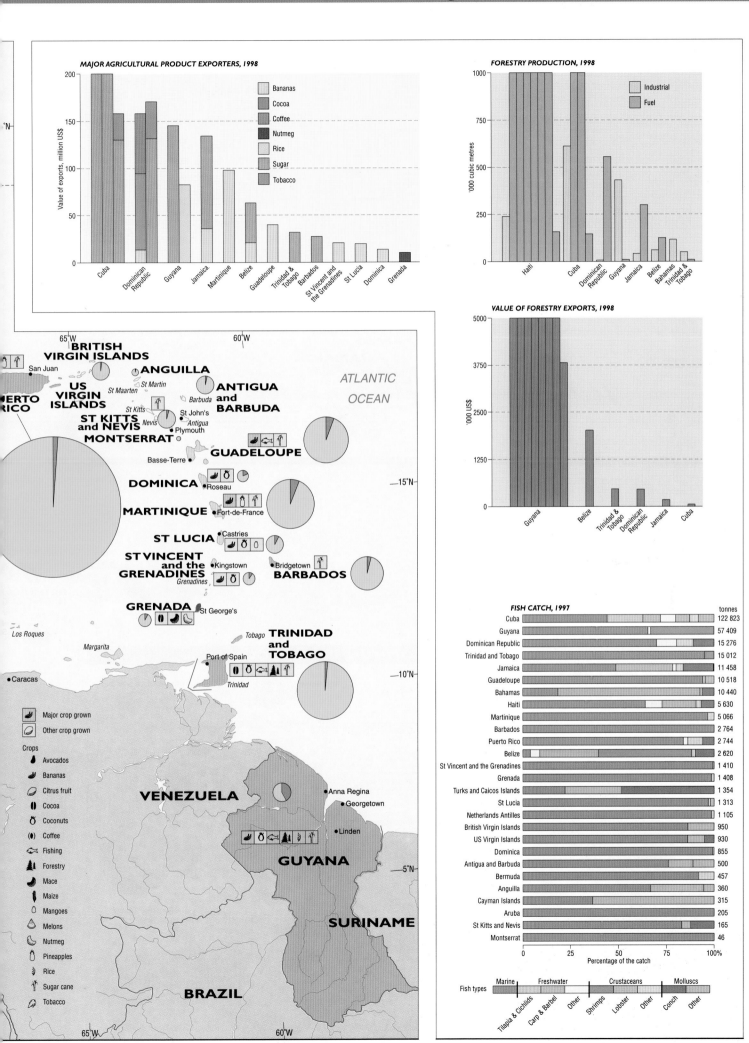

MAJOR AGRICULTURAL PRODUCT EXPORTERS, 1998

Value of exports, million US$

Legend:
- Bananas
- Cocoa
- Coffee
- Nutmeg
- Rice
- Sugar
- Tobacco

Countries: Cuba, Dominican Republic, Guyana, Jamaica, Martinique, Belize, Guadeloupe, Trinidad & Tobago, Barbados, St Vincent and the Grenadines, St Lucia, Dominica, Grenada

FORESTRY PRODUCTION, 1998

'000 cubic metres

Legend:
- Industrial
- Fuel

Countries: Haiti, Cuba, Dominican Republic, Guyana, Jamaica, Belize, Bahamas, Trinidad & Tobago

VALUE OF FORESTRY EXPORTS, 1998

'000 US$

Countries: Guyana, Belize, Trinidad & Tobago, Dominican Republic, Jamaica, Cuba

FISH CATCH, 1997

Country	tonnes
Cuba	122 823
Guyana	57 409
Dominican Republic	15 276
Trinidad and Tobago	15 012
Jamaica	11 458
Guadeloupe	10 518
Bahamas	10 440
Haiti	5 630
Martinique	5 066
Barbados	2 764
Puerto Rico	2 744
Belize	2 620
St Vincent and the Grenadines	1 410
Grenada	1 408
Turks and Caicos Islands	1 354
St Lucia	1 313
Netherlands Antilles	1 105
British Virgin Islands	950
US Virgin Islands	930
Dominica	855
Antigua and Barbuda	500
Bermuda	457
Anguilla	360
Cayman Islands	315
Aruba	205
St Kitts and Nevis	165
Montserrat	46

Percentage of the catch

Fish types:
- Marine
- Freshwater (Tilapia & Cichlids, Carp & Barbel, Other)
- Crustaceans (Shrimps, Lobster, Other)
- Molluscs (Conch, Other)

Map labels:
BRITISH VIRGIN ISLANDS, ANGUILLA, US VIRGIN ISLANDS, ANTIGUA and BARBUDA, ST KITTS and NEVIS, MONTSERRAT, GUADELOUPE, DOMINICA, MARTINIQUE, ST LUCIA, ST VINCENT and the GRENADINES, BARBADOS, GRENADA, TRINIDAD and TOBAGO, PUERTO RICO, VENEZUELA, GUYANA, SURINAME, BRAZIL

San Juan, St Maarten, St Martin, Barbuda, St Kitts, Nevis, St John's, Antigua, Plymouth, Basse-Terre, Roseau, Fort-de-France, Castries, Kingstown, Grenadines, Bridgetown, St George's, Tobago, Port of Spain, Trinidad, Los Roques, Margarita, Caracas, Anna Regina, Georgetown, Linden

ATLANTIC OCEAN

15°N, 10°N, 5°N, 65°W, 60°W

Legend:
- Major crop grown
- Other crop grown

Crops:
- Avocados
- Bananas
- Citrus fruit
- Cocoa
- Coconuts
- Coffee
- Fishing
- Forestry
- Mace
- Maize
- Mangoes
- Melons
- Nutmeg
- Pineapples
- Rice
- Sugar cane
- Tobacco

COUNTRY	GDP, 1998 million US$	GDP per capita, US$
Anguilla	86.0	6935.5
Antigua and Barbuda	563.6	8062.9
Aruba	1728.0	18 501.1
Bahamas	4120.0	14 061.4
Barbados	1964.4	7362.8
Belize	532.0	2230.6
Bermuda	1900.0	29 687.5
British Virgin Islands	588.7	30 984.2
Cayman Islands	745.0	19 761.3
Cuba	17300.0	1556.3
Dominica	238.5	3146.4
Dominican Republic	15900.0	1931.5
Grenada	299.1	2988.0
Guadeloupe	3700.0	8767.8
Guyana	615.7	796.1
Haiti	3900.0	490.4
Jamaica	6489.9	2523.5
Martinique	4240.0	10 899.7
Montserrat	33.1	8275.0
Netherlands Antilles	2441.3	11 647.4
Puerto Rico	34817.0	9019.9
St Kitts and Nevis	259.7	6380.8
St Lucia	571.7	3811.3
St Vincent and the Grenadines	282.9	2548.6
Trinidad and Tobago	5868.2	4573.8
Turks and Caicos	137.8	8612.5
US Virgin Islands	not available	not available

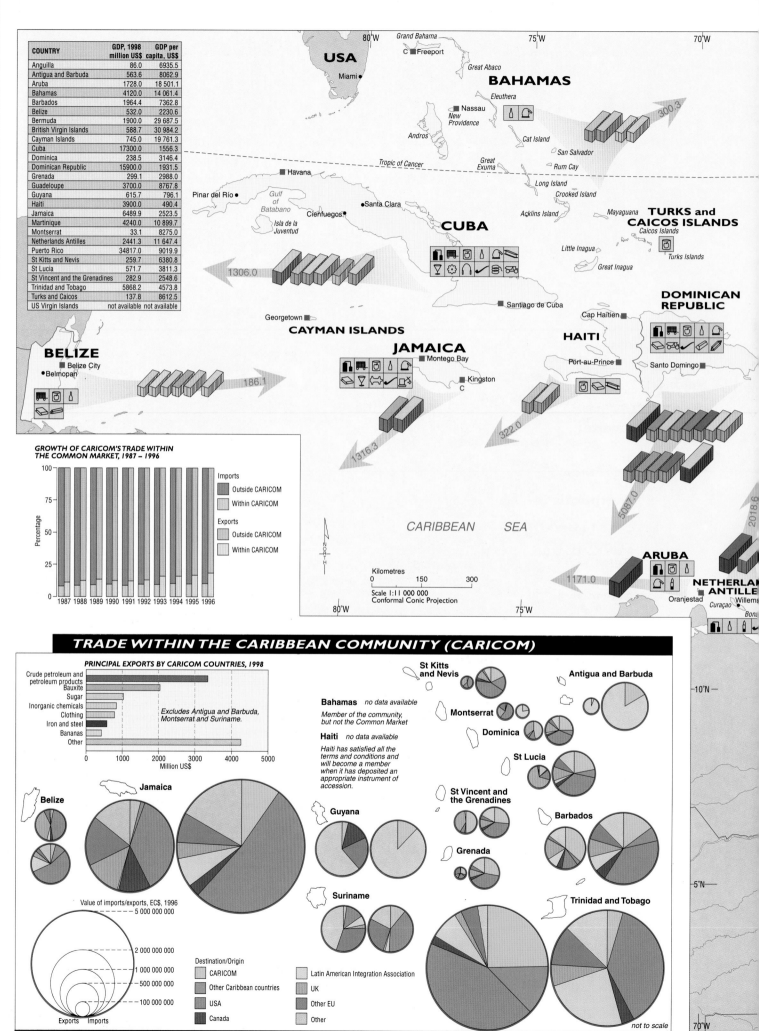

GROWTH OF CARICOM'S TRADE WITHIN THE COMMON MARKET, 1987 – 1996

Imports
Outside CARICOM
Within CARICOM

Exports
Outside CARICOM
Within CARICOM

Percentage
100 / 75 / 50 / 25 / 0
1987 1988 1989 1990 1991 1992 1993 1994 1995 1996

TRADE WITHIN THE CARIBBEAN COMMUNITY (CARICOM)

PRINCIPAL EXPORTS BY CARICOM COUNTRIES, 1998

Crude petroleum and petroleum products
Bauxite
Sugar
Inorganic chemicals
Clothing
Iron and steel
Bananas
Other

Excludes Antigua and Barbuda, Montserrat and Suriname.

0 1000 2000 3000 4000 5000
Million US$

Bahamas no data available
Member of the community, but not the Common Market

Haiti no data available
Haiti has satisfied all the terms and conditions and will become a member when it has deposited an appropriate instrument of accession.

St Kitts and Nevis
Antigua and Barbuda
Montserrat
Dominica
St Lucia
St Vincent and the Grenadines
Grenada
Barbados
Guyana
Suriname
Trinidad and Tobago
Belize
Jamaica

Value of imports/exports, EC$, 1996
5 000 000 000
2 000 000 000
1 000 000 000
500 000 000
100 000 000
Exports   Imports

Destination/Origin
CARICOM
Other Caribbean countries
USA
Canada
Latin American Integration Association
UK
Other EU
Other

not to scale

© Copyright Macmillan Education Ltd

Major export commodities

- Bananas
- Bauxite/Alumina
- Chemicals
- Clothes
- Cocoa
- Coffee
- Electrical components
- Electrical machinery
- Ferro-nickel
- Footwear
- Fruit juice
- Gold
- Headgear
- Jewellery
- Marine products
- Medical instruments
- Nickel
- Nutmeg
- Oil and petroleum
- Rice
- Rum
- Soap products
- Sugar
- Timber
- Tobacco
- Transport equipment
- Others

Value of exports, million US$
- Over 2000
- 1000 to 2000
- 500 to 1000
- 50 to 500
- 10 to 50
- Under 10

300.3 Total value of exports

Major industries

- Bauxite mining
- Beverages
- Cement
- Chemicals
- Diamond mining
- Electrical
- Electronics assembly
- Electroplating
- Food processing
- Forestry
- Furniture
- Gold mining
- Gypsum mining
- Metal processing
- Nickel mining
- Oil refining
- Plastics
- Pulp paper
- Soap and cosmetics
- Sugar factory
- Tannery
- Textiles
- Tobacco
- Vehicle assembly

- Major commercial port
- C Container port

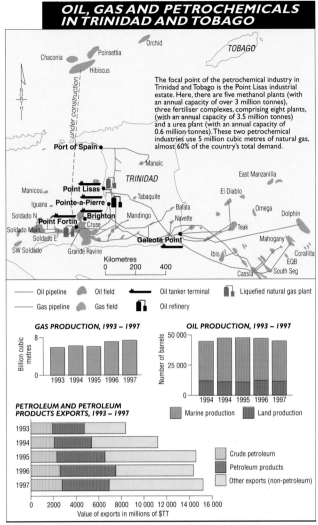

OIL, GAS AND PETROCHEMICALS IN TRINIDAD AND TOBAGO

The focal point of the petrochemical industry in Trinidad and Tobago is the Point Lisas industrial estate. Here, there are five methanol plants (with an annual capacity of over 3 million tonnes), three fertiliser complexes, comprising eight plants, (with an annual capacity of 3.5 million tonnes) and a urea plant (with an annual capacity of 0.6 million tonnes). These two petrochemical industries use 5 million cubic metres of natural gas, almost 60% of the country's total demand.

- Oil pipeline
- Gas pipeline
- Oil field
- Gas field
- Oil tanker terminal
- Oil refinery
- Liquefied natural gas plant

GAS PRODUCTION, 1993 – 1997

OIL PRODUCTION, 1993 – 1997
- Marine production
- Land production

PETROLEUM AND PETROLEUM PRODUCTS EXPORTS, 1993 – 1997
- Crude petroleum
- Petroleum products
- Other exports (non-petroleum)

Value of exports in millions of $TT

BAUXITE MINING AND PROCESSING IN JAMAICA

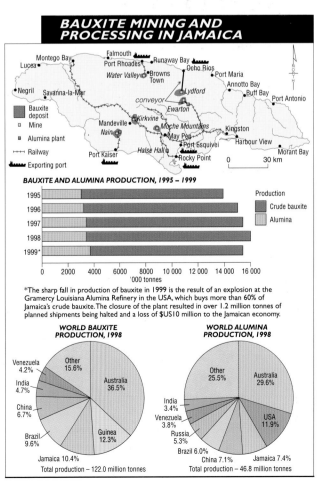

- Bauxite deposit
- Mine
- Alumina plant
- Railway
- Exporting port

BAUXITE AND ALUMINA PRODUCTION, 1995 – 1999
- Production
- Crude bauxite
- Alumina

'000 tonnes

*The sharp fall in production of bauxite in 1999 is the result of an explosion at the Gramercy Louisiana Alumina Refinery in the USA, which buys more than 60% of Jamaica's crude bauxite. The closure of the plant resulted in over 1.2 million tonnes of planned shipments being halted and a loss of $US10 million to the Jamaican economy.

WORLD BAUXITE PRODUCTION, 1998
- Australia 36.5%
- Other 15.6%
- Venezuela 4.2%
- India 4.7%
- China 6.7%
- Brazil 9.6%
- Jamaica 10.4%
- Guinea 12.3%
- Total production – 122.0 million tonnes

WORLD ALUMINA PRODUCTION, 1998
- Australia 29.6%
- Other 25.5%
- USA 11.9%
- Jamaica 7.4%
- China 7.1%
- Brazil 6.0%
- Russia 5.3%
- Venezuela 3.8%
- India 3.4%
- Total production – 46.8 million tonnes

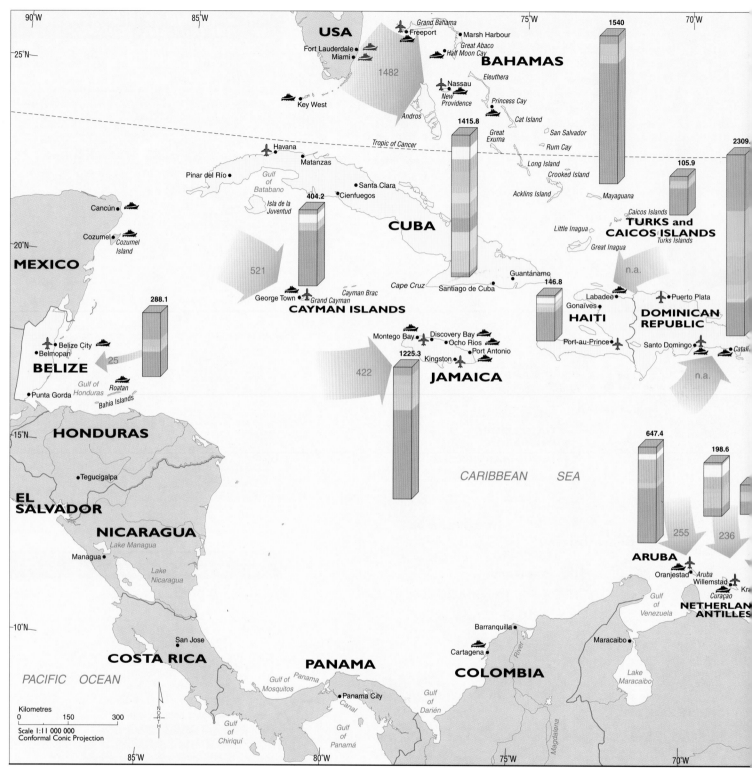

STOPOVER TOURISTS, 1994 – 1998

Number of tourists in millions

1994 | 1995 | 1996 | 1997 | 1998

CRUISE TOURISTS, 1994 – 1998

Number of tourists in millions

1994 | 1995 | 1996 | 1997 | 1998

The figures for cruise passenger arrivals represent the sum of arrivals at individual destinations. As most cruise ships stop at more than one destination, this figure is considerably larger than the actual number of passengers visiting the region.

TOURIST EXPENDITURE, 1994 – 1998

Million US$

1994 | 1995 | 1996 | 1997 | 1998

TOURIST ARRIVALS BY MONTH, 1998

Number of tourists in thousands

Winter   Summer

D J F M A M J J A S O N D
Months

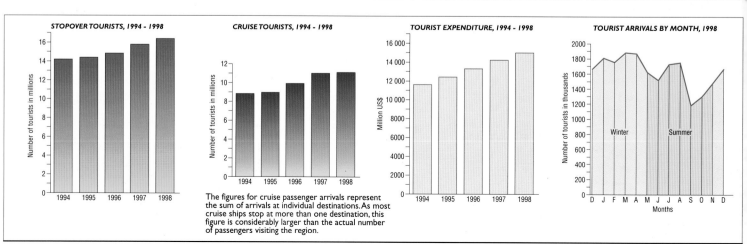

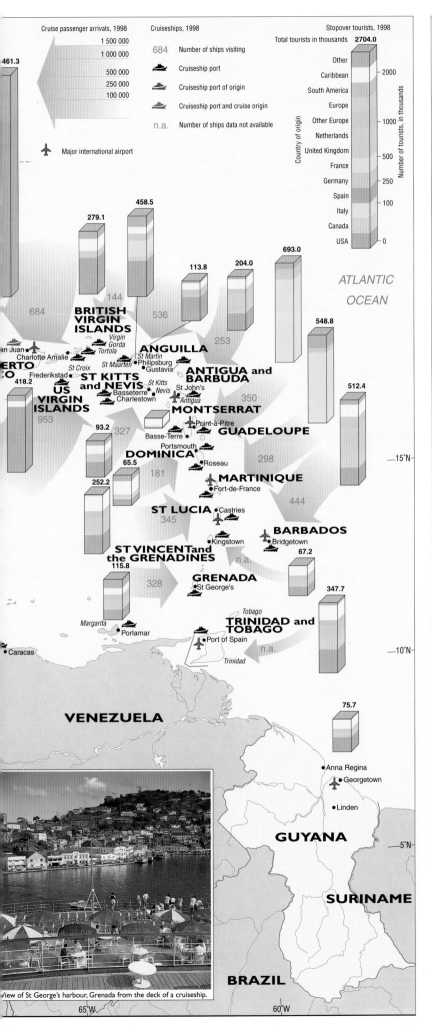

Cruise passenger arrivals, 1998
- 1 500 000
- 1 000 000
- 500 000
- 250 000
- 100 000

461.3

Cruiseships, 1998

684 Number of ships visiting

🚢 Cruiseship port

🚢 Cruiseship port of origin

🚢 Cruiseship port and cruise origin

n.a. Number of ships data not available

✈ Major international airport

Stopover tourists, 1998

Total tourists in thousands 2704.0

Country of origin:
- Other
- Caribbean
- South America
- Europe
- Other Europe
- Netherlands
- United Kingdom
- France
- Germany
- Spain
- Italy
- Canada
- USA

Number of tourists, in thousands: 2000, 1000, 500, 250, 100, 0

ATLANTIC OCEAN

279.1   458.5   113.8   204.0   693.0

684   144   536   253   548.8

BRITISH VIRGIN ISLANDS
Virgin Gorda   *Tortola*

an Juan   Charlotte Amalie   St Croix   Frederikstad

ERTO CO   418.2

US VIRGIN ISLANDS   953

ANGUILLA
St Martin   Philipsburg   *St Maarten*   •Gustavia

ST KITTS and NEVIS
St Kitts   •Nevis   Basseterre•   Charlestown

ANTIGUA and BARBUDA
St John's•   *Antigua*   512.4

MONTSERRAT   350

•Point-à-Pitre
Basse-Terre•   GUADELOUPE   327

93.2   Portsmouth•
DOMINICA   298
65.5   •Roseau   181

MARTINIQUE
•Fort-de-France   444

252.2

ST LUCIA   •Castries   345

•Kingstown

ST VINCENT and the GRENADINES

BARBADOS
•Bridgetown   67.2   n.a.

115.8   328   GRENADA
•St George's   347.7

Margarita   *Tobago*
•Porlamar   TRINIDAD and TOBAGO
•Port of Spain   n.a.   *Trinidad*

•Caracas

VENEZUELA   75.7

•Anna Regina   •Georgetown

•Linden

GUYANA

SURINAME

BRAZIL

View of St George's harbour, Grenada from the deck of a cruiseship.

65°W   60°W   5°N   10°N   15°N

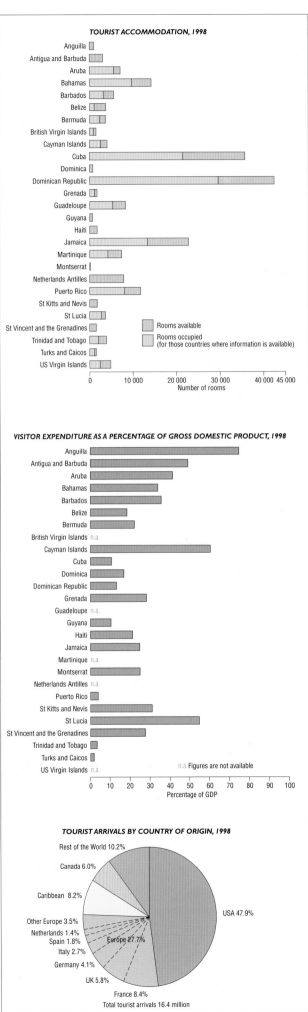

TOURIST ACCOMMODATION, 1998

- Anguilla
- Antigua and Barbuda
- Aruba
- Bahamas
- Barbados
- Belize
- Bermuda
- British Virgin Islands
- Cayman Islands
- Cuba
- Dominica
- Dominican Republic
- Grenada
- Guadeloupe
- Guyana
- Haiti
- Jamaica
- Martinique
- Montserrat
- Netherlands Antilles
- Puerto Rico
- St Kitts and Nevis
- St Lucia
- St Vincent and the Grenadines
- Trinidad and Tobago
- Turks and Caicos
- US Virgin Islands

Rooms available
Rooms occupied (for those countries where information is available)

Number of rooms: 0, 10 000, 20 000, 30 000, 40 000, 45 000

VISITOR EXPENDITURE AS A PERCENTAGE OF GROSS DOMESTIC PRODUCT, 1998

- Anguilla
- Antigua and Barbuda
- Aruba
- Bahamas
- Barbados
- Belize
- Bermuda
- British Virgin Islands n.a.
- Cayman Islands
- Cuba
- Dominica
- Dominican Republic
- Grenada
- Guadeloupe n.a.
- Guyana
- Haiti
- Jamaica
- Martinique n.a.
- Montserrat
- Netherlands Antilles n.a.
- Puerto Rico
- St Kitts and Nevis
- St Lucia
- St Vincent and the Grenadines
- Trinidad and Tobago
- Turks and Caicos
- US Virgin Islands n.a.

n.a. Figures are not available

Percentage of GDP: 0, 10, 20, 30, 40, 50, 60, 70, 80, 90, 100

TOURIST ARRIVALS BY COUNTRY OF ORIGIN, 1998

- Rest of the World 10.2%
- Canada 6.0%
- Caribbean 8.2%
- Other Europe 3.5%
- Netherlands 1.4%
- Spain 1.8%
- Italy 2.7%
- Germany 4.1%
- UK 5.8%
- France 8.4%
- Europe 27.7%
- USA 47.9%

Total tourist arrivals 16.4 million

WORLD STATISTICS

Country – Official name	Capital city	Area (km²)	Population (millions) 1997	Official language/s	Official currency	GDP per capita US$ 1997	Life expectancy male/female	Illiterate adults % male/female
AFRICA								
Algeria – People's Democratic Republic of Algeria	**Algiers**	2 381 741	29.3	Arabic	Algerian dinar	1097	67/70	29/55
Angola – Republic of Angola	**Luanda**	1 246 700	11.7	Portuguese	Redjusted kwanza	663	45/48	44/72
Benin – Republic of Benin	**Porto Novo**	112 622	5.8	French	CFA franc *	364	52/55	55/81
Botswana – Republic of Botswana	**Gaborone**	600 372	1.5	English	Pula	3209	46/48	30/25
Burkina Faso – Democratic Republic of Burkina Faso	**Ouagadougou**	274 200	10.5	French	CFA franc *	160	44/45	71/90
Burundi – Republic of Burundi	**Bujumbura**	27 834	6.4	Kirundi, French	Burundi franc	126	41/44	48/67
Cameroon – Republic of Cameroon	**Yaoundé**	475 442	13.9	French, English	CFA franc *	617	53/56	23/38
Cape Verde – Republic of Cape Verde	**Praia**	4033	0.4	Portuguese	Cape Verde escudo	833	65/71	19/39
Central African Republic – Central African Republic	**Bangui**	622 984	3.4	French, Sango	CFA franc *	364	43/47	46/73
Chad – Republic of Chad	**N'Djaména**	1 284 000	7.2	French, Arabic	CFA franc *	149	46/49	38/65
Comoros – Federal Islamic Republic of Comoros	**Moroni**	2171	0.6	French, Arabic	Comorian franc	334	57/60	37/52
Congo DR – Democratic Republic of the Congo	**Kinshasa**	2 345 409	46.7	French	Zaïre	52	50/52	13/32
Congo – Republic of the Congo	**Brazzaville**	342 000	2.7	French	CFA franc *	702	48/51	17/33
Côte d'Ivoire – Republic of the Ivory Coast	**Yamoussoukro**	322 463	14.2	French	CFA franc *	731	46/47	51/69
Djibouti – Republic of Djibouti	**Djibouti**	22 000	0.6	French, Arabic	Djibouti franc	979	49/52	40/67
Egypt – Arab Republic of Egypt	**Cairo**	1 001 449	60.3	Arabic	Egyptian pound	1168	65/68	36/62
Equatorial Guinea – Republic of Equatorial Guinea	**Malabo**	28 051	0.4	Spanish	CFA franc *	349	48/52	11/33
Eritrea – State of Eritrea	**Asmara**	117 598	3.8	Arabic, Tigrinya	Nakfa	173	49/52	-
Ethiopia – Federal Democratic Republic of Ethiopia	**Addis Ababa**	1 104 301	59.8	Amharic	Ethiopian birr	104	42/44	60/74
Gabon – Gabonese Republic	**Libreville**	267 667	1.2	French	CFA franc *	4611	51/54	26/47
Gambia, The – Republic of the Gambia	**Banjul**	11 295	1.2	English	Dalasi	323	45/49	62/76
Ghana – Republic of Ghana	**Accra**	238 537	18.0	English	Cedi	398	58/62	25/47
Guinea – Republic of Guinea	**Conakry**	245 857	6.9	French	Guinean franc	535	46/47	50/78
Guinea-Bissau – Republic of Guinea-Bissau	**Bissau**	36 125	1.1	Portuguese	CFA franc *	96	43/46	52/84
Kenya – Republic of Kenya	**Nairobi**	582 646	28.6	English	Kenya shilling	356	51/53	14/31
Lesotho – Kingdom of Lesotho	**Maseru**	30 355	2.0	Sesotho, English	Loti	505	55/57	30/8
Liberia – Republic of Liberia	**Monrovia**	111 369	2.1	English	Liberian dollar	1242	46/48	38/72
Libya – Great Socialist People's Libyan Arab Jamahiriya	**Tripoli**	1 759 540	5.2	Arabic	Libyan dinar	5621	68/72	13/40
Madagascar – Republic of Madagascar	**Antananarivo**	587 041	14.1	Malagasy	Malagasy franc	122	56/59	12/27
Malaŵi – Republic of Malaŵi	**Lilongwe**	118 484	10.3	Chichewa, English	Malawi kwacha	234	39/40	28/59
Mali – Republic of Mali	**Bamako**	1 240 000	10.3	French	CFA franc *	244	52/55	60/75
Mauritania – Islamic Republic of Mauritania	**Nouakchott**	1 030 700	2.5	Arabic	Ouguiya	388	52/55	51/73
Mauritius – Republic of Mauritius	**Port Louis**	2045	1.1	English	Mauritius rupee	3688	68/75	14/22
Morocco – Kingdom of Morocco	**Rabat**	446 550	27.3	Arabic	Dirham	1246	65/68	42/69
Mozambique – Republic of Mozambique	**Maputo**	801 590	16.6	Portuguese	Metical	94	44/47	45/77
Namibia – Republic of Namibia	**Windhoek**	824 292	1.6	English	Namibia dollar	2046	52/53	20/22
Niger – Republic of Niger	**Niamey**	1 267 000	9.8	French	CFA franc *	191	47/50	79/93
Nigeria – Federal Republic of Nigeria	**Abuja**	923 768	117.9	English, French	Naira	1376	49/51	34/53
Rwanda – Republic of Rwanda	**Kigali**	26 338	7.9	Kinyarwanda, Fr, English	Rwanda franc	170	39/42	31/48
São Tomé & Príncipe – Democratic Republic of São Tomé & Príncipe	**São Tomé**	964	0.1	Portuguese	Dobra	318	62/65	-
Senegal – Republic of Senegal	**Dakar**	196 192	8.8	French	CFA franc *	519	50/54	57/77
Seychelles – Republic of Seychelles	**Victoria**	280	0.1	English, French, Creole	Seychelles rupee	7304	65/74	-
Sierra Leone – Republic of Sierra Leone	**Freetown**	71 740	4.7	English	Leone	260	36/39	55/82
Somalia – Somali Democratic Republic	**Mogadishu**	637 657	9.6	Somali, Arabic	Somali shilling	169	45/49	64/86
South Africa – Republic of South Africa	**Pretoria** (see p. 36)	1 221 037	40.6	Afrikaans, English, 9 loc	Rand	3331	51/58	16/18
Sudan – Republic of Sudan	**Khartoum**	2 505 813	27.7	Arabic	Sudanese pound	59	54/56	37/62
Swaziland – Kingdom of Swaziland	**Mbabane**	17 363	1.0	siSwati, English	Lilangeni	1420	58/62	22/25
Tanzania – United Republic of Tanzania	**Dodoma**	945 087	31.3	English, Kiswahili	Tanzanian shilling	-	47/50	-
Togo – Republic of Togo	**Lomé**	56 785	4.3	French	CFA franc *	327	48/50	33/65
Tunisia – Republic of Tunisia	**Tunis**	163 610	9.2	Arabic	Tunisian dinar	2063	68/71	24/47
Uganda – Republic of Uganda	**Kampala**	236 036	20.3	English	Uganda shilling	313	39/40	26/50
Western Sahara (SADR) ** – Sahrawi Arab Democratic Republic	**El Aaiún**	266 769	0.3	Arabic	Dirham	-	48/51	-
Zambia – Republic of Zambia	**Lusaka**	752 614	9.4	English	Zambian kwacha	450	39/41	18/35
Zimbabwe – Republic of Zimbabwe	**Harare**	390 580	11.5	English	Zimbabwe dollar	802	44/45	6/14
EUROPE								
Albania – Republic of Albania	**Tiranë**	28 748	3.3	Albanian	Lek	732	70/75	0/0
Andorra – Principality of Andorra	**Andorra-la-Vella**	453	0.05	Catalan	Fr. franc, Sp. peseta	13 670	-	0/0
Austria – Republic of Austria	**Vienna**	83 849	8.1	German	Schilling	25 465	74/80	0/0
Belarus – Republic of Belarus	**Minsk**	207 600	10.3	Belorussian, Russian	Rouble	1331	62/74	1/2
Belgium – Kingdom of Belgium	**Brussels**	30 513	10.2	Flemish (Dutch), French	Belgian franc	23 948	74/81	0/0
Bosnia and Herzegovina – Republic of Bosnia and Herzegovina	**Sarajevo**	51 130	2.3	Serbo-Croat	Dinar	938	70/76	0/0
Bulgaria – Republic of Bulgaria	**Sofia**	110 912	8.3	Bulgarian	Lev	1212	68/75	1/3
Croatia – Republic of Croatia	**Zagreb**	56 537	4.8	Serbo-Croat (Croatian)	Kuna	4352	69/77	0/0
Czech Republic – Czech Republic	**Prague**	78 860	10.3	Czech	Koruna	5052	70/77	0/0
Denmark – Kingdom of Denmark	**Copenhagen**	43 069	5.3	Danish	Danish krone	30 718	73/78	0/0
Estonia – Republic of Estonia	**Tallinn**	45 100	1.5	Estonian	Kroon	3239	63/74	0/0
Finland – Republic of Finland	**Helsinki**	337 032	5.3	Finnish, Swedish	Markka	23 309	73/81	0/0
France – French Republic	**Paris**	547 026	58.6	French	French franc	23 843	74/82	0/0
Germany – Federal Republic of Germany	**Berlin**	356 755	82.1	German	Deutsche mark	25 468	74/80	0/0
Greece – Hellenic Republic	**Athens**	131 944	10.5	Greek	Drachma	11 181	76/81	2/6
Hungary – Hungarian Republic	**Budapest**	93 030	10.2	Hungarian	Forint	4502	67/75	1/1
Iceland – Republic of Iceland	**Reykjavik**	103 000	0.3	Icelandic	Icelandic króna	27 181	77/81	0/0
Ireland – Republic of Ireland	**Dublin**	70 283	3.7	Irish, English	Irish pound	20 603	74/79	0/0
Italy – Italian Republic	**Rome**	301 225	57.5	Italian	Italian lira	19 962	75/81	1/2
Latvia – Republic of Latvia	**Riga**	63 700	2.5	Latvian	Lats	2246	62/74	1/1
Liechtenstein – Principality of Liechtenstein	**Vaduz**	157	0.03	German	Swiss franc	35 170	66/73	0/0
Lithuania – Republic of Lithuania	**Vilnius**	65 200	3.7	Lithuania	Litas	2578	64/76	1/1
Luxembourg – Grand Duchy of Luxembourg	**Luxembourg**	2586	0.4	Fr, Ger, Letzeburgesch	Lux. franc	37 785	73/80	0/0
Macedonia, Former Yugoslav Republic of – Republic of Macedonia	**Skopje**	25 416	2.0	Macedonian	Denar	1671	70/74	0/0
Malta – Republic of Malta	**Valletta**	316	0.4	Maltese, English	Maltese lira	8718	75/79	10/9
Moldova – Republic of Moldova	**Kishinev**	33 700	4.3	Moldovan (Romanian)	Leu	870	64/71	0/0
Monaco – Principality of Monaco	**Monaco**	1	0.03	French	French franc	23 843	-	0/0
Netherlands – Kingdom of the Netherlands	**Amsterdam**	40 844	15.6	Dutch	Guilder	23 270	75/81	0/0
Norway – Kingdom of Norway	**Oslo**	324 219	4.4	Norwegian	Norwegian krone	34 890	75/81	0/0
Poland – Polish Republic	**Warsaw**	312 677	38.7	Polish	Zloty	3505	68/77	1/1
Portugal – Portuguese Republic	**Lisbon**	92 082	9.9	Portuguese	Portuguese escudo	10 269	72/79	7/13
Romania – Romania	**Bucharest**	237 500	22.6	Romanian	Leu	1545	66/74	1/4
Russia – Russian Federation	**Moscow**	17 075 380	147.3	Russian	Rouble	3028	61/73	1/2
San Marino – Republic of San Marino	**San Marino**	61	0.025	Italian	Italian lira	19 962	73/79	0/0
Slovakia – The Slovak Republic	**Bratislava**	40 010	5.4	Slovak	Slovak koruna	3621	69/77	0/0
Slovenia – Republic of Slovenia	**Ljubljana**	20 251	2.0	Slovene	Tolar	9122	71/78	1/1
Spain – Kingdom of Spain	**Madrid**	504 782	39.3	Spanish, 3 loc	Spanish peseta	13 412	74/81	2/4
Sweden – Kingdom of Sweden	**Stockholm**	449 964	8.8	Swedish	Swedish krona	25 718	76/81	0/0
Switzerland – Swiss Confederation	**Bern**	41 288	7.1	German, French, Italian	Swiss franc	35 170	75/82	0/0
Ukraine – Ukraine	**Kiev**	603 700	50.7	Ukrainian	Hyrvna	973	64/74	-
United Kingdom – United Kingdom of Great Britain & Northern Ireland	**London**	244 046	59.0	English	Pound sterling	21 921	74/80	0/0
Vatican City – State of the Vatican City	**Vatican City**	.44	.001	Italian	Italian lira	-	-	0/0
Yugoslavia – Federal Republic of Yugoslavia	**Belgrade**	153 597	10.6	Serbo-Croat (Serbian)	Dinar	1600	69/74	-

* CFA = Colonial French African   loc = local languages   **Western Sahara (SADR) is currently occupied by Morocco

Country – Official name	Capital city	Area (km²)	Population (millions) 1997	Official language/s	Official currency	GDP per capita US$ 1997	Life expectancy male/female	Illiterate adults % male/female
ASIA								
Afghanistan– Islamic State of Afghanistan	Kabul	652 225	21.9	Pashto, Dari	Afghani	286	45/46	54/84
Armenia – Republic of Armenia	Yerevan	29 800	3.8	Armenian	Dram	458	67/73	1/1
Azerbaijan – Republic of Azerbaijan	Baku	86 600	7.6	Azeri	Manat	496	65/74	1/1
Bahrain – State of Bahrain	Manama	622	0.6	Arabic	Bahraini dinar	9522	71/75	11/20
Bangladesh– People's Republic of Bangladesh	Dhaka	148 393	123.1	Bengali	Taka	286	58/58	51/74
Bhutan – Kingdom of Bhutan	Thimphu	47 000	1.7	Dzongkha	Ngultrum	197	59/62	44/72
Brunei – State of Brunei Darussalam	Bandar Seri Begawan	5765	0.3	Malay	Brunei dollar (Ringgit)	17 890	73/78	7/15
Burma – Union of Myanmar	Rangoon	676 552	46.0	Burmese	Kyat	274	58/61	12/22
Cambodia – Kingdom of Cambodia	Phnom Penh	181 035	10.9	Khmer	Riel	159	51/55	9/10
China – People's Republic of China	Beijing	9 572 900	1234.3	Chinese (Mandarin)	Renminbi (Yuan)	745	68/72	10/27
Cyprus – Republic of Cyprus	Nicosia	9251	0.7	Greek, Turkish	Cyprus pound	11 106	75/80	2/7
Georgia – Republic of Georgia	Tbilisi	69 700	5.4	Georgian	Lari	966	68/76	1/1
India – Republic of India	New Delhi	3 165 596	953	Hindi, English	Indian rupee	402	62/63	34/62
Indonesia – Republic of Indonesia	Jakarta	1 904 569	200.6	Bahasa Indonesia	Rupiah	1055	63/67	10/22
Iran – Islamic Republic of Iran	Tehran	1 648 000	63.1	Farsi (Persian)	Iranian rial	2466	68/70	21/37
Iraq – Republic of Iraq	Baghdad	434 924	21.4	Arabic	Iraqi dinar	7037	60/63	29/55
Israel – State of Israel	Jerusalem	21 920	5.8	Hebrew, Arabic	Shekel	15 800	75/79	3/7
Japan – Nippon (Land of the Rising Sun)	Tokyo	377 727	125.4	Japanese	Yen	33 265	76/82	0/0
Jordan – Hashemite Kingdom of Jordan	Amman	97 740	5.7	Arabic	Jordan dinar	1306	69/71	9/20
Kazakstan – Republic of Kazakstan	Astana	2 715 100	16.5	Kazak	Tenge	1255	63/72	1/1
Korea, North – People's Democratic Republic of Korea	Pyongyang	122 762	24.3	Korean	Won	232	69/75	-
Korea, South – Republic of Korea	Seoul	99 263	45.4	Korean	Won	9677	68/76	1/5
Kuwait – State of Kuwait	Kuwait	17 818	1.8	Arabic	Kuwaiti dinar	17 533	74/78	18/24
Kyrgyzstan – Kyrgyz Republic	Bishkek	198 500	4.6	Kyrgyz, Russian	Som	380	63/72	1/1
Laos – Lao People's Democratic Republic	Vientiane	236 800	5.0	Lao	Kip	348	52/54	31/56
Lebanon – Republic of Lebanon	Beirut	10 452	3.8	Arabic	Lebanese pound	4546	68/72	9/23
Malaysia – Federation of Malaysia	Kuala Lumpur	329 749	20.6	Malay	Malaysian ringgit	4665	70/74	11/21
Maldives – Republic of Maldives	Malé	298	0.25	Divehi	Rufiyaa	1325	66/63	5/5
Mongolia – Mongolian Republic	Ulan Bator	1 565 000	2.3	Halh mongol	Tugrik	375	64/67	11/23
Nepal – Kingdom of Nepal	Kathmandu	140 797	23.2	Nepalese	Nepalese rupee	217	58/57	46/81
Oman – Sultanate of Oman	Muscat	212 459	2.3	Arabic	Omani rial	6751	69/73	25/49
Pakistan – Islamic Republic of Pakistan	Islamabad	796 095	144.5	Urdu	Pakistan rupee	466	63/65	46/76
Philippines – Republic of the Philippines	Manila	300 000	72.0	Pilipino, English	Philippine piso	1151	66/70	6/6
Qatar – State of Qatar	Doha	11 000	0.7	Arabic	Qatari riyal	16 166	70/75	21/20
Saudi Arabia – Kingdom of Saudi Arabia	Riyadh	2 149 690	19.4	Arabic	Saudi rial	6921	70/73	20/40
Singapore – Republic of Singapore	Singapore	641	3.0	Malay, Ch, Eng, Tamil	Singapore dollar	28 107	75/79	4/14
Sri Lanka – Democratic Socialist Republic of Sri Lanka	Colombo	65 609	18.6	Sinhala, Tamil	Sri Lankan rupee	826	71/75	6/13
Syria – Syrian Arab Republic	Damascus	185 180	15.6	Arabic	Syrian pound	4343	67/71	15/46
Taiwan – Republic of China	Taipei	35 760	21.4	Chinese (Mandarin)	New Taiwan dollar	-	72/78	
Tajikistan – Republic of Tajikistan	Dushanbe	143 100	5.9	Tajik	Tajik rouble	178	64/70	1/1
Thailand – Kingdom of Thailand	Bangkok	514 000	60.7	Thai	Baht	2576	66/72	4/8
Turkey – Republic of Turkey	Ankara	780 576	63.9	Turkish	Turkish lira	3026	66/72	8/28
Turkmenistan – Republic of Turkmenistan	Ashkhabad	488 100	4.6	Turkmen	Manat	188	62/69	1/1
United Arab Emirates – United Arab Emirates	Abu Dhabi	83 600	1.9	Arabic	UAE dirham	20 203	74/76	27/25
Uzbekistan– Republic of Uzbekistan	Tashkent	449 600	23.2	Uzbek	Som	426	64/71	1/1
Vietnam– Socialist Republic of Vietnam	Hanoi	329 556	76.6	Vietnamese	Dong	330	65/70	5/12
Yemen – Republic of Yemen	Sana'a	527 968	14.7	Arabic	Yemeni riyal	318	57/58	38/82
NORTH AMERICA								
Antigua and Barbuda– Antigua and Barbuda	St John's	442	0.1	English	E Caribbean dollar	8791	68/73	-
Bahamas – Commonwealth of the Bahamas	Nassau	13 935	0.3	English	Bahamian dollar	13 047	71/72	5/4
Barbados – Barbados	Bridgetown	431	0.3	English	Barbados dollar	8178	70/76	2/3
Belize – Belize	Belmopan	22 965	0.2	English	Belize dollar	2788	69/73	-
Canada – Canada	Ottawa	9 976 139	30.3	English, French	Canadian dollar	20 082	76/82	0/0
Costa Rica – Republic of Costa Rica	San José	50 700	3.5	Spanish	Costa Rican colon	2540	74/79	5/5
Cuba – Republic of Cuba	Havana	110 861	11.1	Spanish	Cuban peso	2100	74/77	4/4
Dominica – Commonwealth of Dominica	Roseau	751	0.1	English	E Caribbean dollar	3427	71/76	0/0
Dominican Republic– Dominican Republic	Santo Domingo	49 734	8.1	Spanish	Peso oro	1841	71/75	18/19
El Salvador – Republic of El Salvador	San Salvador	21 041	5.9	Spanish	Salvadorian colón	1935	66/72	21/27
Grenada – Grenada	St George's	344	0.1	English	E Caribbean dollar	3353	63/66	-
Guatemala – Republic of Guatemala	Guatemala City	108 889	10.5	Spanish	Quetzal	1691	61/67	27/42
Haiti – Republic of Haiti	Port-au-Prince	27 750	7.5	French, Créole	Gourde	398	47/51	53/59
Honduras– Republic of Honduras	Tegucigalpa	112 088	6.0	Spanish	Lempira	785	68/72	30/31
Jamaica – Jamaica	Kingston	10 991	2.6	English	Jamaican dollar	2634	73/77	20/11
Mexico – United States of Mexico	Mexico City	1 927 547	94.3	Spanish	Mexican peso	4265	67/75	8/13
Nicaragua – Republic of Nicaragua	Managua	130 000	4.7	Spanish	Córdoba	431	66/71	37/37
Panama – Republic of Panama	Panama City	77 082	2.7	Spanish	Balboa	3159	72/76	9/10
St Kitts and Nevis – Federation of St Kitts and Nevis	Basseterre	306	0.04	English	E Caribbean dollar	6405	68/74	-
St Lucia – Saint Lucia	Castries	616	0.1	English	E Caribbean dollar	4031	69/76	-
St Vincent and the Grenadines – St Vincent and the Grenadines	Kingstown	388	0.1	English	E Caribbean dollar	2543	71/74	-
United States of America – United States of America	Washington DC	9 372 614	267.6	English	US dollar	28 789	73/80	0/0
SOUTH AMERICA								
Argentina – Argentine Republic	Buenos Aires	2 766 889	35.7	Spanish	Peso	9070	70/77	4/4
Bolivia – Republic of Bolivia	La Paz, Sucre	1 098 581	7.6	Spanish	Boliviano	996	60/63	10/25
Brazil – Federative Republic of Brazil	Brasília	8 511 996	163.7	Portuguese	Real	4930	63/71	17/17
Chile – Republic of Chile	Santiago	756 945	14.6	Spanish	Chilean peso	5271	72/78	5/5
Colombia – Republic of Colombia	Bogotá	1 138 914	40.0	Spanish	Colombian peso	2384	67/74	9/10
Ecuador– Republic of Ecuador	Quito	283 561	11.9	Spanish	Sucre	1648	67/72	8/12
Guyana – Co-operative Republic of Guyana	Georgetown	214 969	0.7	English	Guyana dollar	881	61/67	1/3
Paraguay – Republic of Paraguay	Asunción	406 752	5.1	Spanish	Guaraní	1961	66/72	7/10
Peru – Republic of Peru	Lima	1 285 216	24.4	Sp, Quechua, Aymara	Nuevo sol	2674	66/71	7/17
Suriname – Republic of Suriname	Paramaribo	163 265	0.4	Dutch	Suriname guilder	3733	67/73	5/9
Trinidad and Tobago – Republic of Trinidad and Tobago	Port of Spain	5130	1.3	English	Trinidad & Tobago dollar	4397	65/71	1/3
Uruguay – Oriental Republic of Uruguay	Montevideo	176 215	3.3	Spanish	Uruguayan peso	6026	70/78	3/2
Venezuela – Republic of Venezuela	Caracas	912 050	22.8	Spanish	Bolívar	3678	70/76	8/9
AUSTRALASIA								
Australia – Commonwealth of Australia	Canberra	7 682 300	18.5	English	Australian dollar	21 971	75/81	0/0
Cook Islands– Cook Islands	Avarua	236	0.02	English	New Zealand dollar	5213	67/73	-
Fiji – Republic of Fiji	Suva	18 274	0.8	English	Fiji dollar	2733	70/75	6/11
Kiribati – Republic of Kiribati	Bairiki	728	0.07	English	Australian dollar	680	58/63	-
Marshall Islands– Republic of the Marshall Islands	Dalap-Uliga-Darrit (Majuro) 179		0.06	English	US dollar	1661	59/63	-
Micronesia – Federated States of Micronesia	Kolonia	627	0.1	English	US dollar	1899	64/69	-
Nauru – Republic of Nauru	Nauru	21	0.009	Nauruan, English	Australian dollar	-	-	-
New Zealand– New Zealand	Wellington	269 057	3.8	English, Maori	New Zealand dollar	17 359	74/79	0/0
Niue – Niue	Alofi	259	0.004	English	New Zealand dollar	-	-	-
Palau – Republic of Palau	Koror	464	0.02	Palauan, English	US dollar	5811	65/69	-
Papua New Guinea– Papua New Guinea	Port Moresby	462 840	4.5	English	Kina	1031	57/58	19/37
Samoa – Independent State of Samoa	Apia	2842	0.2	Samoan, English	Tala	1094	69/73	-
Solomon Islands – Solomon Islands	Honiara	28 446	0.4	English	Solomon I dollar	845	69/73	-
Tonga – Kingdom of Tonga	Nuku'alofa	699	0.1	Tongan, English	Pa'anga	1788	67/71	-
Tuvalu – Tuvalu	Funafuti	158	0.009	Tuvaluan, English	Australian dollar	-	59/60	-
Vanuatu – Republic of Vanuatu	Vila	14 763	0.2	Bislama, French, English	Vatu	1420	65/69	-

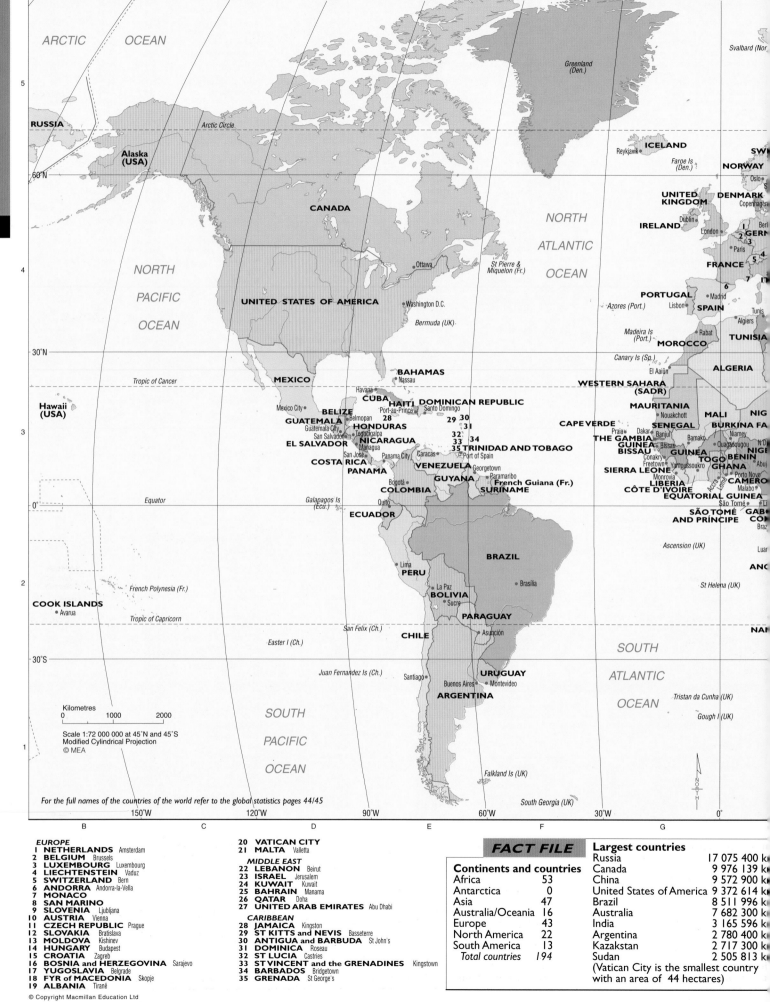

EUROPE
1 NETHERLANDS Amsterdam
2 BELGIUM Brussels
3 LUXEMBOURG Luxembourg
4 LIECHTENSTEIN Vaduz
5 SWITZERLAND Bern
6 ANDORRA Andorra-la-Vella
7 MONACO
8 SAN MARINO
9 SLOVENIA Ljubljana
10 AUSTRIA Vienna
11 CZECH REPUBLIC Prague
12 SLOVAKIA Bratislava
13 MOLDOVA Kishinev
14 HUNGARY Budapest
15 CROATIA Zagreb
16 BOSNIA and HERZEGOVINA Sarajevo
17 YUGOSLAVIA Belgrade
18 FYR of MACEDONIA Skopje
19 ALBANIA Tiranë

20 VATICAN CITY
21 MALTA Valletta

MIDDLE EAST
22 LEBANON Beirut
23 ISRAEL Jerusalem
24 KUWAIT Kuwait
25 BAHRAIN Manama
26 QATAR Doha
27 UNITED ARAB EMIRATES Abu Dhabi

CARIBBEAN
28 JAMAICA Kingston
29 ST KITTS and NEVIS Basseterre
30 ANTIGUA and BARBUDA St John's
31 DOMINICA Roseau
32 ST LUCIA Castries
33 ST VINCENT and the GRENADINES Kingstown
34 BARBADOS Bridgetown
35 GRENADA St George's

FACT FILE

Continents and countries	
Africa	53
Antarctica	0
Asia	47
Australia/Oceania	16
Europe	43
North America	22
South America	13
Total countries	**194**

Largest countries

Russia	17 075 400 k
Canada	9 976 139 k
China	9 572 900 k
United States of America	9 372 614 k
Brazil	8 511 996 k
Australia	7 682 300 k
India	3 165 596 k
Argentina	2 780 400 k
Kazakstan	2 717 300 k
Sudan	2 505 813 k

(Vatican City is the smallest country with an area of 44 hectares)

For the full names of the countries of the world refer to the global statistics pages 44/45

ARCTIC OCEAN

CANADA

Alaska (USA)

RUSSIA

Moscow

STONIA
ATVIA
HUANIA
ELARUS
ND
UKRAINE
Kiev
N3
Minsk

KAZAKSTAN

Astana

MONGOLIA

Ulan Bator

NORTH
PACIFIC

OCEAN

60°N

MANIA
Bucharest
BULGARIA
GEORGIA
ARMENIA
ECE
TURKEY
CYPRUS
Nicosia
SYRIA
23
Damascus
JORDAN
Amman
IRAQ
Baghdad
Cairo
EGYPT

Tbilisi
AZERBAIJAN
Ankara
Yerevan
Baku
TURKMENISTAN
Ashkhabad
22
Tehran
IRAN
24

UZBEKISTAN
Tashkent
KYRGYZSTAN
Bishkek
Dushanbe
TAJIKISTAN
Kabul
AFGHANISTAN
Islamabad

Beijing

NORTH
KOREA
Pyongyang
Seoul
SOUTH
KOREA

JAPAN
Tokyo

30°N

SAUDI ARABIA

Riyadh
25 26
27
Muscat
OMAN

PAKISTAN
New Delhi
NEPAL
Kathmandu
BHUTAN
Thimphu

BANGLADESH
Dhaka

CHINA

T'ai-pei

TAIWAN

ERITREA
Asmara
Khartoum
Sana'a
YEMEN
SUDAN
DJIBOUTI
Djibouti
RAL
CAN
BLIC
ETHIOPIA
Addis Ababa
UGANDA
Kampala
KENYA
Nairobi
NDA
Kigali
mbura
BURUNDI
GO
REP.)
Dodoma
TANZANIA
COMOROS
Moroni
AMBIA
usaka
Lilongwe
MALAWI
Harare
ZIMBABWE
TSWANA
MOZAMBIQUE
Pretoria
Maputo
Mbabane
SWAZILAND
Maseru
LESOTHO
TH AFRICA

INDIA
BURMA
Rangoon
THAILAND
Bangkok
LAOS
Vientiane
CAMBODIA
Phnom Penh
VIETNAM
Hanoi

Manila
PHILIPPINES

Northern
Marianas
(USA)
Guam (USA)

MICRONESIA
PALAU
Palikir

MARSHALL
ISLANDS
Majuro

SRI LANKA
Colombo
Male
MALDIVES

Mogadishu
SOMALIA

SEYCHELLES
Victoria

Chagos Arch (UK)

BRUNEI
Bandar Seri Begawan
Kuala Lumpur
MALAYSIA
SINGAPORE

Jakarta

INDONESIA
Dili
EAST
TIMOR
(see addendum on
page 3 of the atlas)
Port Moresby

PAPUA
NEW GUINEA

SOLOMON
ISLANDS
Honiara

NAURU
Nauru

Bairiki

KIRIBATI

TUVALU
Funafuti

SAMOA
Apia
American
Samoa (USA)

MADAGASCAR
Antananarivo
MAURITIUS
Port Louis
Réunion (Fr.)

Christmas I (Aust.)

Cocos Is (Aust.)

INDIAN

OCEAN

AUSTRALIA

New Caledonia
(Fr.)

VANUATU
Vila
Suva
FIJI

NIUE
Avarua
Nuku'alofa
TONGA
COOK IS

30°S

Canberra

Norfolk I (Aust.)
Lord Howe I (Aust.)

NEW
ZEALAND
Wellington

Chatham Is (N.Z.)

Kerguelen Is (Fr.)

Heard I (Aust.)

Auckland Is (N.Z.)

Macquarie I (Aust.)

International Date Line

rgest population	(millions)
ina	1234.3
ia	953.0
ited States of America	265.8
onesia	200.6
azil	164.4
ssia	146.7
kistan	144.5
an	125.4
ngladesh	123.1
geria	115.0

he smallest population is Vatican City
h a population of 1000 people)

Recently independent nations

Palau – 1994 (formerly part of islands of Micronesia)
Czech Republic – 1993 (formerly part of Czechoslovakia)
Slovakia – 1993 (formerly part of Czechoslovakia)
Bosnia and Herzegovina – 1992 (formerly part of Yugoslavia)
Croatia – 1991 (formerly part of Yugoslavia)
Slovenia – 1991 (formerly part of Yugoslavia)
Former Yugoslav Republic of Macedonia – 1991 (formerly part
    of Yugoslavia)
Armenia, Azerbaijan, Belarus, Georgia, Kazakstan, Kyrgyzstan,
Moldova, Russia, Tajikistan, Turkmenistan, Ukraine and
    Uzbekistan – 1991 (formerly part of USSR)
Estonia, Latvia and Lithuania – 1990 (formerly part of USSR)

Some disputed areas

Bougainville – Independence/Papua New Guinea
Chechnya – Independence/Russia
Falkland Islands – Argentina/United Kingdom
Jammu and Kashmir – Pakistan/India/China
Kuril Islands – Russia/Japan
Northern Ireland – Independence/United Kingdom
Palestine – Independence/Israel
Spratly Islands – Philippines/Vietnam/Malaysia/Taiwan
Taiwan – Taiwan/China
Tibet – Independence/China
Timor – Independence/Indonesia
Western Sahara (SADR) – Independence/Morocco

48

POPULATION DENSITY

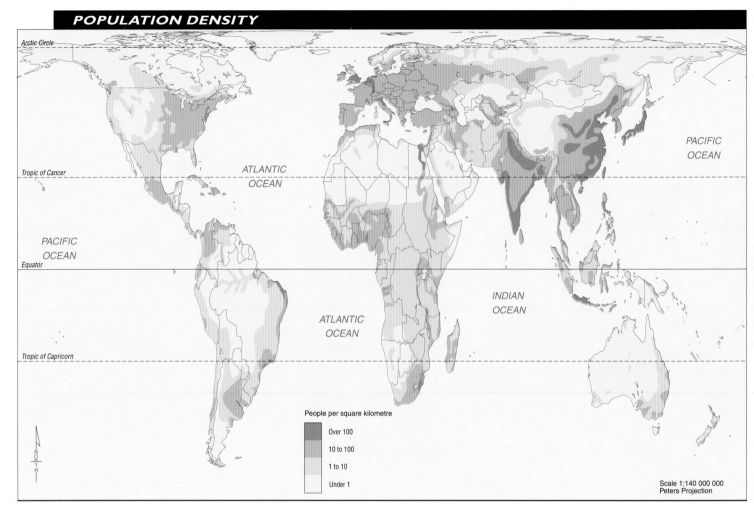

Arctic Circle
Tropic of Cancer
PACIFIC OCEAN
ATLANTIC OCEAN
Equator
PACIFIC OCEAN
INDIAN OCEAN
ATLANTIC OCEAN
Tropic of Capricorn

People per square kilometre

Over 100
10 to 100
1 to 10
Under 1

Scale 1:140 000 000
Peters Projection

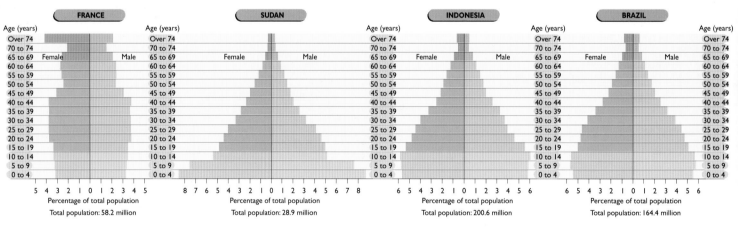

FRANCE

Age (years) | Age (years)
Over 74
70 to 74
65 to 69 Female   Male
60 to 64
55 to 59
50 to 54
45 to 49
40 to 44
35 to 39
30 to 34
25 to 29
20 to 24
15 to 19
10 to 14
5 to 9
0 to 4

5 4 3 2 1 0 1 2 3 4 5
Percentage of total population
Total population: 58.2 million

SUDAN

Age (years) | Age (years)
Female   Male

8 7 6 5 4 3 2 1 0 1 2 3 4 5 6 7 8
Percentage of total population
Total population: 28.9 million

INDONESIA

Age (years) | Age (years)
Female   Male

6 5 4 3 2 1 0 1 2 3 4 5 6
Percentage of total population
Total population: 200.6 million

BRAZIL

Age (years) | Age (years)
Female   Male

6 5 4 3 2 1 0 1 2 3 4 5 6
Percentage of total population
Total population: 164.4 million

CANADA

Age (years) | Age (years)
Over 74
70 to 74
65 to 69 Female   Male
60 to 64
55 to 59
50 to 54
45 to 49
40 to 44
35 to 39
30 to 34
25 to 29
20 to 24
15 to 19
10 to 14
5 to 9
0 to 4

6 5 4 3 2 1 0 1 2 3 4 5 6
Percentage of total population
Total population: 29.8 million

NEW ZEALAND

Age (years) | Age (years)
Female   Male

6 5 4 3 2 1 0 1 2 3 4 5 6
Percentage of total population
Total population: 3.6 million

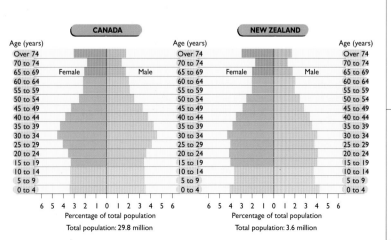

LARGEST CITIES
(population in millions)

1975		1996		2000 (estimate)	
New York	19.8	Tokyo	23.4	Mexico City	31.0
Tokyo	17.7	Mexico City	22.9	São Paulo	25.8
Mexico City	11.9	New York	21.8	Tokyo	24.2
Shanghai	11.6	São Paulo	19.9	New York	22.8
Los Angeles	10.8	Shanghai	17.7	Shanghai	22.7
São Paulo	10.7	Beijing	15.3	Beijing	19.9
London	10.4	Rio de Janeiro	14.7	Rio de Janeiro	19.0
Buenos Aires	9.3	Los Angeles	13.3	Mumbai (Bombay)	17.1
Rhine - Ruhr	9.3	Mumbai (Bombay)	12.0	Kolkata (Calcutta)	16.7
Paris	9.2	Kolkata (Calcutta)	11.9	Jakarta	16.6
Rio de Janeiro	8.9	Seoul	11.8	Seoul	14.2
Beijing	8.7	Buenos Aires	11.4	Los Angeles	14.2

WORLD POPULATION
(1996 – 5771 million)

Asia
North America
South America
Africa
Europe
Australia/ Oceania

LARGEST COUNTRIES
(population in millions)

1	China	1234.3
2	India	953.0
3	USA	265.8
4	Indonesia	200.6
5	Brazil	164.4
6	Russia	146.7
7	Pakistan	144.5
8	Japan	125.4
9	Bangladesh	123.1
10	Nigeria	115.0

POPULATION GROWTH

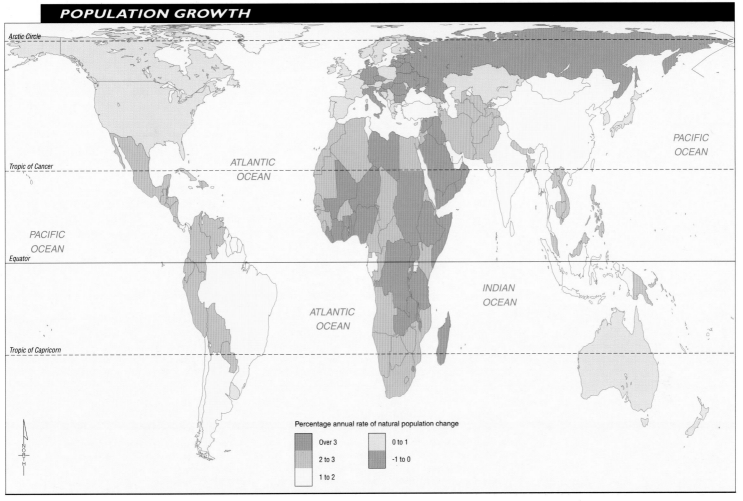

Percentage annual rate of natural population change

Over 3		0 to 1	
2 to 3		-1 to 0	
1 to 2			

URBANISATION

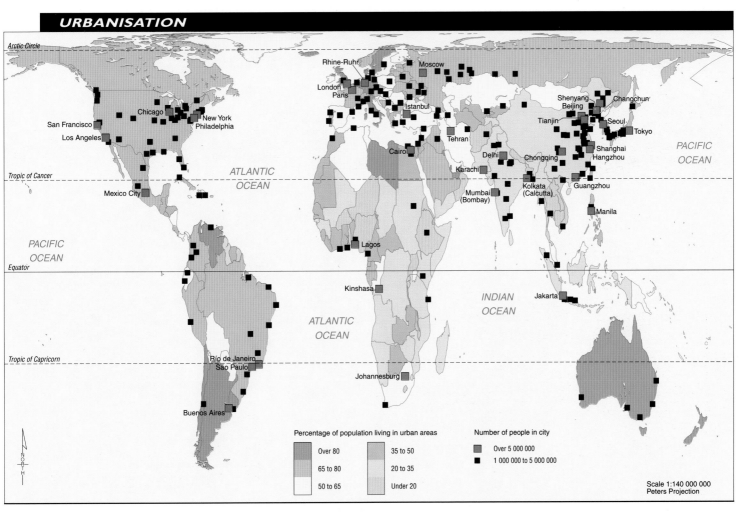

Percentage of population living in urban areas

Over 80		35 to 50	
65 to 80		20 to 35	
50 to 65		Under 20	

Number of people in city

Over 5 000 000	
1 000 000 to 5 000 000	

Scale 1:140 000 000
Peters Projection

MIGRATION

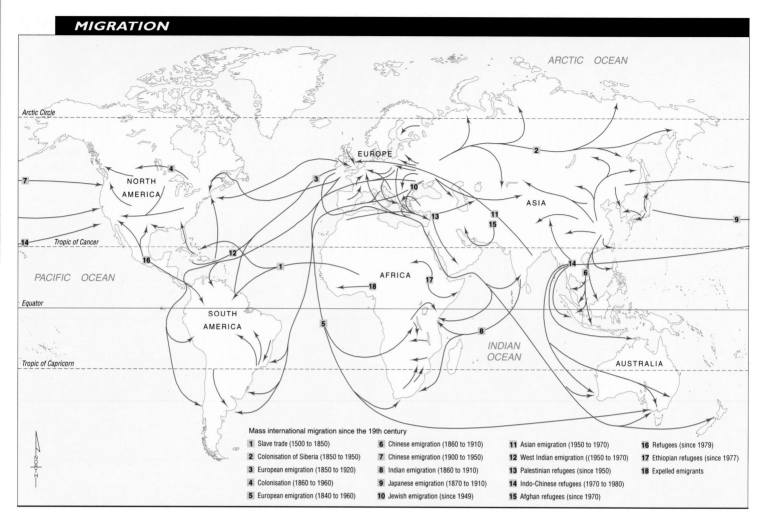

Mass international migration since the 19th century

1 Slave trade (1500 to 1850)	**6** Chinese emigration (1860 to 1910)	**11** Asian emigration (1950 to 1970)	**16** Refugees (since 1979)
2 Colonisation of Siberia (1850 to 1950)	**7** Chinese emigration (1900 to 1950)	**12** West Indian emigration ((1950 to 1970)	**17** Ethiopian refugees (since 1977)
3 European emigration (1850 to 1920)	**8** Indian emigration (1860 to 1910)	**13** Palestinian refugees (since 1950)	**18** Expelled emigrants
4 Colonisation (1860 to 1960)	**9** Japanese emigration (1870 to 1910)	**14** Indo-Chinese refugees (1970 to 1980)	
5 European emigration (1840 to 1960)	**10** Jewish emigration (since 1949)	**15** Afghan refugees (since 1970)	

REFUGEES

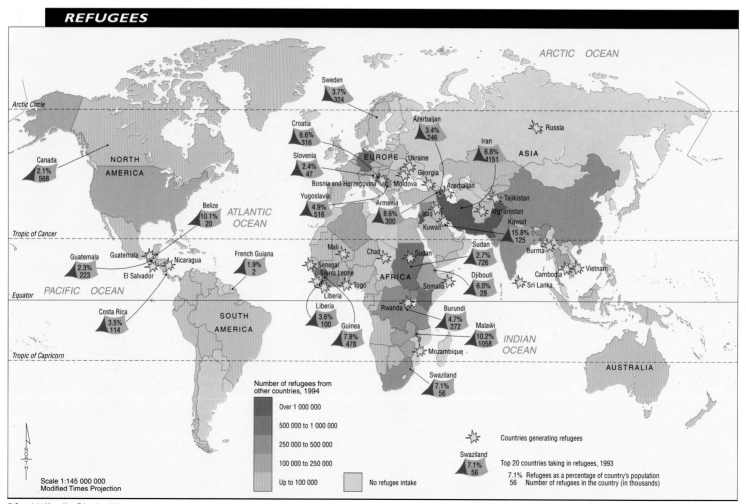

Number of refugees from other countries, 1994

- Over 1 000 000
- 500 000 to 1 000 000
- 250 000 to 500 000
- 100 000 to 250 000
- Up to 100 000
- No refugee intake

Countries generating refugees

Top 20 countries taking in refugees, 1993

Swaziland
7.1%
56

7.1% Refugees as a percentage of country's population
56 Number of refugees in the country (in thousands)

Scale 1:145 000 000
Modified Times Projection

© Copyright Macmillan Education Ltd

50

LANGUAGES

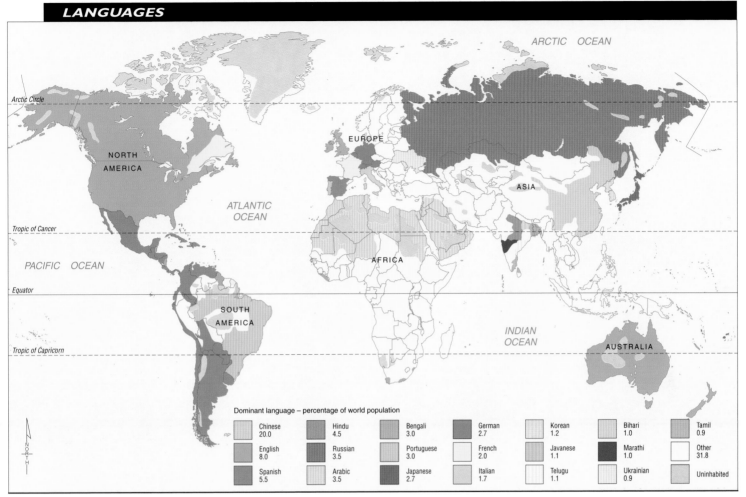

Dominant language – percentage of world population

Chinese 20.0	Hindu 4.5	Bengali 3.0
English 8.0	Russian 3.5	Portuguese 3.0
Spanish 5.5	Arabic 3.5	Japanese 2.7
German 2.7	Korean 1.2	Bihari 1.0
French 2.0	Javanese 1.1	Marathi 1.0
Italian 1.7	Telugu 1.1	Ukrainian 0.9
Tamil 0.9	Other 31.8	Uninhabited

RELIGION

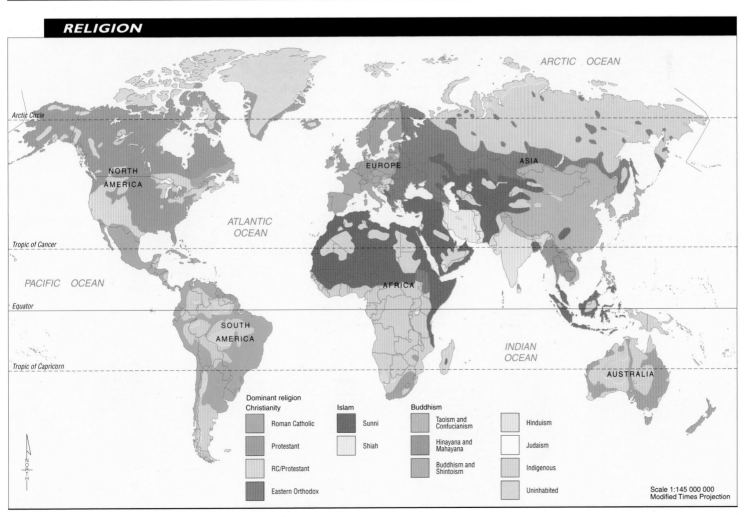

Dominant religion

Christianity
- Roman Catholic
- Protestant
- RC/Protestant
- Eastern Orthodox

Islam
- Sunni
- Shiah

Buddhism
- Taoism and Confucianism
- Hinayana and Mahayana
- Buddhism and Shintoism
- Uninhabited

- Hinduism
- Judaism
- Indigenous

Scale 1:145 000 000
Modified Times Projection

INFANT MORTALITY

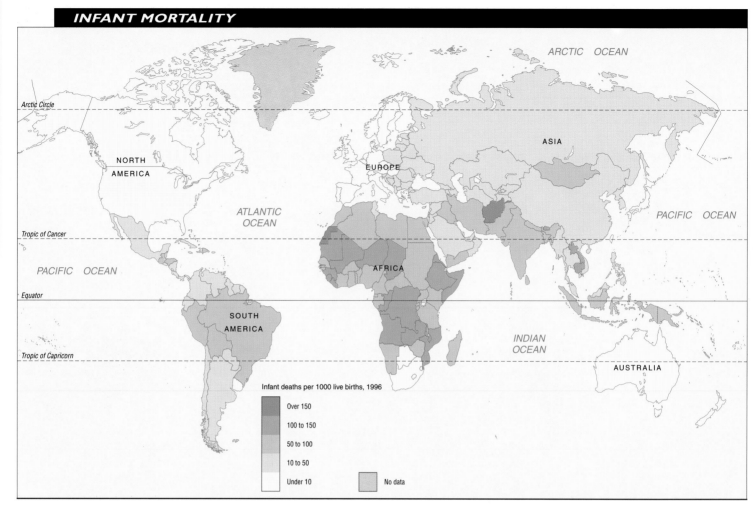

Infant deaths per 1000 live births, 1996

- Over 150
- 100 to 150
- 50 to 100
- 10 to 50
- Under 10
- No data

LIFE EXPECTANCY

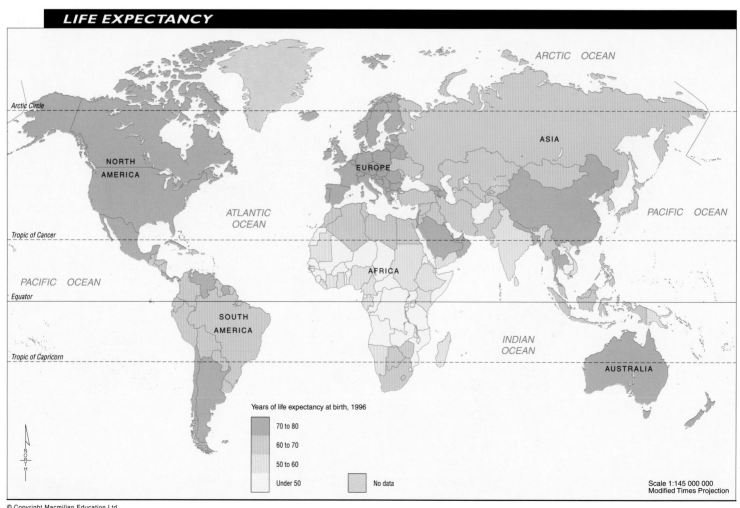

Years of life expectancy at birth, 1996

- 70 to 80
- 60 to 70
- 50 to 60
- Under 50
- No data

Scale 1:145 000 000
Modified Times Projection

ADULT LITERACY

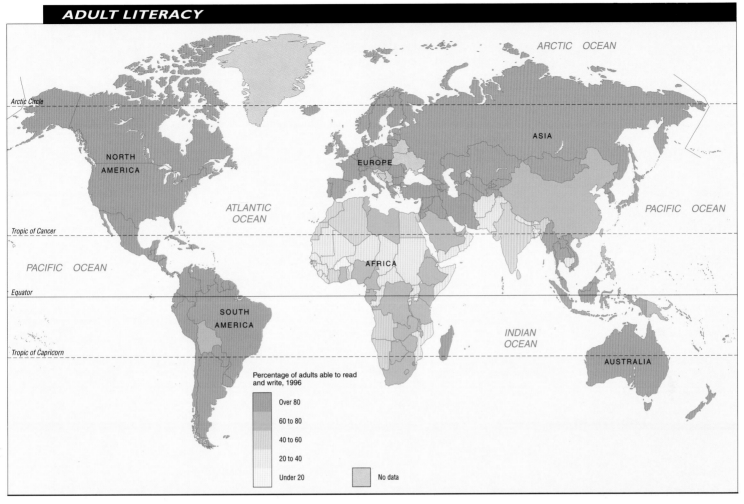

Percentage of adults able to read and write, 1996

- Over 80
- 60 to 80
- 40 to 60
- 20 to 40
- Under 20
- No data

ACCESS TO MEDIA

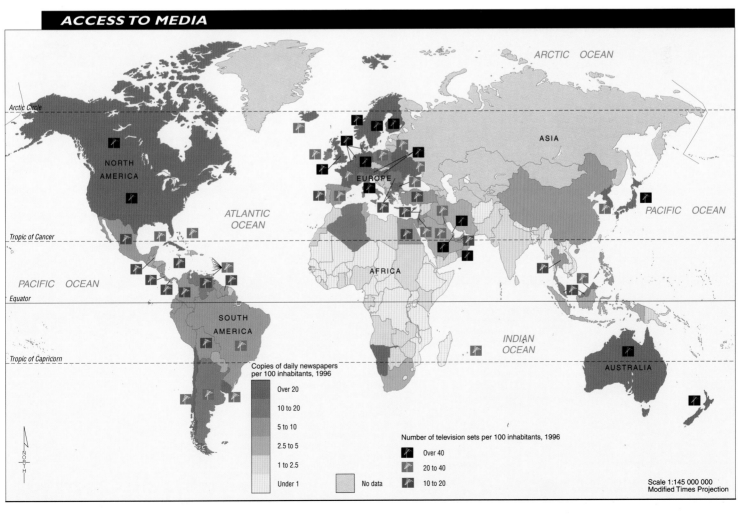

Copies of daily newspapers per 100 inhabitants, 1996

- Over 20
- 10 to 20
- 5 to 10
- 2.5 to 5
- 1 to 2.5
- Under 1
- No data

Number of television sets per 100 inhabitants, 1996

- Over 40
- 20 to 40
- 10 to 20

Scale 1:145 000 000
Modified Times Projection

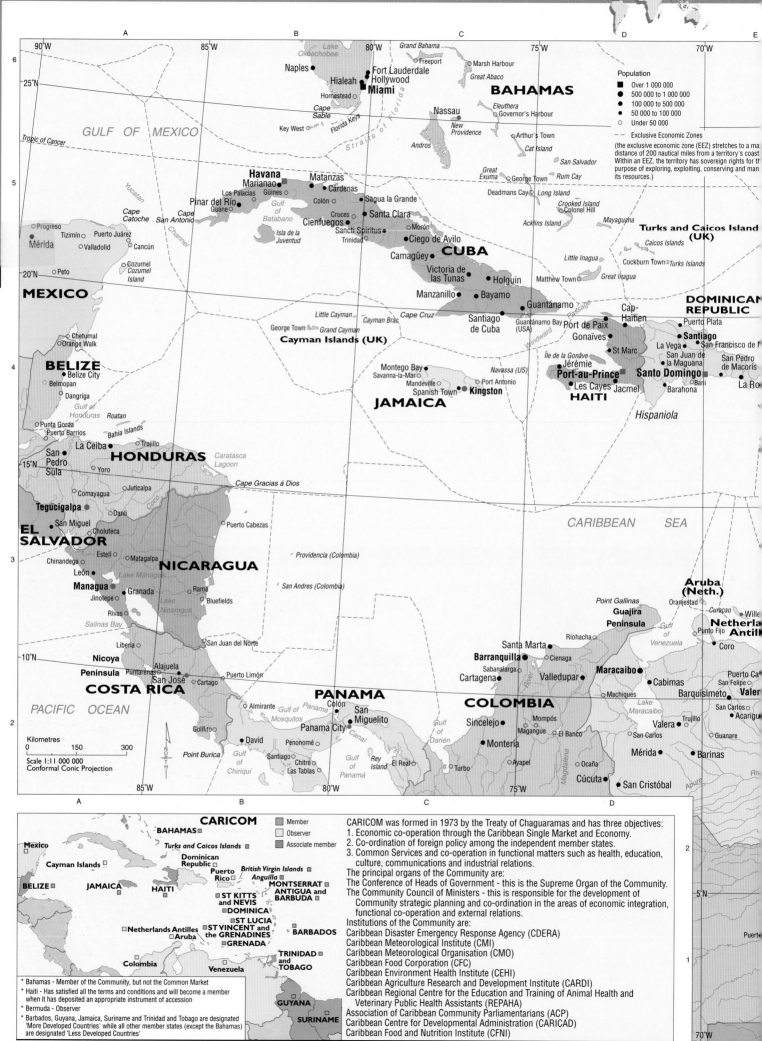

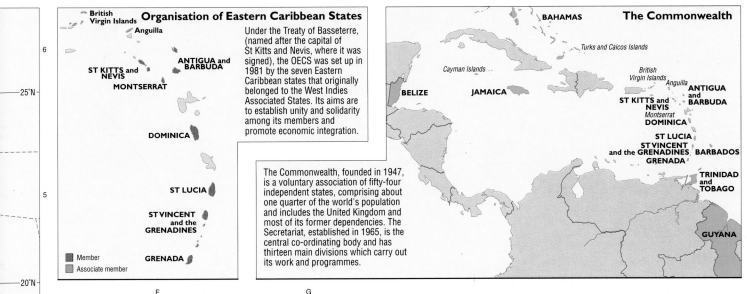

Organisation of Eastern Caribbean States

Under the Treaty of Basseterre, (named after the capital of St Kitts and Nevis, where it was signed), the OECS was set up in 1981 by the seven Eastern Caribbean states that originally belonged to the West Indies Associated States. Its aims are to establish unity and solidarity among its members and promote economic integration.

British Virgin Islands
Anguilla
ST KITTS and NEVIS
ANTIGUA and BARBUDA
MONTSERRAT
DOMINICA
ST LUCIA
ST VINCENT and the GRENADINES
GRENADA

■ Member
■ Associate member

The Commonwealth

The Commonwealth, founded in 1947, is a voluntary association of fifty-four independent states, comprising about one quarter of the world's population and includes the United Kingdom and most of its former dependencies. The Secretariat, established in 1965, is the central co-ordinating body and has thirteen main divisions which carry out its work and programmes.

BAHAMAS
Turks and Caicos Islands
Cayman Islands
British Virgin Islands
Anguilla
ANTIGUA and BARBUDA
ST KITTS and NEVIS
Montserrat
DOMINICA
ST LUCIA
ST VINCENT and the GRENADINES
BARBADOS
GRENADA
TRINIDAD and TOBAGO
GUYANA
BELIZE
JAMAICA

Other organisations

Association of Caribbean States (ACS)

Founded in 1994 the ACS aims to promote economic integration and co-operation in the region; to undertake concerted action to protect the environment (particularly the Caribbean Sea); and to co-operate in the areas of science and technology, health, transport, education and culture. All the CARICOM countries are members plus Colombia, Costa Rica, Cuba, Dominican Republic, El Salvador, Guatemala, Haiti, Honduras, Mexico, Panama, Nicaragua, Suriname and Venezuela.

CARIBCAN was created by the Canadian government in 1986 to give preferential, duty free, access to the Canadian market for almost all imports from the Commonwealth Caribbean countries (and associate members). For members see the Commonwealth map above.

Caribbean Basin Initiative (CBI)

The CBI is a US programme to promote economic development in beneficiary countries, especially through investment in non-traditional sectors of their economies. Beneficiary countries are all the CARICOM countries, Central America (with the exception of Mexico), Aruba, BVI, Dominican Rep., and Neths. Antilles.

Organisation of American States (OAS)

The OAS was founded in 1948 to foster peace, security, mutual understanding and co-operation among the nations of the Western Hemisphere. All the independent countries of North, Central and South America and the Caribbean are members with the exception of Cuba, which was suspended in 1962.

The Lomé Convention for African, Caribbean and Pacific (ACP) Countries

Under the first Lomé Convention (1975) the European Community (now called the European Union), committed funds for aid and investment to developing countries. A special provision has been made for over 99% of ACP exports (mainly agricultural) to enter the EU market duty free. All the independent Caribbean countries with the exception of Cuba are ACP states.

REGIONAL STATISTICS

COUNTRY	CAPITAL	AREA (in km²)	STATUS	LANGUAGE
Anguilla	The Valley	96	British	English
Antigua and Barbuda	St John's	442	Independent	English
Aruba	Oranjestad	193	Dutch	Dutch and Papiamento
Bahamas	Nassau	13 939	Independent	English
Barbados	Bridgetown	430	Independent	English
Belize	Belmopan	22 965	Independent	English
Bermuda	Hamilton	53	British	English
British Virgin Islands	Road Town	153	British	English
Cayman Islands	George Town	259	British	English
Cuba	Havana	110 860	Independent	Spanish
Dominica	Roseau	750	Independent	English
Dominican Republic	Santo Domingo	48 422	Independent	Spanish
Grenada	St George's	344	Independent	English
Guadeloupe	Basse-Terre	1 780	French	French
Guyana	Georgetown	214 969	Independent	English
Haiti	Port-au-Prince	27 750	Independent	French and Creole
Jamaica	Kingston	10 991	Independent	English
Martinique	Fort-de-France	1 100	French	French
Montserrat	Plymouth	102	British	English
Netherlands Antilles	Willemstad	800	Dutch	Dutch and Papiamento
Puerto Rico	San Juan	8 959	American	Spanish and English
St Kitts and Nevis	Basseterre	267	Independent	English
St Lucia	Castries	616	Independent	English
St Vincent and the Grenadines	Kingstown	389	Independent	English
Trinidad and Tobago	Port of Spain	5 128	Independent	English
Turks and Caicos Islands	Cockburn Town	430	British	English
US Virgin Islands	Charlotte Amalie	355	American	English

ATLANTIC OCEAN

British Virgin Islands
Road Town
The Valley
Anguilla (UK)
St Martin (France)
St Maarten
Charlotte Amalie
St Croix
US Virgin Islands
Neth. Antilles
Basseterre
St Kitts Nevis
ST KITTS and NEVIS
Barbuda
St John's
Antigua
ANTIGUA and BARBUDA
Plymouth
Montserrat (UK)
Guadeloupe (France)
Pointe-à-Pitre
Basse-Terre
Marie Galante
DOMINICA
Roseau
Martinique (France)
Fort-de-France
ST LUCIA
Castries
ST VINCENT and the GRENADINES
Kingstown
Grenadines
BARBADOS
Bridgetown
GRENADA
St George's
Orchila
Los Roques
Blanquilla
Tobago
Scarborough
Galera Point
TRINIDAD and TOBAGO
Margarita
La Tortuga
Porlamar
Carúpano
Güiria
Port of Spain
Arima
Cumaná
Punta La Cruz
San Fernando
Trinidad
Barcelona
Maturín
San Juan de los Morros
Zaraza
de la Pascua
Tucupita
bozo
El Tigre
San José de Amacuro
Ciudad Guayana
Ciudad Bolívar
Guasipati
Anna Regina
El Callao
Georgetown
La Paragua
Bartica
New Amsterdam
Rockstone
Linden
Corriverton
Totness
VENEZUELA
GUYANA
Angel Falls
Caicara
Caura
Caroní
Essequibo
SURINAME
ernando de Atabapo
Boa Vista
BRAZIL
Branco
Caracas
San Juan
Mayagüez
Puerto Rico (USA)

San recibo

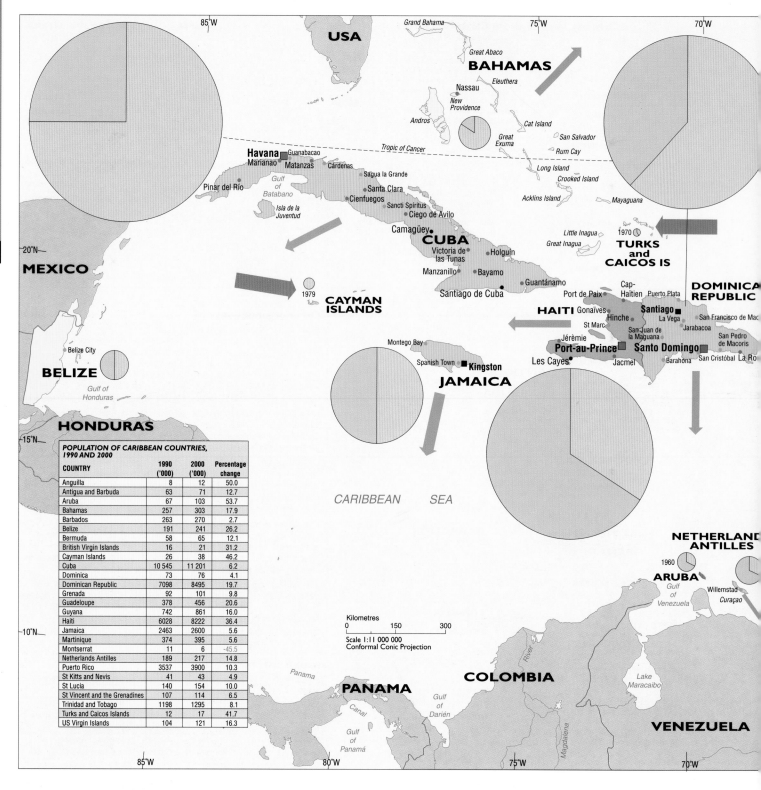

POPULATION OF CARIBBEAN COUNTRIES, 1990 AND 2000			
COUNTRY	1990 ('000)	2000 ('000)	Percentage change
Anguilla	8	12	50.0
Antigua and Barbuda	63	71	12.7
Aruba	67	103	53.7
Bahamas	257	303	17.9
Barbados	263	270	2.7
Belize	191	241	26.2
Bermuda	58	65	12.1
British Virgin Islands	16	21	31.2
Cayman Islands	26	38	46.2
Cuba	10 545	11 201	6.2
Dominica	73	76	4.1
Dominican Republic	7098	8495	19.7
Grenada	92	101	9.8
Guadeloupe	378	456	20.6
Guyana	742	861	16.0
Haiti	6028	8222	36.4
Jamaica	2463	2600	5.6
Martinique	374	395	5.6
Montserrat	11	6	-45.5
Netherlands Antilles	189	217	14.8
Puerto Rico	3537	3900	10.3
St Kitts and Nevis	41	43	4.9
St Lucia	140	154	10.0
St Vincent and the Grenadines	107	114	6.5
Trinidad and Tobago	1198	1295	8.1
Turks and Caicos Islands	12	17	41.7
US Virgin Islands	104	121	16.3

Kilometres
0   150   300
Scale 1:11 000 000
Conformal Conic Projection

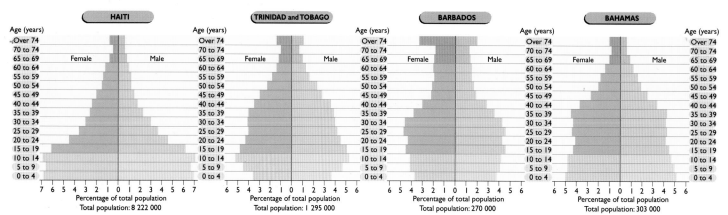

HAITI

Age (years)

Over 74
70 to 74
65 to 69   Female   Male
60 to 64
55 to 59
50 to 54
45 to 49
40 to 44
35 to 39
30 to 34
25 to 29
20 to 24
15 to 19
10 to 14
5 to 9
0 to 4

7 6 5 4 3 2 1 0 1 2 3 4 5 6 7
Percentage of total population
Total population: 8 222 000

TRINIDAD and TOBAGO

Age (years)

Over 74
70 to 74
65 to 69   Female   Male
60 to 64
55 to 59
50 to 54
45 to 49
40 to 44
35 to 39
30 to 34
25 to 29
20 to 24
15 to 19
10 to 14
5 to 9
0 to 4

6 5 4 3 2 1 0 1 2 3 4 5 6
Percentage of total population
Total population: 1 295 000

BARBADOS

Age (years)

Over 74
70 to 74
65 to 69   Female   Male
60 to 64
55 to 59
50 to 54
45 to 49
40 to 44
35 to 39
30 to 34
25 to 29
20 to 24
15 to 19
10 to 14
5 to 9
0 to 4

6 5 4 3 2 1 0 1 2 3 4 5 6
Percentage of total population
Total population: 270 000

BAHAMAS

Age (years)

Over 74
70 to 74
65 to 69   Female   Male
60 to 64
55 to 59
50 to 54
45 to 49
40 to 44
35 to 39
30 to 34
25 to 29
20 to 24
15 to 19
10 to 14
5 to 9
0 to 4

6 5 4 3 2 1 0 1 2 3 4 5 6
Percentage of total population
Total population: 303 000

URBAN POPULATION

Number of people

- Over 1 000 000
- 500 000 to 1 000 000
- 250 000 to 500 000
- 100 000 to 250 000
- 50 000 to 100 000

POPULATION DENSITY

People per km²

- Over 500
- 250 to 500
- 100 to 250
- 50 to 100
- Under 50

CARIBBEAN POPULATION, 1960 - 2000

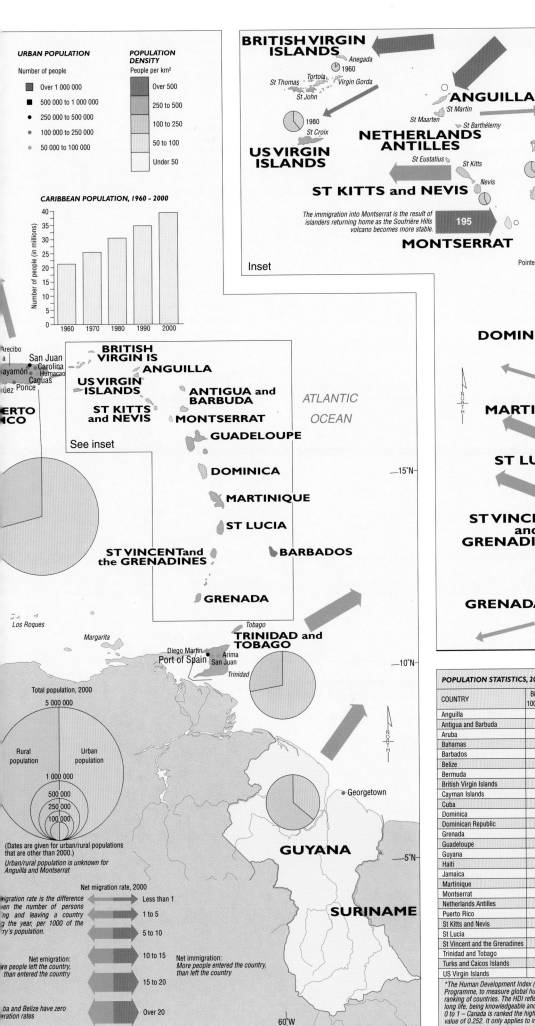

Total population, 2000

Rural population / Urban population

5 000 000
1 000 000
500 000
250 000
100 000

(Dates are given for urban/rural populations that are other than 2000.)
Urban/rural population is unknown for Anguilla and Montserrat

Net migration rate, 2000

...igration rate is the difference ...en the number of persons ...ng and leaving a country ...g the year, per 1000 of the ...'s population.

- Less than 1
- 1 to 5
- 5 to 10
- 10 to 15
- 15 to 20
- Over 20

Net emigration:
...re people left the country, ...an entered the country

Net immigration:
More people entered the country, than left the country

...ba and Belize have zero ...ration rates

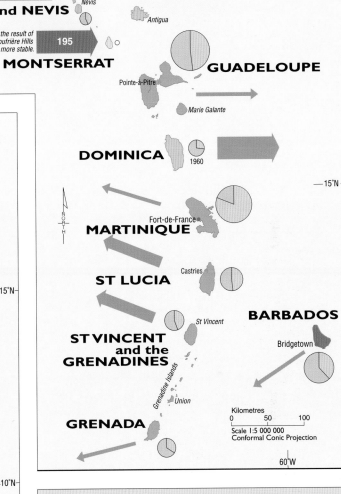

The immigration into Montserrat is the result of islanders returning home as the Soufrière Hills volcano becomes more stable.

195

ATLANTIC OCEAN

Kilometres
0   50   100
Scale 1:5 000 000
Conformal Conic Projection

POPULATION STATISTICS, 2000

COUNTRY	Birth rate per 1000 population	Death rate per 1000 population	Life expectancy Male	Life expectancy Female	HDI* rank	HDI* value
Anguilla	15.3	5.8	73	79	-	-
Antigua and Barbuda	20.2	6.0	68	73	37	0.833
Aruba	13.1	6.1	75	82	-	-
Bahamas	21.8	5.2	71	72	33	0.844
Barbados	13.6	8.7	70	76	30	0.858
Belize	32.3	4.8	69	73	58	0.777
Bermuda	12.5	7.4	75	79	-	-
British Virgin Islands	15.3	4.5	75	76	-	-
Cayman Islands	14.2	5.1	76	81	-	-
Cuba	12.7	7.3	74	77	56	0.783
Dominica	18.3	7.3	71	76	51	0.798
Dominican Republic	25.2	4.7	71	75	87	0.729
Grenada	23.2	8.0	63	66	54	0.785
Guadeloupe	17.3	6.0	74	80	-	-
Guyana	17.9	8.4	61	67	96	0.709
Haiti	32.0	15.1	47	51	150	0.440
Jamaica	18.5	5.5	73	77	83	0.735
Martinique	16.1	6.4	79	77	-	-
Montserrat	17.5	7.5	76	80	-	-
Netherlands Antilles	16.9	6.4	73	77	-	-
Puerto Rico	15.5	7.7	71	80	-	-
St Kitts and Nevis	19.1	9.4	68	74	47	0.798
St Lucia	22.2	5.4	69	76	88	0.728
St Vincent and the Grenadines	18.3	6.2	71	74	79	0.738
Trinidad and Tobago	13.8	8.8	65	71	50	0.793
Turks and Caicos Islands	25.7	4.8	71	76	-	-
US Virgin Islands	16.0	5.4	74	82	-	-

*The Human Development Index (HDI) is constructed every year by the United Nations Development Programme, to measure global human development in one simple composite index and to produce a ranking of countries. The HDI reflects achievements in the most basic human capabilities - leading a long life, being knowledgeable and enjoying a decent standard of living. The HDI value ranges from 0 to 1 – Canada is ranked the highest with a value of 0.935 and Sierra Leone the lowest with a value of 0.252. It only applies to independent countries and not dependencies.

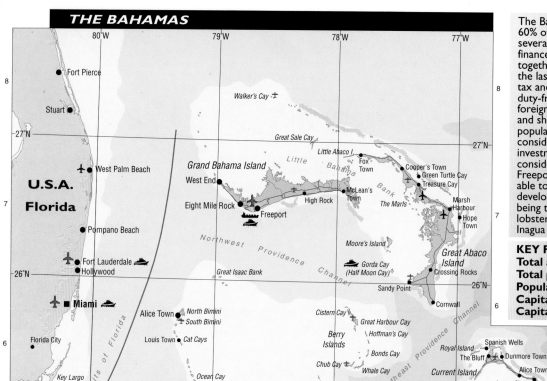

THE BAHAMAS

The Bahamas depends on tourism for some 60% of its GDP and employment, spread over several sectors of the economy. Offshore finance is also of considerable importance and together these have shown a healthy growth in the last decade. The Bahamas has no income tax and in addition the town of Freeport is a duty-free zone which has attracted major foreign investment, notably in pharmaceuticals and ship repairing. The Out Islands, as the less populated islands are known, have developed considerably since the 1970's with major investments in infrastructure, so that despite considerable population loss to Nassau and Freeport, they are much more self-sufficient and able to benefit increasingly from the extensive development of the last ten years. Apart from being the world's fourth largest exporter of lobster, the Bahamas also exports salt from Inagua and sand from Ocean Cay in the Biminis.

KEY FACTS
Total area – 13 868 km²
Total population – 302 836 (2000)
Population density – 22 people per km²
Capital city – Nassau
Capital population – 171 500

Map legend

- ■ Capital city
- ● Important town
- • Other settlement
- — District boundary
- ⚓ Major port
- 🚢 Cruiseship port
- ✈ Major international airport
- ✈ Regional airport
- ✈ Other airport

NEW PROVIDENCE ISLAND – ECONOMIC ACTIVITY

Scale 1:290 000

Legend:
- Forest
- Urban area
- Public land
- Swamp/mangrove
- ● Commercial centre
- 🏛 Major tourist area
- ↗ Pine trees

Kilometres
0   5   10

Places on New Providence Island: Gambier Village, Cable Beach, Nassau, Paradise Island, Lake Killarney, Sports ground, Sandilands Village, Industrial estate, Lyford Cay, Nassau International Airport, Carmichael Village, (bulk oil terminal and port), Clifton, Commonwealth Brewery, Adelaide, Coral Harbour, Bacardi Rum Plant

Kilometres
0   50   100
Scale 1:3 000 000
Conformal Conic Projection

GRAND BAHAMA ISLAND

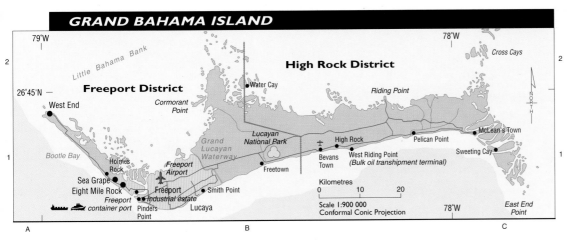

POPULATION GROWTH 1963 - 2000

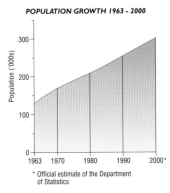

* Official estimate of the Department of Statistics

DOMESTIC EXPORTS, 1998

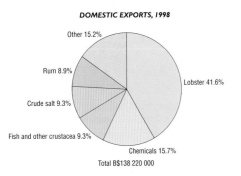

Other 15.2%
Rum 8.9%
Crude salt 9.3%
Fish and other crustacea 9.3%
Chemicals 15.7%
Lobster 41.6%

Total B$138 220 000

ORIGIN OF TOURISTS, 1998

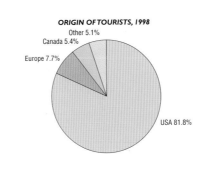

Other 5.1%
Canada 5.4%
Europe 7.7%
USA 81.8%

TOURIST ARRIVALS, 1995 - 1999

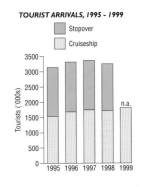

Stopover
Cruiseship

n.a.

GROSS DOMESTIC PRODUCT BY ECONOMIC ACTIVITY, 1995

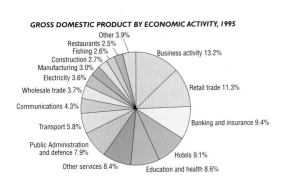

Other 3.9%
Restaurants 2.5%
Fishing 2.6%
Construction 2.7%
Manufacturing 3.0%
Electricity 3.6%
Wholesale trade 3.7%
Communications 4.3%
Transport 5.8%
Public Administration and defence 7.9%
Other services 8.4%
Education and health 8.6%
Hotels 9.1%
Banking and insurance 9.4%
Retail trade 11.3%
Business activity 13.2%

NUMBER OF HOTEL ROOMS BY ISLAND, 1996

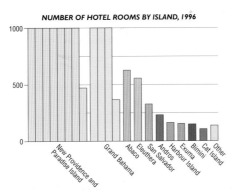

New Providence and Paradise Island, Grand Bahama, Abaco, Eleuthera, San Salvador, Andros, Harbour Island, Exuma, Bimini, Cat Island, Other

TOURIST EXPENDITURE, 1995 - 1999

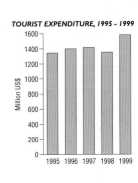

Island/Cay	Area (km²)	Population 1990	% of total population	Density (people per km²)
Total Bahamas	13868	255 049		18.4
New Providence and Paradise Island	210	172 196	67.5	820.0
Grand Bahama	1373	40 898	16.0	30.0
Abaco Islands and Cays	1666	10 003	3.9	6.0
Acklins	389	405	0.2	1.0
Andros	5957	8 177	3.2	1.3
Berry Islands	31	628	0.3	20.3
Bimini Islands and Cays	28	1 639	0.6	58.5
Cat Island	388	1 698	0.7	4.4
Conception Island	10	0		
Crooked Island and Long Cay	233	412	0.2	2.0
Eleuthera	518	10 584	4.1	20.4
Exuma Island and Cays	291	3 556	1.4	12.2
Great Inagua	1544	985	0.4	0.6
Little Inagua	127	0		
Little San Salvador	10	0		
Long Island	448	2 949	1.2	6.6
Mayaguana	285	312	0.1	1.1
Plana Cays	15	0		
Ragged Island Range and Jumentos	33	89		2.7
Rum Cay	78	53		0.7
Samana Cays	39	0		
San Salvador	153	465	0.2	3.0
Other small islands, cays and rocks	23	0		

CUBA

CUBA

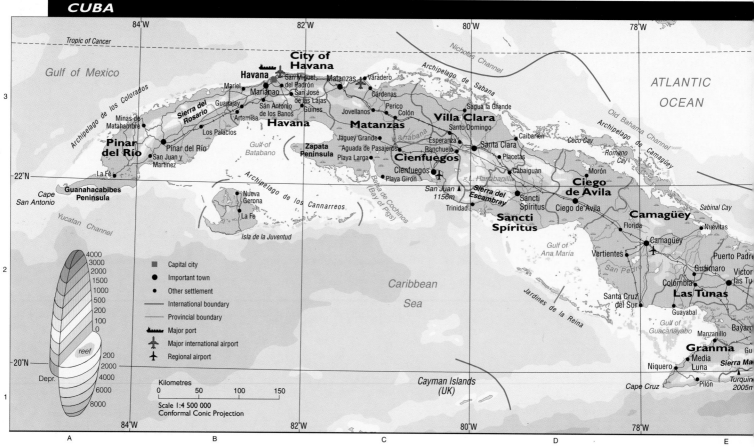

Capital city
Important town
Other settlement
International boundary
Provincial boundary
Major port
Major international airport
Regional airport

Kilometres
0   50   100   150
Scale 1:4 500 000
Conformal Conic Projection

ECONOMIC ACTIVITY

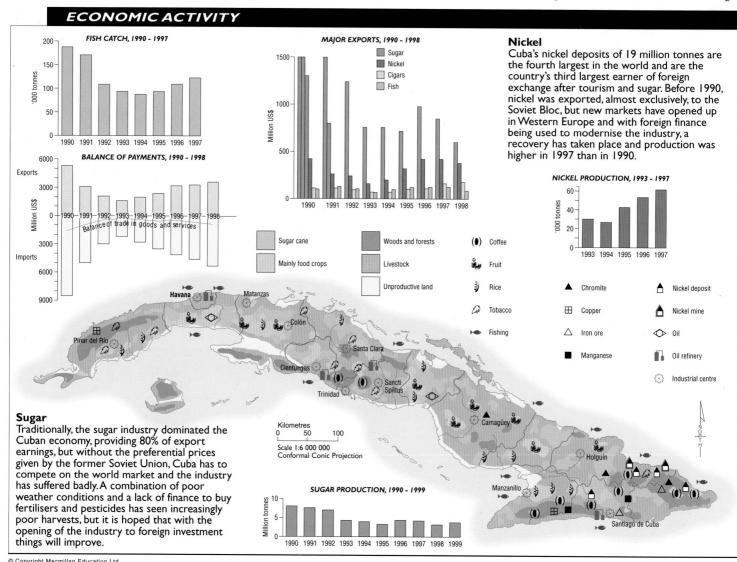

FISH CATCH, 1990 - 1997

'000 tonnes

1990 1991 1992 1993 1994 1995 1996 1997

BALANCE OF PAYMENTS, 1990 - 1998

Million US$

Exports

1990 1991 1992 1993 1994 1995 1996 1997 1998

Imports

Balance of trade in goods and services

MAJOR EXPORTS, 1990 - 1998

Million US$

- Sugar
- Nickel
- Cigars
- Fish

1990 1991 1992 1993 1994 1995 1996 1997 1998

- Sugar cane
- Mainly food crops
- Woods and forests
- Livestock
- Unproductive land
- Coffee
- Fruit
- Rice
- Tobacco
- Fishing
- Chromite
- Copper
- Iron ore
- Manganese
- Nickel deposit
- Nickel mine
- Oil
- Oil refinery
- Industrial centre

Nickel

Cuba's nickel deposits of 19 million tonnes are the fourth largest in the world and are the country's third largest earner of foreign exchange after tourism and sugar. Before 1990, nickel was exported, almost exclusively, to the Soviet Bloc, but new markets have opened up in Western Europe and with foreign finance being used to modernise the industry, a recovery has taken place and production was higher in 1997 than in 1990.

NICKEL PRODUCTION, 1993 - 1997

'000 tonnes

1993 1994 1995 1996 1997

Kilometres
0   50   100
Scale 1:6 000 000
Conformal Conic Projection

Sugar

Traditionally, the sugar industry dominated the Cuban economy, providing 80% of export earnings, but without the preferential prices given by the former Soviet Union, Cuba has to compete on the world market and the industry has suffered badly. A combination of poor weather conditions and a lack of finance to buy fertilisers and pesticides has seen increasingly poor harvests, but it is hoped that with the opening of the industry to foreign investment things will improve.

SUGAR PRODUCTION, 1990 - 1999

Million tonnes

1990 1991 1992 1993 1994 1995 1996 1997 1998 1999

Cuba is one of the last bastions of Communist rule in the world and is governed by bodies of People's Power. The highest ranking body of People's Power is the National Assembly which elects the members of the Council of State, the supreme governing body of the Cuban state. The Head of State is Fidel Castro, who is also First Secretary of the Communist Party of Cuba. Traditionally, Cuba has had close political and economic links with the former Soviet Union, benefiting from preferential trade agreements. With the break-up of the Soviet Union and its subsequent move towards free market economies, Cuba has become increasingly isolated in an effort to remain faithful to its communist tradition.

KEY FACTS
Total area – 110 860 km²
Total population – 11 116 000 (1998)
Population density – 100 people per km²
Capital – Havana
Capital population – 2 175 995

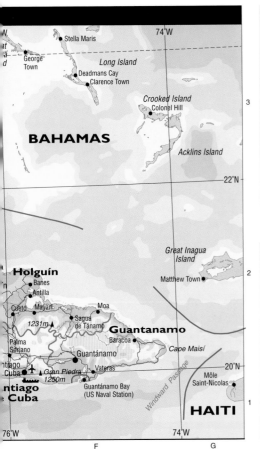

ANNUAL RAINFALL

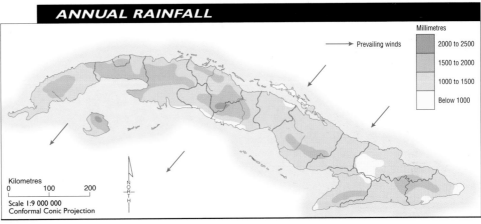

TOURISM

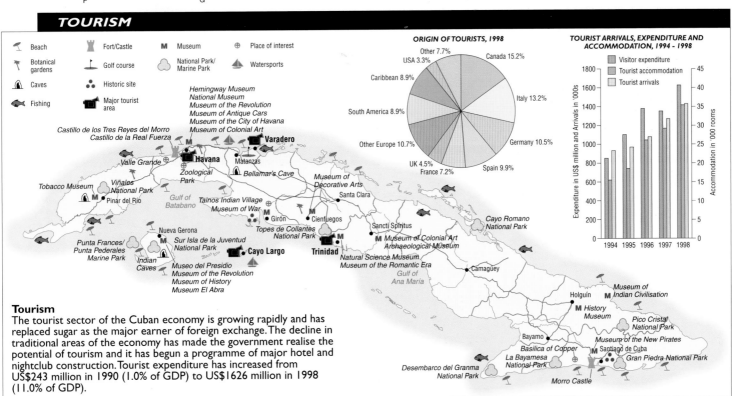

ORIGIN OF TOURISTS, 1998

Other 7.7% / USA 3.3% / Canada 15.2% / Caribbean 8.9% / Italy 13.2% / South America 8.9% / Germany 10.5% / Other Europe 10.7% / UK 4.5% / France 7.2% / Spain 9.9%

Tourism
The tourist sector of the Cuban economy is growing rapidly and has replaced sugar as the major earner of foreign exchange. The decline in traditional areas of the economy has made the government realise the potential of tourism and it has begun a programme of major hotel and nightclub construction. Tourist expenditure has increased from US$243 million in 1990 (1.0% of GDP) to US$1626 million in 1998 (11.0% of GDP).

FACT FILE

Before the break-up of the Soviet Union, Cuba was the designated sugar producer for the Moscow dominated eastern European economic bloc, while in return Russia provided Cuba's oil imports. The preferential prices in this trade formed the basis of the country's economy, but with the collapse of the Sovet bloc, sugar and oil had to be traded at world market prices and Cuba's economy suffered a sharp downward spiral.
Tough economic measures, a recovery in the sugar industry and an upsurge in tourism has halted the decline and in the last few years Cuba's economy has started a slow recovery.

JAMAICA

JAMAICA

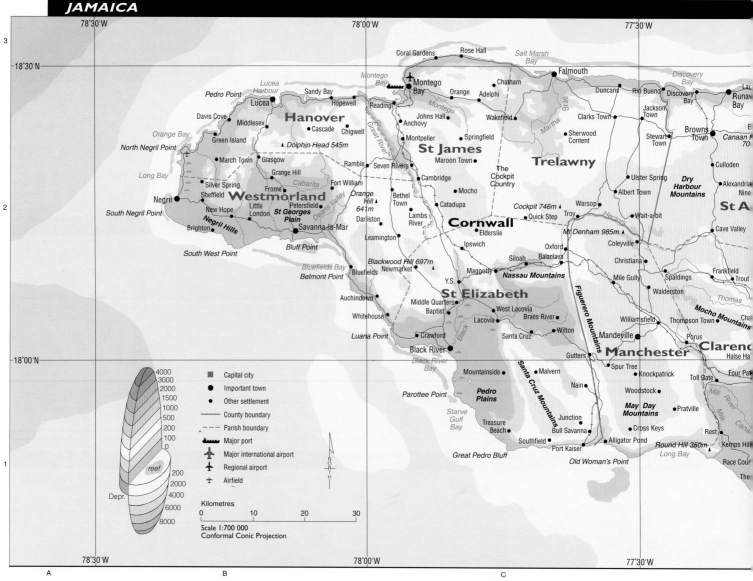

Capital city
Important town
Other settlement
County boundary
Parish boundary
Major port
Major international airport
Regional airport
Airfield

Scale 1:700 000
Conformal Conic Projection

Kilometres
0   10   20   30

POPULATION

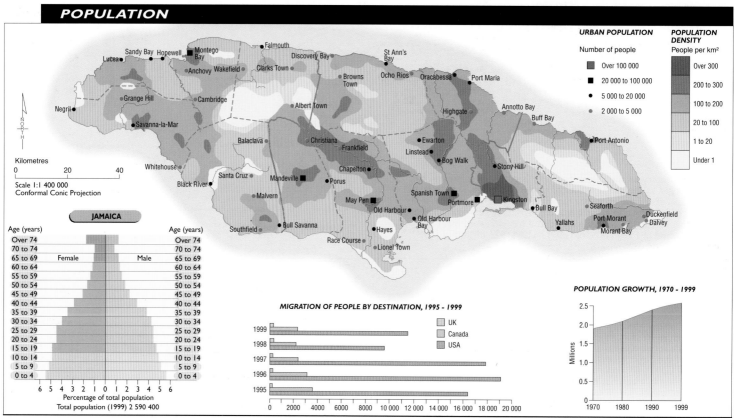

URBAN POPULATION

Number of people
Over 100 000
20 000 to 100 000
5 000 to 20 000
2 000 to 5 000

POPULATION DENSITY
People per km²
Over 300
200 to 300
100 to 200
20 to 100
1 to 20
Under 1

Kilometres
0   20   40
Scale 1:1 400 000
Conformal Conic Projection

JAMAICA

Age (years)   Age (years)
Over 74   Over 74
70 to 74   70 to 74
65 to 69   Female   Male   65 to 69
60 to 64   60 to 64
55 to 59   55 to 59
50 to 54   50 to 54
45 to 49   45 to 49
40 to 44   40 to 44
35 to 39   35 to 39
30 to 34   30 to 34
25 to 29   25 to 29
20 to 24   20 to 24
15 to 19   15 to 19
10 to 14   10 to 14
5 to 9   5 to 9
0 to 4   0 to 4
6 5 4 3 2 1 0 1 2 3 4 5 6
Percentage of total population
Total population (1999) 2 590 400

MIGRATION OF PEOPLE BY DESTINATION, 1995 - 1999
UK
Canada
USA
1999
1998
1997
1996
1995
0   2000 4000 6000 8000 10 000 12 000 14 000 16 000 18 000 20 000

POPULATION GROWTH, 1970 - 1999
2.5
2.0
1.5
1.0
0.5
0
Millions
1970   1980   1990   1999

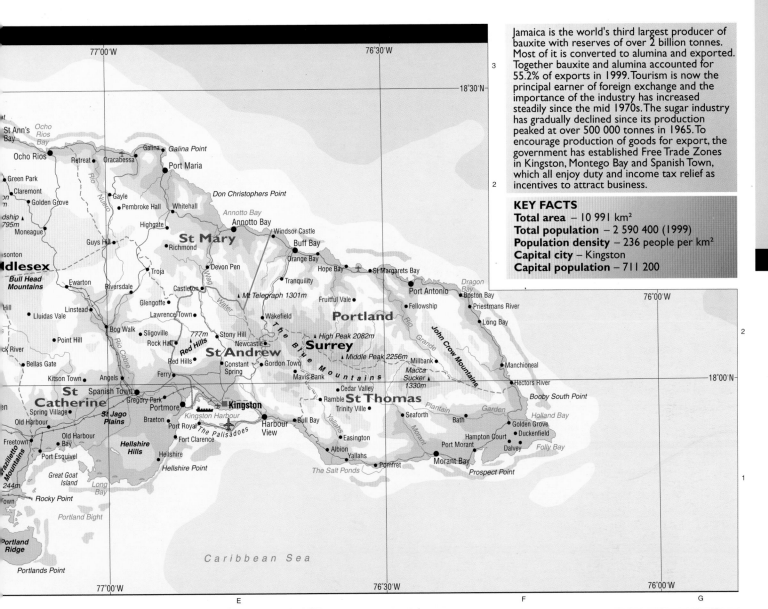

Jamaica is the world's third largest producer of bauxite with reserves of over 2 billion tonnes. Most of it is converted to alumina and exported. Together bauxite and alumina accounted for 55.2% of exports in 1999. Tourism is now the principal earner of foreign exchange and the importance of the industry has increased steadily since the mid 1970s. The sugar industry has gradually declined since its production peaked at over 500 000 tonnes in 1965. To encourage production of goods for export, the government has established Free Trade Zones in Kingston, Montego Bay and Spanish Town, which all enjoy duty and income tax relief as incentives to attract business.

KEY FACTS
Total area – 10 991 km²
Total population – 2 590 400 (1999)
Population density – 236 people per km²
Capital city – Kingston
Capital population – 711 200

TOURISM

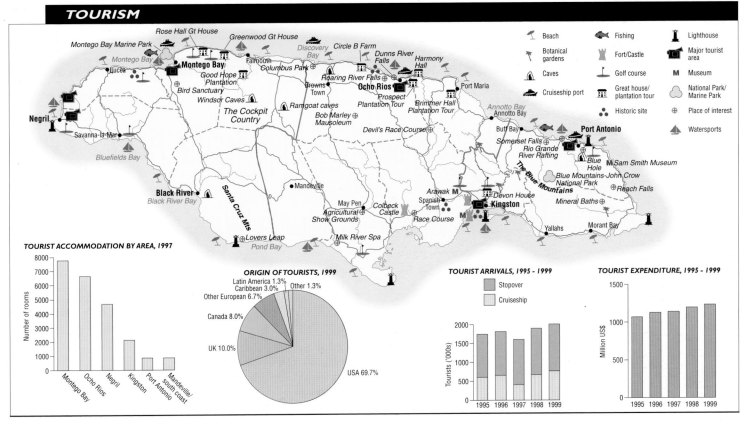

Key:
- Beach
- Botanical gardens
- Caves
- Cruiseship port
- Fishing
- Fort/Castle
- Golf course
- Great house/plantation tour
- Historic site
- Lighthouse
- Major tourist area
- M Museum
- National Park/Marine Park
- Place of interest
- Watersports

TOURIST ACCOMMODATION BY AREA, 1997
(Number of rooms; areas: Montego Bay, Ocho Rios, Negril, Kingston, Port Antonio, Mandeville/south coast)

ORIGIN OF TOURISTS, 1999
- Latin America 1.3%
- Caribbean 3.0%
- Other 1.3%
- Other European 6.7%
- Canada 8.0%
- UK 10.0%
- USA 69.7%

TOURIST ARRIVALS, 1995 - 1999
- Stopover
- Cruiseship
(Tourists ('000s); 1995, 1996, 1997, 1998, 1999)

TOURIST EXPENDITURE, 1995 - 1999
(Million US$; 1995, 1996, 1997, 1998, 1999)

JAMAICA

ECONOMIC ACTIVITY

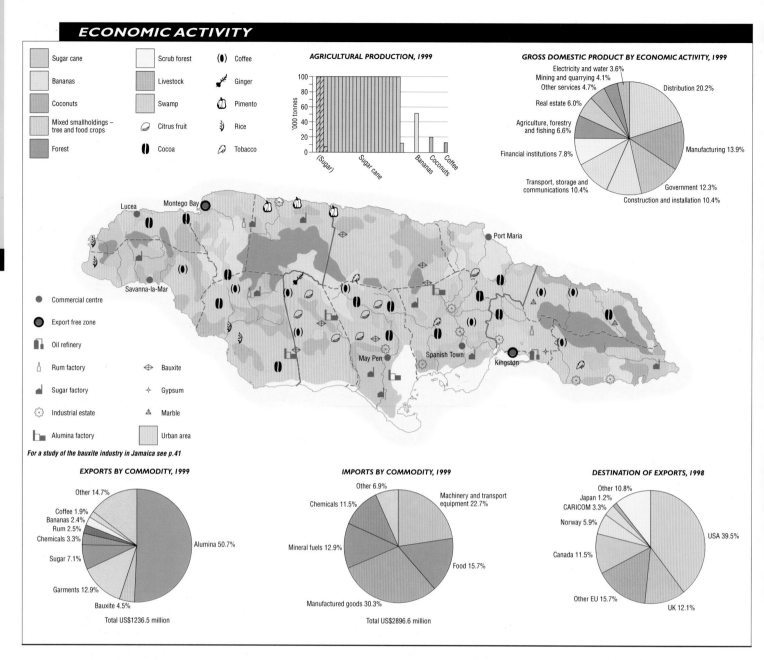

Sugar cane
Bananas
Coconuts
Mixed smallholdings –
tree and food crops
Forest

Scrub forest
Livestock
Swamp

Citrus fruit
Cocoa

Coffee
Ginger
Pimento
Rice
Tobacco

● Commercial centre
◉ Export free zone
▮ Oil refinery
🍾 Rum factory
▬ Sugar factory
❀ Industrial estate
▬ Alumina factory
⬥ Bauxite
✦ Gypsum
△ Marble
▭ Urban area

For a study of the bauxite industry in Jamaica see p.41

AGRICULTURAL PRODUCTION, 1999

'000 tonnes (0–100): (Sugar), Sugar cane, Bananas, Coconuts, Coffee

GROSS DOMESTIC PRODUCT BY ECONOMIC ACTIVITY, 1999

Electricity and water 3.6%
Mining and quarrying 4.1%
Other services 4.7%
Real estate 6.0%
Agriculture, forestry and fishing 6.6%
Financial institutions 7.8%
Transport, storage and communications 10.4%
Construction and installation 10.4%
Government 12.3%
Manufacturing 13.9%
Distribution 20.2%

EXPORTS BY COMMODITY, 1999

Other 14.7%
Coffee 1.9%
Bananas 2.4%
Rum 2.5%
Chemicals 3.3%
Sugar 7.1%
Garments 12.9%
Bauxite 4.5%
Alumina 50.7%

Total US$1236.5 million

IMPORTS BY COMMODITY, 1999

Other 6.9%
Chemicals 11.5%
Mineral fuels 12.9%
Manufactured goods 30.3%
Machinery and transport equipment 22.7%
Food 15.7%

Total US$2896.6 million

DESTINATION OF EXPORTS, 1998

Other 10.8%
Japan 1.2%
CARICOM 3.3%
Norway 5.9%
Canada 11.5%
Other EU 15.7%
UK 12.1%
USA 39.5%

ANNUAL RAINFALL

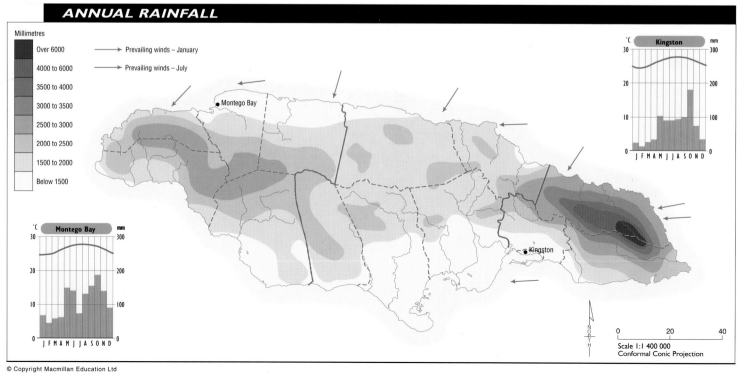

Millimetres
Over 6000
4000 to 6000
3500 to 4000
3000 to 3500
2500 to 3000
2000 to 2500
1500 to 2000
Below 1500

→ Prevailing winds – January
→ Prevailing winds – July

Kingston
Montego Bay

Scale 1:1 400 000
Conformal Conic Projection

0   20   40

CAYMAN ISLANDS

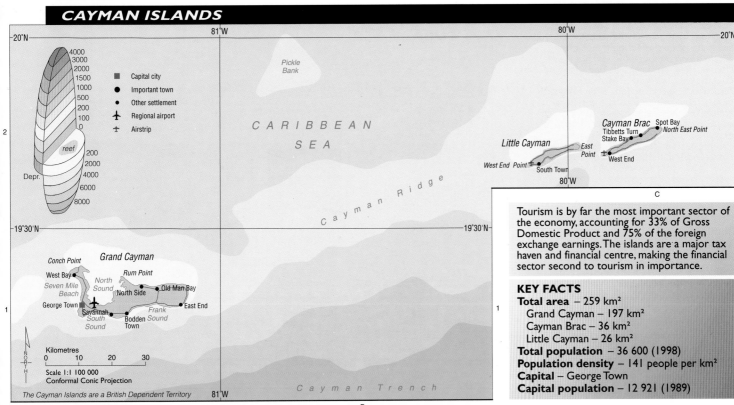

4000
3000
1500
1000
500
200
100
0

- ■ Capital city
- ● Important town
- • Other settlement
- ✈ Regional airport
- ✈ Airstrip

reef

200
2000
4000
6000
8000

Depr.

CARIBBEAN SEA

Pickle Bank

Cayman Ridge

Cayman Brac
Spot Bay
Tibbetts Turn
Stake Bay   North East Point
West End

Little Cayman
East Point
West End Point   South Town

80°W

C

Grand Cayman
Conch Point
West Bay
Rum Point
Seven Mile Beach
North Sound
North Side   Old Man Bay
George Town
Savannah
Bodden Town
Frank Sound
South Sound
East End

Kilometres
0   10   20   30

Scale 1:1 100 000
Conformal Conic Projection

The Cayman Islands are a British Dependent Territory

A   B

Tourism is by far the most important sector of the economy, accounting for 33% of Gross Domestic Product and 75% of the foreign exchange earnings. The islands are a major tax haven and financial centre, making the financial sector second to tourism in importance.

65

KEY FACTS
Total area – 259 km²
 Grand Cayman – 197 km²
 Cayman Brac – 36 km²
 Little Cayman – 26 km²
Total population – 36 600 (1998)
Population density – 141 people per km²
Capital – George Town
Capital population – 12 921 (1989)

LAND USE

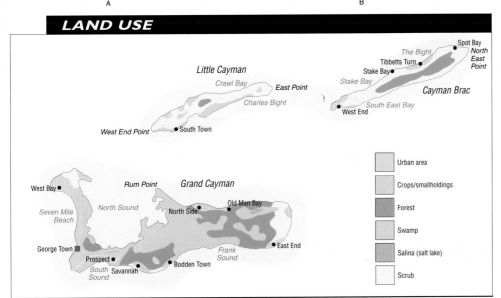

Little Cayman
Crawl Bay   East Point
Charles Bight
West End Point   South Town

Cayman Brac
Spot Bay
The Bight   North East Point
Tibbetts Turn
Stake Bay
Stake Bay
West End   South East Bay

Grand Cayman
West Bay   Rum Point
Seven Mile Beach   North Sound
North Side   Old Man Bay
George Town
Prospect
Savannah   Bodden Town   East End
South Sound   Frank Sound

- Urban area
- Crops/smallholdings
- Forest
- Swamp
- Salina (salt lake)
- Scrub

GROSS DOMESTIC PRODUCT BY ECONOMIC ACTIVITY, 1998

Other 37.5%
Tourism 33.0%
Industry 14.0%
Financial services 15.5%

TOURIST EXPENDITURE, 1994 – 1998

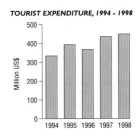

Million US$
500
400
300
200
100
0
1994 1995 1996 1997 1998

TOURIST ARRIVALS, 1994 – 1998

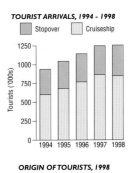

■ Stopover □ Cruiseship

Tourists ('000s)
1250
1000
750
500
250
0
1994 1995 1996 1997 1998

TOURISM

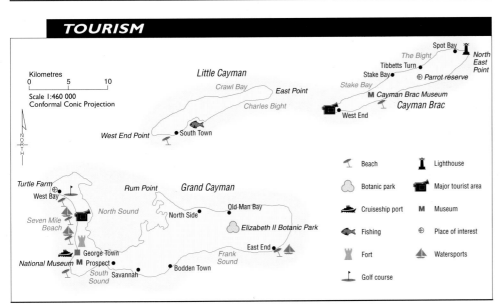

Kilometres
0   5   10

Scale 1:460 000
Conformal Conic Projection

Little Cayman
Crawl Bay   East Point
Charles Bight
West End Point   South Town

Cayman Brac
Spot Bay
The Bight   North East Point
Tibbetts Turn
Stake Bay   Parrot reserve
Stake Bay   Cayman Brac Museum
West End

Grand Cayman
Turtle Farm
West Bay   Rum Point
Seven Mile Beach   North Sound
North Side   Old Man Bay
Elizabeth II Botanic Park
East End
George Town
National Museum   Prospect
Savannah   Bodden Town
South Sound   Frank Sound

- Beach
- Botanic park
- Cruiseship port
- Fishing
- Fort
- Golf course
- Lighthouse
- Major tourist area
- M Museum
- Place of interest
- Watersports

ORIGIN OF TOURISTS, 1998

Other Caribbean 1.2%
Other European 2.7%   Other 2.9%
Canada 4.5%
UK 5.9%
Jamaica 9.7%
USA 73.1%

HAITI and the DOMINICAN REPUBLIC

HAITI

Political instability and years of economic sanctions by the international community have had a devastating effect on the Haitian economy. Even though the sanctions were lifted in 1994, Haiti remains one of the poorest countries in the Western Hemisphere. Agriculture, which has long been Haiti's dominant economic activity, has suffered greatly and the countryside is today considered to be the most environmentally degraded in the Western Hemisphere. The production of export crops has declined considerably, and offshore manufacturing, utilising low cost labour on duty-free industrial estates, is now the biggest earner of foreign exchange.

KEY FACTS

Total area – 27 750 km²
Total population – 7 336 000 (1996)
Population density – 264 people per km²
Capital city – Port-au-Prince
Capital population – 1 140 000

HAITI

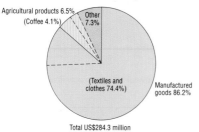

EXPORTS BY COMMODITY, 1998

Agricultural products 6.5%
(Coffee 4.1%)
Other 7.3%
(Textiles and clothes 74.4%)
Manufactured goods 86.2%

Total US$284.3 million

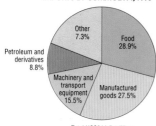

IMPORTS BY COMMODITY, 1998

Other 7.3%
Food 28.9%
Petroleum and derivatives 8.8%
Machinery and transport equipment 15.5%
Manufactured goods 27.5%

Total US$811.5 million

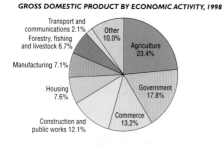

GROSS DOMESTIC PRODUCT BY ECONOMIC ACTIVITY, 1998

Transport and communications 2.1%
Forestry, fishing and livestock 6.7%
Manufacturing 7.1%
Housing 7.6%
Construction and public works 12.1%
Commerce 13.2%
Government 17.8%
Agriculture 23.4%
Other 10.0%

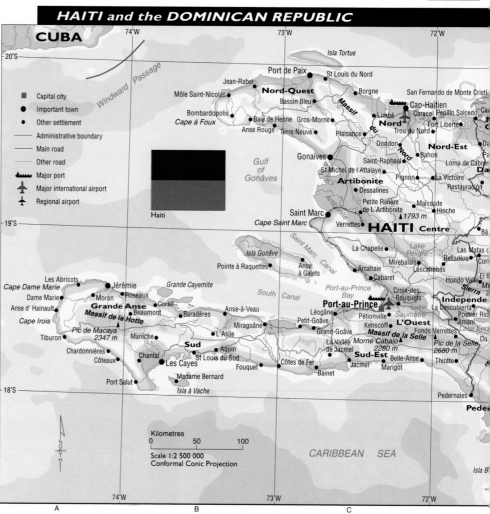

HAITI and the DOMINICAN REPUBLIC

CUBA

Windward Passage

Capital city
Important town
Other settlement
Administrative boundary
Main road
Other road
Major port
Major international airport
Regional airport

Isla Tortue
Port de Paix   St Louis du Nord
Jean-Rabel   Borgne   San Fernando de Monte Cristi
Môle Saint-Nicolas   Nord-Ouest   Bassin Bleu   Cap-Haïtien
Bombardopolis   Caracol Pepillo Salcedo
Cape á Foux   Baie de Henne   Gros-Morne   Limbé   Nord   Fort Liberté
Anse Rouge   Terre Neuve   Plaisance   Trou du Nord   Nord-Est
Dondon   Bahon
Gonaïves   St Michel de l'Attalaye   Saint-Raphaël   Loma de Cabrer
Artibonite   Dessalines   Pignon   La Victoire   Restauración
Petite Rivière   Maissade
Saint Marc   de L'Artibonite   Hinche
Cape Saint Marc   Verrettes   HAITI Centre

Gulf of Gonâves

Isla Gonâve   La Chapelle   Lake Péligre   Las Matas   Belladère
Mirebalais   Lascahobas
Pointe à Raquettes   Anse à Galets   Arcahaie   Cabaret   Hondo Valle   Sierra
Croix-des-Bouquets   Independe
Les Abricots   Jérémie   Grande Cayemite   Port-au-Prince   La Descubierta
Cape Dame Marie   Roseaux   Bay   Pétionville   Postrer Río
Dame Marie   Morón   Corail   Anse-à-Veau   Port-au-Prince   Saumâtre   Jimaní   Lake En
Anse d' Hainault   Grande Anse   Beaumont   Baradères   Miragoâne   Léogâne   Kenscoff   Fonds Verrettes
Cape Irois   Massif de la Hotte   Petit-Goâve   Massif de la Selle   Pic de la Selle   2680 m
Pic de Macaya   L'Asile   Grand-Goâve   La Vallée   Morne Cabaio   2280 m
2347 m   Maniche   Sud   de Jacmel   Sud-Est   Belle-Anse   Thiotte
Tiburon   Aquin   Côtes de Fer   Jacmel   Marigot
Chardonnières   Chantal   St Louis du Sud   Fouquet   Bainet
Côteaux   Les Cayes   Pederneros
Madame Bernard   Peder
Port Salut   Isla à Vache   Peder

Kilometres
0   50   100
Scale 1:2 500 000
Conformal Conic Projection

CARIBBEAN   SEA

Isla B

A   B   C

ECONOMIC ACTIVITY

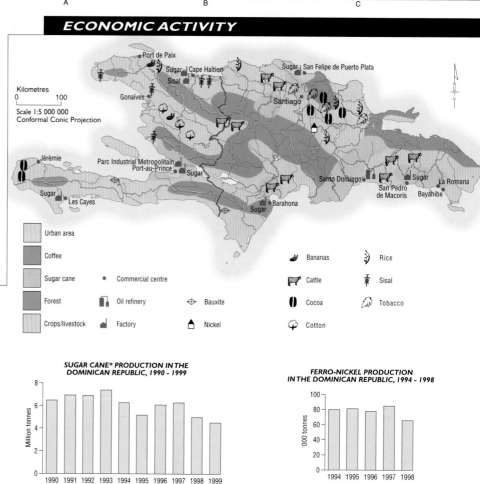

Kilometres
0   100
Scale 1:5 000 000
Conformal Conic Projection

Port de Paix   Sugar   Cape Haïtien   Sugar   San Felipe de Puerto Plata
Sisal
Gonaïves   Santiago
Jérémie   Parc Industrial Metropolitain   Port-au-Prince   Sugar
Sugar   Santo Domingo   Sugar   La Romana
Les Cayes   San Pedro   de Macorís   Bayahibe
Barahona
Sugar

Urban area
Coffee
Sugar cane
Forest
Crops/livestock
Commercial centre
Oil refinery
Factory
Bauxite
Nickel

Bananas   Rice
Cattle   Sisal
Cocoa   Tobacco
Cotton

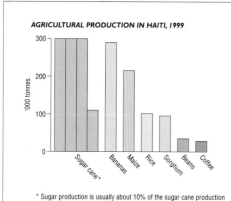

AGRICULTURAL PRODUCTION IN HAITI, 1999

'000 tonnes

Sugar cane *   Bananas   Maize   Rice   Sorghum   Beans   Coffee

* Sugar production is usually about 10% of the sugar cane production

SUGAR CANE* PRODUCTION IN THE DOMINICAN REPUBLIC, 1990 - 1999

Million tonnes

1990 1991 1992 1993 1994 1995 1996 1997 1998 1999

FERRO-NICKEL PRODUCTION IN THE DOMINICAN REPUBLIC, 1994 - 1998

'000 tonnes

1994 1995 1996 1997 1998

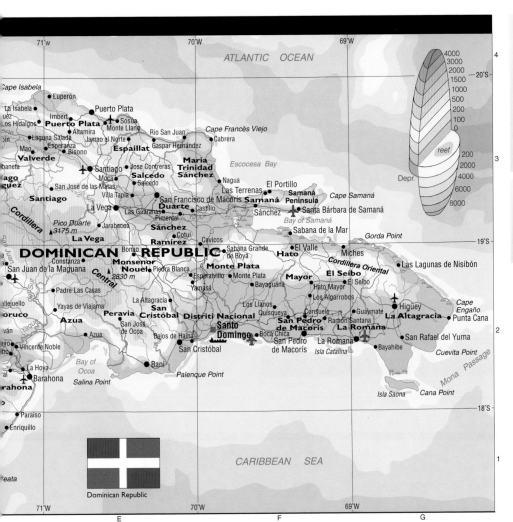

DOMINICAN REPUBLIC

In the past agriculture, and especially sugar, has been an important contributor to the economy of the Dominican Republic. The sugar industry has suffered from under-investment, labour problems (traditionally Haitian labour has been used) and falling world prices. Like many Caribbean countries unable to meet quotas stipulated in bilateral agreements (mainly with the USA), it often has to import refined sugar for domestic use. Tourism has become a strong growth industry, while the manufacturing sector has been growing rapidly, especially in the free-trade zones.

KEY FACTS

Total area – 48 422 km²
Total population – 8 052 000 (1996)
Population density – 166 people per km²
Capital city – Santo Domingo
Capital population – 2 138 262

DOMINICAN REPUBLIC

EXPORTS BY COMMODITY, 1998

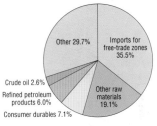

Tobacco 1.3%
Coffee 1.4%
Cocoa 1.8%
Ferro-nickel 2.7%
Sugar 2.8%
Other 7.8%
Exports from free-trade zones 82.2%

Total US$4988.7 million

IMPORTS BY COMMODITY, 1998

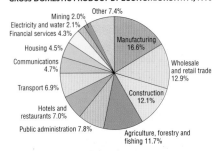

Other 29.7%
Imports for free-trade zones 35.5%
Crude oil 2.6%
Refined petroleum products 6.0%
Consumer durables 7.1%
Other raw materials 19.1%

Total US$7597.0 million

GROSS DOMESTIC PRODUCT BY ECONOMIC ACTIVITY, 1998

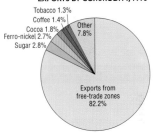

Mining 2.0%
Other 7.4%
Electricity and water 2.1%
Financial services 4.3%
Housing 4.5%
Communications 4.7%
Transport 6.9%
Hotels and restaurants 7.0%
Public administration 7.8%
Manufacturing 16.6%
Wholesale and retail trade 12.9%
Construction 12.1%
Agriculture, forestry and fishing 11.7%

ANNUAL RAINFALL

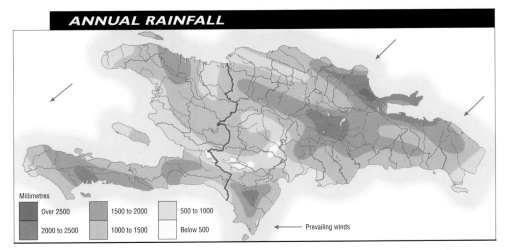

Millimetres
Over 2500
2000 to 2500
1500 to 2000
1000 to 1500
500 to 1000
Below 500

→ Prevailing winds

TOURISM — DOMINICAN REPUBLIC

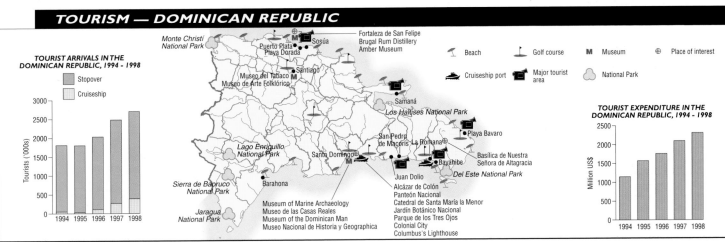

TOURIST ARRIVALS IN THE DOMINICAN REPUBLIC, 1994 - 1998

Stopover
Cruiseship

Tourists ('000s)
3000
2500
2000
1500
1000
500
0
1994 1995 1996 1997 1998

🏖 Beach
⚓ Cruiseship port
⛳ Golf course
🏨 Major tourist area
Ⓜ Museum
☁ National Park
⊕ Place of interest

Monte Christi National Park
Puerto Plata
Playa Dorada
Sosúa
Fortaleza de San Felipe
Brugal Rum Distillery
Amber Museum
Santiago
Museo del Tabaco
Museo de Arte Folklórico
Samaná
Los Haitises National Park
Lago Enriquillo National Park
Santo Domingo
San Pedro de Macorís
La Romana
Playa Bavaro
Basílica de Nuestra Señora de Altagracia
Bayahibe
Del Este National Park
Juan Dolio
Sierra de Baoruco National Park
Barahona
Jaragua National Park
Museum of Marine Archaeology
Museo de las Casas Reales
Museum of the Dominican Man
Museo Nacional de Historia y Geographica
Alcázar de Colón
Panteón Nacional
Catedral de Santa María la Menor
Jardín Botánico Nacional
Parque de los Tres Ojos
Colonial City
Columbus's Lighthouse

TOURIST EXPENDITURE IN THE DOMINICAN REPUBLIC, 1994 - 1998

Million US$
2500
2000
1500
1000
500
0
1994 1995 1996 1997 1998

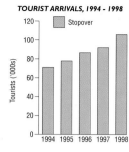

TURKS AND CAICOS ISLANDS

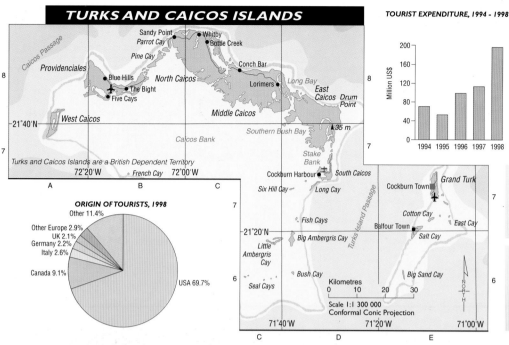

Turks and Caicos Islands are a British Dependent Territory

TOURIST EXPENDITURE, 1994 - 1998

TOURIST ARRIVALS, 1994 - 1998

Stopover

ORIGIN OF TOURISTS, 1998

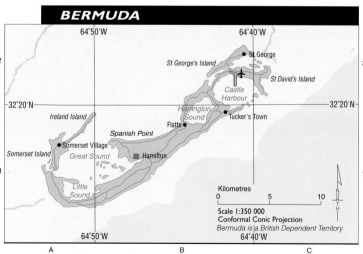

Other 11.4%
Other Europe 2.9%
UK 2.1%
Germany 2.2%
Italy 2.6%
Canada 9.1%
USA 69.7%

Tourism and offshore financial services dominate the economy of Turks and Caicos. There is little agriculture and the islands' principal natural resource is fisheries, with lobster and conch being the most important exports.

KEY FACTS
Total area – 430 km²
Total population – 15 000
Population density – 35 people per km²
Capital city – Cockburn Town
Capital population – 3100

PROVIDENCIALES

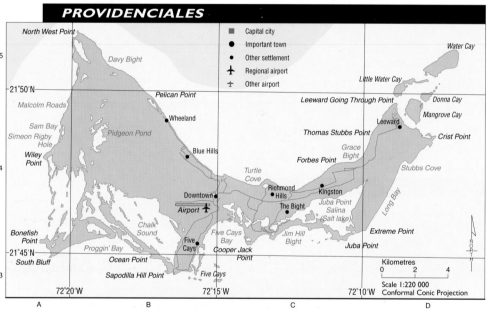

Capital city
Important town
Other settlement
Regional airport
Other airport

Scale 1:220 000
Conformal Conic Projection

GRAND TURK

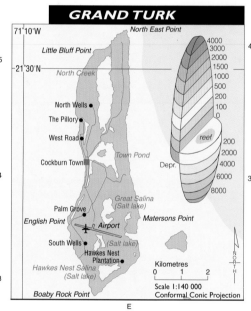

Scale 1:140 000
Conformal Conic Projection

BERMUDA

St George
St George's Island
St David's Island
Castle Harbour
Ireland Island
Harrington Sound
Tucker's Town
Flatts
Spanish Point
Somerset Village
Hamilton
Somerset Island
Great Sound
Little Sound

Kilometres
0   5   10
Scale 1:350 000
Conformal Conic Projection
Bermuda is a British Dependent Territory

TOURIST EXPENDITURE, 1994 - 1998

TOURIST ARRIVALS, 1994 - 1998

Stopover
Cruiseship

ORIGIN OF TOURISTS, 1998

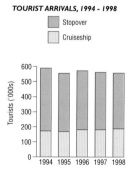

Other 4.1%
UK 8.2%
Canada 9.1%
USA 78.6%

Bermuda's economy is largely dependent on tourism and international business. Many international companies especially insurers, are attracted by a favourable tax environment and Bermuda operates the world's fifth largest flag of convenience shipping fleet.

KEY FACTS
Total area – 53 km²
Total population – 60 144 (1996)
Population density – 1135 people per km²
Capital city – Hamilton
Capital population – 4680 (1991)

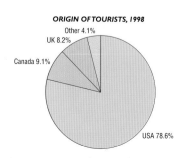

68

PUERTO RICO

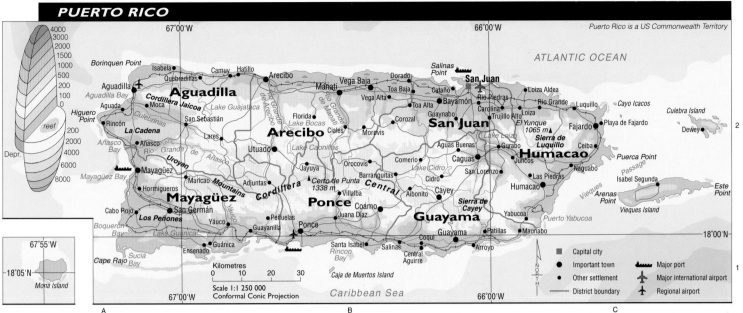

Puerto Rico is a US Commonwealth Territory

ATLANTIC OCEAN

Caribbean Sea

Scale 1:1 250 000
Conformal Conic Projection

■ Capital city	⚓ Major port
● Important town	✈ Major international airport
• Other settlement	✈ Regional airport
— District boundary	

Puerto Rico's economy is dominated by manufacturing, which accounted for over 40% of GDP in 1997. The sector has moved away from the old labour intensive industries such as food, tobacco and garments, towards the capital intensive industries such as pharmaceuticals, chemicals and machinery. The service sector, and in particular finance, is the second largest contributor to GDP and with over three million stopover tourists and one million cruise passengers, tourism is another major revenue earner. The USA received over 91% of Puerto Rico's exports in 1998.

KEY FACTS
Total area – 8959 km²
Total population – 3 888 000 (1999)
Population density – 434 people per km²
Capital city – San Juan
Capital population – 439 427 (1998)

ANNUAL RAINFALL

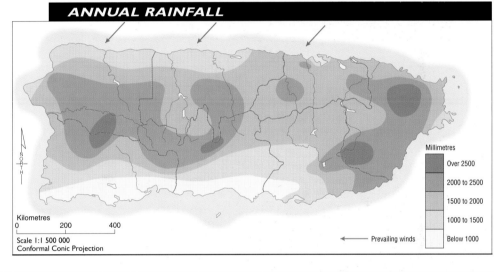

Kilometres
0   200   400

Scale 1:1 500 000
Conformal Conic Projection

Millimetres	
	Over 2500
	2000 to 2500
	1500 to 2000
	1000 to 1500
	Below 1000

← Prevailing winds

ECONOMIC ACTIVITY

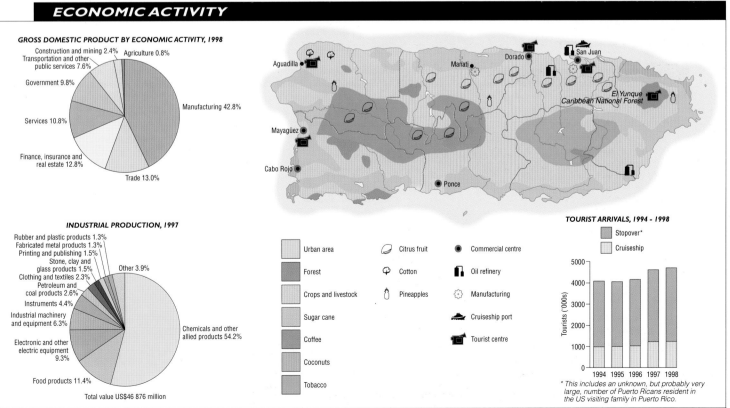

GROSS DOMESTIC PRODUCT BY ECONOMIC ACTIVITY, 1998

- Construction and mining 2.4%
- Agriculture 0.8%
- Transportation and other public services 7.6%
- Government 9.8%
- Services 10.8%
- Finance, insurance and real estate 12.8%
- Trade 13.0%
- Manufacturing 42.8%

INDUSTRIAL PRODUCTION, 1997

- Rubber and plastic products 1.3%
- Fabricated metal products 1.3%
- Printing and publishing 1.5%
- Stone, clay and glass products 1.5%
- Clothing and textiles 2.3%
- Petroleum and coal products 2.6%
- Instruments 4.4%
- Industrial machinery and equipment 6.3%
- Electronic and other electric equipment 9.3%
- Food products 11.4%
- Other 3.9%
- Chemicals and other allied products 54.2%

Total value US$46 876 million

Urban area	⌇ Citrus fruit	● Commercial centre
Forest	♀ Cotton	⛽ Oil refinery
Crops and livestock	▽ Pineapples	⚙ Manufacturing
Sugar cane		⛴ Cruiseship port
Coffee		📷 Tourist centre
Coconuts		
Tobacco		

TOURIST ARRIVALS, 1994 - 1998

■ Stopover*
□ Cruiseship

Tourists ('000s)

	1994	1995	1996	1997	1998
	~4100	~4100	~4200	~4600	~4700

* This includes an unknown, but probably very large, number of Puerto Ricans resident in the US visiting family in Puerto Rico.

70

EASTERN CARIBBEAN

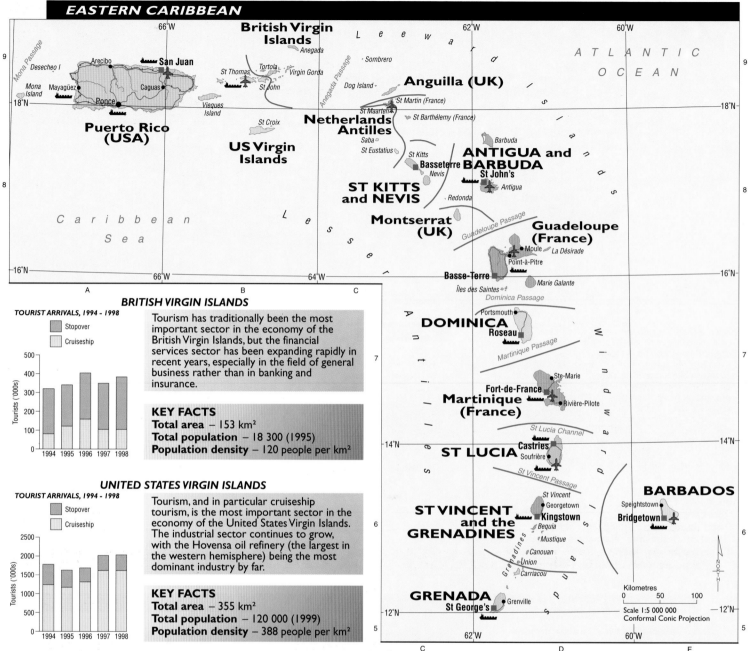

ATLANTIC OCEAN

British Virgin Islands

Mona Passage
Desecheo I
Arecibo
San Juan
Mona Island
Mayagüez
Caguas
Ponce
Puerto Rico (USA)
Vieques Island
US Virgin Islands
St Thomas
Tortola
Virgin Gorda
St John
St Croix

Leeward Islands
Anegada
Sombrero
Dog Island
Anguilla (UK)
St Martin (France)
St Maarten
St Barthélemy (France)
Netherlands Antilles
Saba
St Eustatius
St Kitts
Basseterre
Nevis
ST KITTS and NEVIS
Redonda
Montserrat (UK)

Barbuda
ANTIGUA and BARBUDA
St John's
Antigua

Guadeloupe Passage
Guadeloupe (France)
Moule
La Désirade
Point-à-Pitre
Basse-Terre
Marie Galante
Îles des Saintes
Dominica Passage

Caribbean Sea

Lesser Antilles

DOMINICA
Portsmouth
Roseau
Martinique Passage

Windward Islands

Fort-de-France
Ste-Marie
Martinique (France)
Rivière-Pilote

St Lucia Channel
ST LUCIA
Castries
Soufrière
St Vincent Passage

St Vincent
Georgetown
ST VINCENT and the GRENADINES
Kingstown
Bequia
Mustique
Grenadines
Canouan
Union
Carriacou

BARBADOS
Speightstown
Bridgetown

GRENADA
St George's
Grenville

Kilometres
0 50 100
Scale 1:5 000 000
Conformal Conic Projection

BRITISH VIRGIN ISLANDS

TOURIST ARRIVALS, 1994 - 1998

Stopover
Cruiseship

Tourists ('000s)
500
400
300
200
100
0
1994 1995 1996 1997 1998

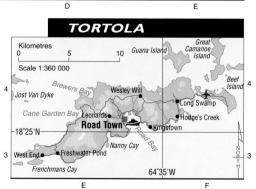

Tourism has traditionally been the most important sector in the economy of the British Virgin Islands, but the financial services sector has been expanding rapidly in recent years, especially in the field of general business rather than in banking and insurance.

KEY FACTS
Total area – 153 km²
Total population – 18 300 (1995)
Population density – 120 people per km²

UNITED STATES VIRGIN ISLANDS

TOURIST ARRIVALS, 1994 - 1998

Stopover
Cruiseship

Tourists ('000s)
2500
2000
1500
1000
500
0
1994 1995 1996 1997 1998

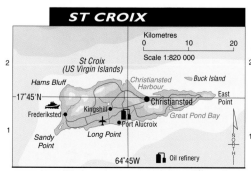

Tourism, and in particular cruiseship tourism, is the most important sector in the economy of the United States Virgin Islands. The industrial sector continues to grow, with the Hovensa oil refinery (the largest in the western hemisphere) being the most dominant industry by far.

KEY FACTS
Total area – 355 km²
Total population – 120 000 (1999)
Population density – 388 people per km²

BRITISH and UNITED STATES VIRGIN ISLANDS

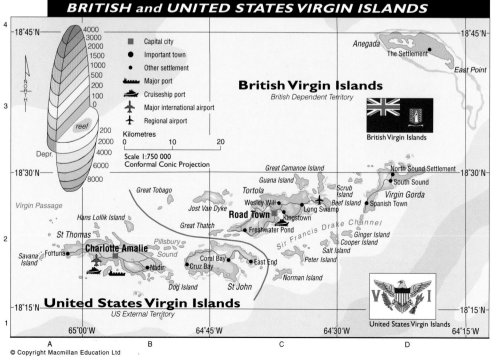

4000
3000
1500
1000
500
200
100
0
reef
200
2000
4000
6000
8000
Depr.

Capital city
Important town
Other settlement
Major port
Cruiseship port
Major international airport
Regional airport

Kilometres
0 10 20
Scale 1:750 000
Conformal Conic Projection

British Virgin Islands
British Dependent Territory

British Virgin Islands

Anegada
The Settlement
East Point
North Sound Settlement
South Sound
Great Camanoe Island
Guana Island
Tortola
Scrub Island
Virgin Gorda
Wesley Will
Long Swamp
Beef Island
Spanish Town
Road Town
Kingstown
Freshwater Pond
Ginger Island
Cooper Island
Salt Island
Peter Island
Sir Francis Drake Channel
Norman Island

Virgin Passage
Great Tobago
Jost Van Dyke
Great Thatch
Hans Lollik Island
Pillsbury Sound
St Thomas
Savana Island
Fortuna
Charlotte Amalie
Nadir
Coral Bay
Cruz Bay
East End
Dog Island
St John

United States Virgin Islands
US External Territory

United States Virgin Islands

TORTOLA

Kilometres
0 5 10
Scale 1:360 000

Guana Island
Great Camanoe Island
Jost Van Dyke
Brewers Bay
Wesley Will
Beef Island
Cane Garden Bay
Leonards
Long Swamp
Road Town
Hodge's Creek
Kingstown
Road Bay
West End
Nanny Cay
Freshwater Pond
Frenchmans Cay

ST CROIX

Kilometres
0 10 20
Scale 1:820 000

St Croix (US Virgin Islands)
Hams Bluff
Christiansted Harbour
Buck Island
Christiansted
East Point
Frederiksted
Kingshill
Port Alucroix
Great Pond Bay
Sandy Point
Long Point

Oil refinery

ST KITTS AND NEVIS

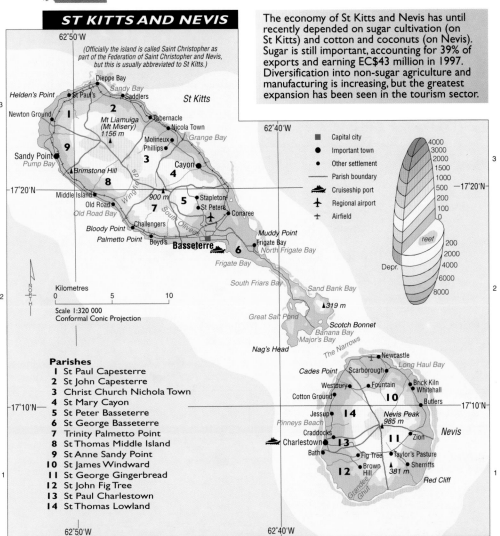

The economy of St Kitts and Nevis has until recently depended on sugar cultivation (on St Kitts) and cotton and coconuts (on Nevis). Sugar is still important, accounting for 39% of exports and earning EC$43 million in 1997. Diversification into non-sugar agriculture and manufacturing is increasing, but the greatest expansion has been seen in the tourism sector.

KEY FACTS
Total area – 267 km²
Total population – 43 500 (1995)
Population density – 163 people per km²
Capital city – Basseterre
Capital population – 16 400

(Officially the island is called Saint Christopher as part of the Federation of Saint Christopher and Nevis, but this is usually abbreviated to St Kitts.)

Map legend:
- ■ Capital city
- ● Important town
- • Other settlement
- — Parish boundary
- Cruiseship port
- Regional airport
- Airfield

Scale 1:320 000
Conformal Conic Projection

Parishes
1 St Paul Capesterre
2 St John Capesterre
3 Christ Church Nichola Town
4 St Mary Cayon
5 St Peter Basseterre
6 St George Basseterre
7 Trinity Palmetto Point
8 St Thomas Middle Island
9 St Anne Sandy Point
10 St James Windward
11 St George Gingerbread
12 St John Fig Tree
13 St Paul Charlestown
14 St Thomas Lowland

ANNUAL RAINFALL

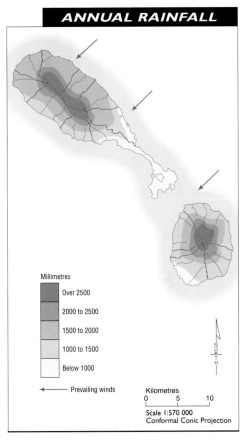

Millimetres
- Over 2500
- 2000 to 2500
- 1500 to 2000
- 1000 to 1500
- Below 1000

← Prevailing winds

Scale 1:570 000
Conformal Conic Projection

71

ECONOMIC ACTIVITY

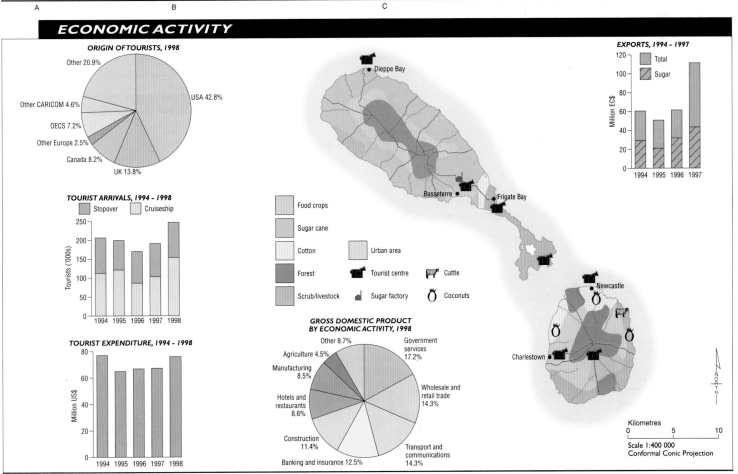

ORIGIN OF TOURISTS, 1998
- USA 42.8%
- UK 13.8%
- Canada 8.2%
- Other Europe 2.5%
- OECS 7.2%
- Other CARICOM 4.6%
- Other 20.9%

EXPORTS, 1994 – 1997
- Total
- Sugar

TOURIST ARRIVALS, 1994 – 1998
- Stopover
- Cruiseship

TOURIST EXPENDITURE, 1994 – 1998

Map legend:
- Food crops
- Sugar cane
- Cotton
- Forest
- Scrub/livestock
- Urban area
- Tourist centre
- Sugar factory
- Cattle
- Coconuts

GROSS DOMESTIC PRODUCT BY ECONOMIC ACTIVITY, 1998
- Government services 17.2%
- Wholesale and retail trade 14.3%
- Transport and communications 14.3%
- Banking and insurance 12.5%
- Construction 11.4%
- Hotels and restaurants 8.6%
- Manufacturing 8.5%
- Agriculture 4.5%
- Other 8.7%

Scale 1:400 000
Conformal Conic Projection

ANTIGUA AND BARBUDA

72

ANTIGUA

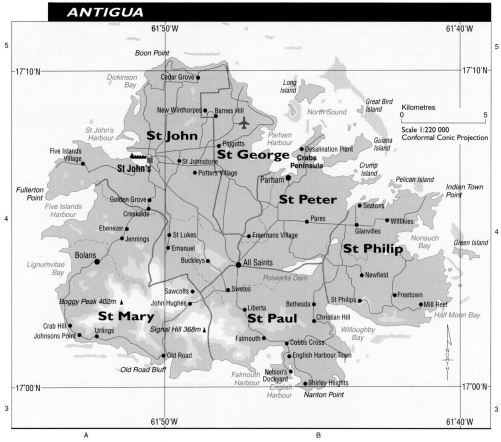

Boon Point
Dickinson Bay
Cedar Grove
Long Island
Great Bird Island
North Sound
New Winthorpes
Barnes Hill
Five Islands Village
St John
St John's Harbour
Piggotts
St George
St Johnstone
Parham Harbour
Desalination Plant
Crabs Peninsula
Guiana Island
St John's
Potters Village
Parham
Crump Island
Pelican Island
Fullerton Point
Golden Grove
St Peter
Indian Town Point
Five Islands Harbour
Creekside
Pares
Seatons
Willikies
Ebenezer
St Lukes
Freemans Village
Glanvilles
Jennings
Nonsuch Bay
Bolans
Emanuel
St Philip
Green Island
Lignumvitae Bay
Buckleys
All Saints
Potworks Dam
Newfield
Sawcolts
Swetes
Boggy Peak 402m
John Hughes
Liberta
Bethesda
St Philips
Freetown
St Mary
Signal Hill 368m
Christian Hill
Mill Reef
Crab Hill
Urlings
St Paul
Falmouth
Willoughby Bay
Johnsons Point
Cobbs Cross
Half Moon Bay
Old Road
English Harbour Town
Old Road Bluff
Falmouth Harbour
Nelson's Dockyard
Shirley Heights
English Harbour
Nanton Point

Kilometres
0   5
Scale 1:220 000
Conformal Conic Projection

Historically, agriculture was the backbone of Antigua and Barbuda's economy, but soil depletion, unfavourable market conditions and inconsistent rainfall patterns has resulted in the decline of this sector of the economy, to be replaced by tourism, which is now the main earner of foreign exchange.

KEY FACTS
Total area – 442 km²
Total population – 71 505 (1998)
Population density – 162 people per km²
Capital city – St John's
Capital population – 30 000

ECONOMIC ACTIVITY

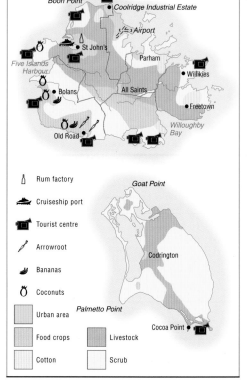

Boon Point
Coolridge Industrial Estate
Airport
St John's
Parham
Five Islands Harbour
Bolans
All Saints
Willikies
Old Road
Freetown
Willoughby Bay

Goat Point
Codrington
Palmetto Point
Cocoa Point

🍶 Rum factory
🚢 Cruiseship port
🐴 Tourist centre
Arrowroot
Bananas
Coconuts
Urban area
Food crops | Livestock
Cotton | Scrub

ANNUAL RAINFALL

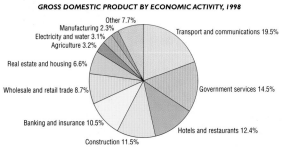

← Prevailing winds
Millimetres
Over 1500
1000 to 1500
Below 1000

Kilometres
0   5   10
Scale 1:500 000
Conformal Conic Projection

BARBUDA

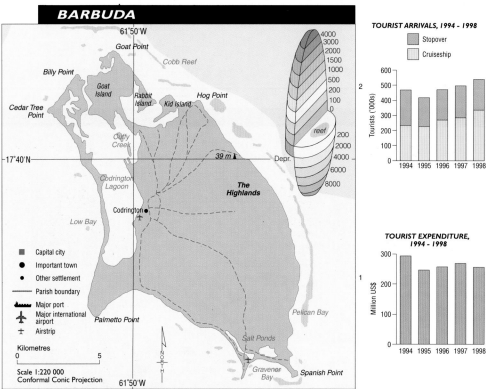

Goat Point
Billy Point
Cobb Reef
Cedar Tree Point
Goat Island
Rabbit Island
Hog Point
Kid Island
Duffy Creek
reef
39 m
Depr.
Codrington Lagoon
The Highlands
Codrington
Low Bay
Palmetto Point
Pelican Bay
Salt Ponds
Gravenor Bay
Spanish Point

■ Capital city
● Important town
• Other settlement
— Parish boundary
⚓ Major port
✈ Major international airport
✈ Airstrip

Kilometres
0   5
Scale 1:220 000
Conformal Conic Projection

TOURIST ARRIVALS, 1994 - 1998
Stopover
Cruiseship

Tourists ('000s)
600, 500, 400, 300, 200, 100, 0
1994 1995 1996 1997 1998

TOURIST EXPENDITURE, 1994 - 1998
Million US$
300, 200, 100, 0
1994 1995 1996 1997 1998

GROSS DOMESTIC PRODUCT BY ECONOMIC ACTIVITY, 1998
Other 7.7%
Manufacturing 2.3%
Electricity and water 3.1%
Agriculture 3.2%
Real estate and housing 6.6%
Wholesale and retail trade 8.7%
Banking and insurance 10.5%
Construction 11.5%
Hotels and restaurants 12.4%
Government services 14.5%
Transport and communications 19.5%

ORIGIN OF TOURISTS, 1998
Other 4.3%
Canada 7.2%
Other Europe 9.6%
USA 32.4%
Caribbean 18.3%
UK 28.2%

© Copyright Macmillan Education Ltd

MONTSERRAT and ANGUILLA

Anguilla
Montserrat

MONTSERRAT

(Situation before Chances Peak volcano erupted in 1995)

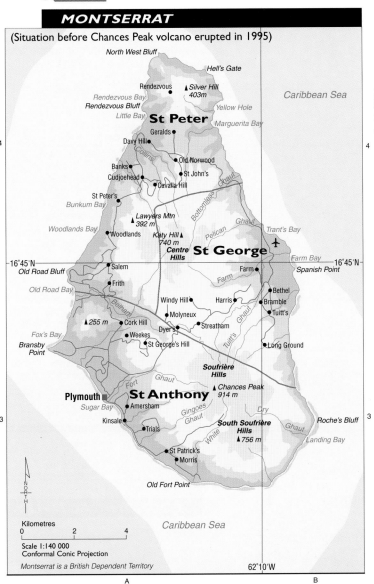

North West Bluff
Hell's Gate
Rendezvous ▲ Silver Hill 403m
Rendezvous Bay
Rendezvous Bluff
Little Bay
Yellow Hole
Caribbean Sea
Marguerita Bay
St Peter
Geralds
Davy Hill
Old Norwood
Banks
St John's
Cudjoehead
Oavalla Hill
St Peter's
Bunkum Bay
▲ Lawyers Mtn 392 m
Woodlands Bay
Woodlands
Katy Hill ▲ 740 m
St George
Centre Hills
Trant's Bay
16°45'N
Old Road Bluff
Salem
Farm
Farm Bay
Spanish Point
Old Road Bay
Frith
Farm
Windy Hill
Harris
Bethel
Bramble
Molyneux
Tuitt's
▲ 255 m
Cork Hill
Streatham
Dyer's
Fox's Bay
Weekes
St George's Hill
Long Ground
Bransby Point
Soufrière Hills
St Anthony
Plymouth ■
Amersham
▲ Chances Peak 914 m
Sugar Bay
Gingoes Ghaut
Kinsale
South Soufrière Hills
Roche's Bluff
Trials
▲ 756 m
Landing Bay
St Patrick's
Morris
Old Fort Point
Caribbean Sea

Kilometres 0 2 4
Scale 1:140 000
Conformal Conic Projection
Montserrat is a British Dependent Territory
62°10'W

TOURIST ARRIVALS, 1994 - 1998

Stopover / Cruiseship

Montserrat has been devastated by the volcanic eruptions that occurred between 1995 and 1997. The island's infrastructure, its airport, port and most of its businesses and farm land have been destroyed, while the capital, Plymouth, has been buried under ash and lava (see page 11 for more details). With the closure of the airport, Montserrat is only accessible by ferry and helicopter, but tourists are still visiting the island and numbers are slowly increasing. Only 4000 of the original 12 000 inhabitants are left and they are trying to establish themselves in the 'safe zone' in the north of the island, but with the volcano still active the future of the island is uncertain.

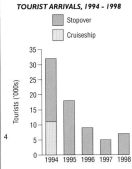

KEY FACTS
Total area – 102 km²
Total population – 4089 (1997)
Population density – 40 people per km²

73

ANNUAL RAINFALL

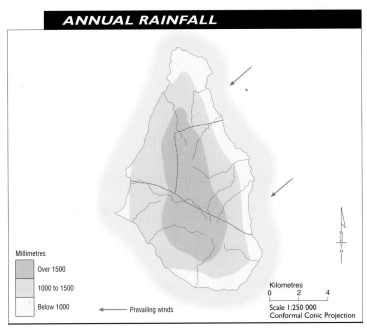

Millimetres
Over 1500
1000 to 1500
Below 1000
← Prevailing winds

Kilometres 0 2 4
Scale 1:250 000
Conformal Conic Projection

ANGUILLA

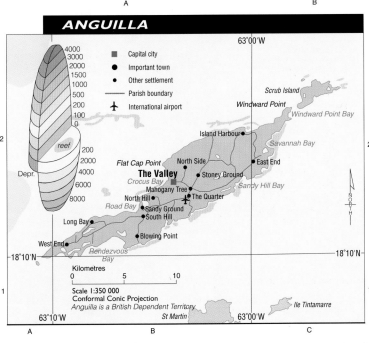

63°00'W
■ Capital city
● Important town
● Other settlement
— Parish boundary
✈ International airport

Scrub Island
Windward Point
Windward Point Bay
Island Harbour
Savannah Bay
Flat Cap Point
North Side
East End
The Valley
Stoney Ground
Crocus Bay
Mahogany Tree
Sandy Hill Bay
North Hill
The Quarter
Sandy Ground
Road Bay
South Hill
Long Bay
Blowing Point
West End
Rendezvous Bay
18°10'N
Ile Tintamarre
St Martin
63°10'W
63°00'W

Kilometres 0 5 10
Scale 1:350 000
Conformal Conic Projection
Anguilla is a British Dependent Territory

TOURIST EXPENDITURE, 1994 - 1998
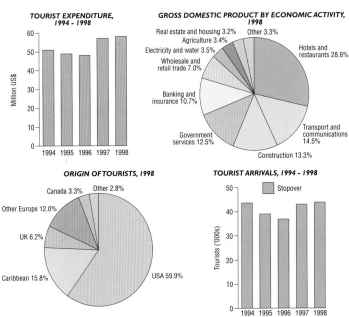

GROSS DOMESTIC PRODUCT BY ECONOMIC ACTIVITY, 1998

Real estate and housing 3.2% / Other 3.3%
Agriculture 3.4%
Electricity and water 3.5%
Wholesale and retail trade 7.0%
Hotels and restaurants 28.6%
Banking and insurance 10.7%
Government services 12.5%
Transport and communications 14.5%
Construction 13.3%

ORIGIN OF TOURISTS, 1998
Canada 3.3% / Other 2.8%
Other Europe 12.0%
UK 6.2%
Caribbean 15.8%
USA 59.9%

TOURIST ARRIVALS, 1994 - 1998
Stopover

Anguilla's traditional industries were boat building, fishing, salt production and livestock rearing. During the 1980s these were replaced by a rapid growth in tourism, which has now become the most important sector of the island's economy accounting for 50% of GDP and over 50% of employment.

KEY FACTS
Total area – 96 km²
Total population – 10 302 (1995)
Population density – 107 people per km²
Capital city – The Valley
Capital population – 2000 (1992)

GUADELOUPE and MARTINIQUE

GUADELOUPE

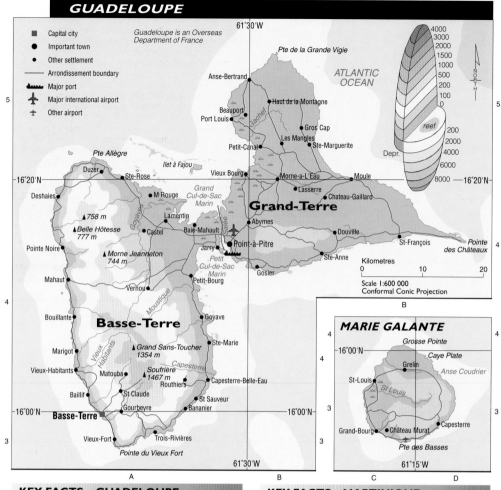

Key
- Capital city
- Important town
- Other settlement
- Arrondissement boundary
- Major port
- Major international airport
- Other airport

Guadeloupe is an Overseas Department of France

61°30'W

ATLANTIC OCEAN

Pte de la Grande Vigie
Anse-Bertrand
Haut de la Montagne
Beauport
Port Louis
Gros Cap
Petit-Canal
Les Mangles
Ste-Marguerite
Vieux Bourg
Morne-a-L'Eau
Moule
Lasserre
Chateau-Gaillard
Grand-Terre
Abymes
Douville
St-François
Point-à-Pitre
Jarry
Ste-Anne
Petit Cul-de-Sac Marin
Gosier
Pointe des Châteaux

Pte Allègre
Duzer
Ste-Rose
Ilet à Fajou
Deshaies
M Rouge
Grand Cul-de-Sac Marin
Lamentin
Castel
Baie-Mahault
Pointe Noire
▲758 m
▲Belle Hôtesse 777 m
▲Morne Jeanneton 744 m
Mahaut
Vernou
Petit-Bourg
Bouillante
Basse-Terre
Goyave
Marigot
Ste-Marie
Vieux-Habitants
▲Grand Sans-Toucher 1354 m
Matouba
Capesterre
▲Soufrière 1467 m
Routhiers
Capesterre-Belle-Eau
Baillif
St Claude
St Sauveur
Basse-Terre
Gourbeyre
Bananier
Vieux-Fort
Trois-Rivières
Pointe du Vieux Fort

16°20'N
16°00'N

Kilometres 0 10 20
Scale 1:600 000
Conformal Conic Projection

MARIE GALANTE

Grosse Pointe
Caye Plate
16°00'N
Grelin
Anse Coudrier
St-Louis
St Louis
Grand-Bourg
Château Murat
Capesterre
Pte des Basses
61°15'W

KEY FACTS – GUADELOUPE
Total area – 1705 km²
Total population – 428 000 (1997)
Population density – 251 people per km²
Capital city – Basse-Terre
Capital population – 25 000

KEY FACTS – MARTINIQUE
Total area – 1080 km²
Total population – 392 000 (1997)
Population density – 363 people per km²
Capital city – Fort-de-France
Capital population – 101 540

MARTINIQUE

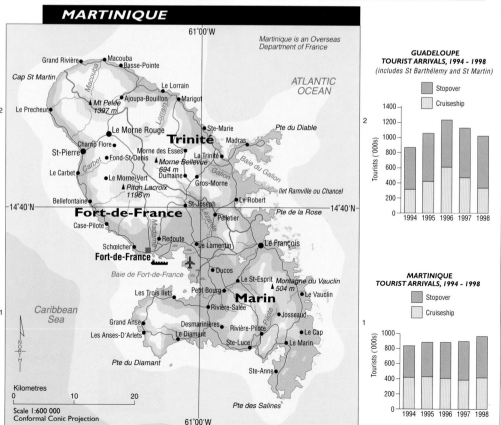

61°00'W

Martinique is an Overseas Department of France

ATLANTIC OCEAN

Grand Rivière
Macouba
Basse-Pointe
Cap St Martin
Le Lorrain
Le Precheur
▲Mt Pelée 1397 m
Ajoupa-Bouillon
Marigot
Ste-Marie
Pte du Diable
Le Morne Rouge
Madras
Champ Flore
Trinité
St-Pierre
Morne des Esses
▲Morne Bellevue 694 m
La Trinité
Fond-St-Denis
Dumaine
Baie du Galion
Le Carbet
▲Le Morne Vert
Gros-Morne
Ilet Ramville ou Chancel
▲Piton Lacroix 1196 m
Bellefontaine
St-Joseph
Le Robert
Pte de la Rose
Fort-de-France
Pelletier
Case-Pilote
Redoute
Le Lamentin
Schœlcher
Le François
Fort-de-France
Baie de Fort-de-France
Ducos
Le St-Esprit
Montagne du Vauclin ▲504 m
Les Trois Ilets
Petit Bourg
Le Vauclin
Marin
Rivière-Salée
Caribbean Sea
Grand Anse
Josseaud
Desmarinières
Rivière-Pilote
Le Cap
Les Anses-D'Arlets
Le Diamant
Le Marin
Ste-Luce
Ste-Anne
Pte du Diamant
Pte des Salines

14°40'N

Kilometres 0 10 20
Scale 1:600 000
Conformal Conic Projection

© Copyright Macmillan Education Ltd

ANNUAL RAINFALL

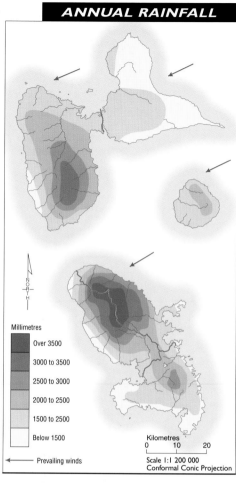

Millimetres
- Over 3500
- 3000 to 3500
- 2500 to 3000
- 2000 to 2500
- 1500 to 2500
- Below 1500

← Prevailing winds

Kilometres 0 10 20
Scale 1:1 200 000
Conformal Conic Projection

GUADELOUPE TOURIST ARRIVALS, 1994 - 1998
(includes St Barthélemy and St Martin)

- Stopover
- Cruiseship

Tourists ('000s)
1400
1200
1000
800
600
400
200
1994 1995 1996 1997 1998

MARTINIQUE TOURIST ARRIVALS, 1994 - 1998

- Stopover
- Cruiseship

Tourists ('000s)
1000
800
600
400
200
0
1994 1995 1996 1997 1998

ECONOMIC ACTIVITY

Moule
St-François
Pointe-à-Pitre
Gosier
Ste-Anne
Basse-Terre

St-Pierre
La Trinité
Schœlcher
Fort-de-France
Anse a L'Ane/Pointe du Bout
Le Diamant
Le Marin
Ste-Anne

Key
- Urban area
- Mixed crops
- Sugar cane
- Forest
- Scrub/livestock
- Commercial centre
- Tourist centre
- Oil refinery
- Sugar factory
- Cruiseship port
- Bananas
- Cattle
- Cocoa
- Coffee
- Pineapples
- Vanilla

DOMINICA

DOMINICA

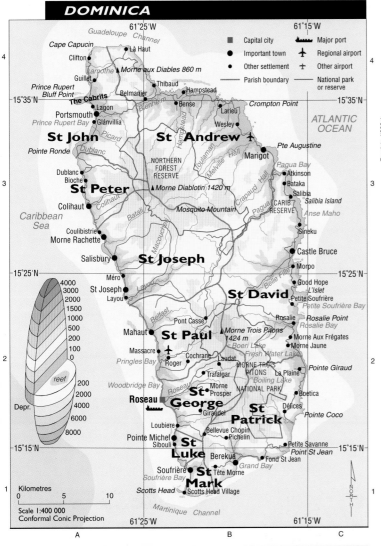

Map legend:
- ■ Capital city
- ● Important town
- • Other settlement
- —— Parish boundary
- 🚢 Major port
- ✈ Regional airport
- ✈ Other airport
- —— National park or reserve

Scale 1:400 000
Conformal Conic Projection

Dominica's economy has long depended on agriculture which has included coffee, limes, sugar and vanilla in the past, and bananas, cocoa, coconuts, bay leaves and citrus today. The mountainous nature of the island encourages tree crops that stabilise the soil. Bananas is the main export crop, but falling prices and insecure markets are making this less certain. Coconuts are widely grown and support a regional export in cooking oils and a wider market for soap products. The island does not lend itself naturally to resort type tourism, but its natural beauty has made it of growing importance to the cruiseship industry and for ecotourism.

KEY FACTS
Total area – 750 km²
Total population – 74 000 (1995)
Population density – 99 people per km²
Capital city – Roseau
Capital population – 20 755

TOURIST ARRIVALS, 1994 - 1998
Tourists ('000s); Stopover / Cruiseship

ANNUAL RAINFALL

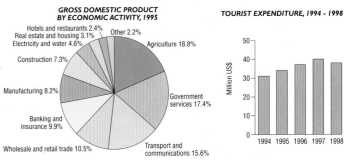

Millimetres
- Over 4000
- 3500 to 4000
- 3000 to 3500
- 2500 to 3000
- 2000 to 2500
- 1500 to 2000
- Below 1500
- ← Prevailing winds

ECONOMIC ACTIVITY

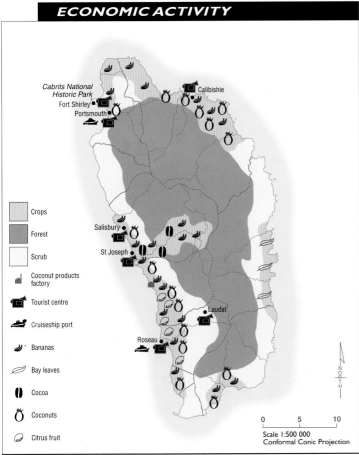

Legend:
- Crops
- Forest
- Scrub
- Coconut products factory
- Tourist centre
- Cruiseship port
- Bananas
- Bay leaves
- Cocoa
- Coconuts
- Citrus fruit

Scale 1:500 000
Conformal Conic Projection

GROSS DOMESTIC PRODUCT BY ECONOMIC ACTIVITY, 1995
- Hotels and restaurants 2.4%
- Real estate and housing 3.1%
- Electricity and water 4.6%
- Construction 7.3%
- Manufacturing 8.2%
- Banking and insurance 9.9%
- Wholesale and retail trade 10.5%
- Transport and communications 15.6%
- Government services 17.4%
- Agriculture 18.8%
- Other 2.2%

TOURIST EXPENDITURE, 1994 - 1998
Million US$

EXPORTS, 1994 - 1998
Million EC$
Bananas / Soap products / Other

ORIGIN OF TOURISTS, 1998
- Other 12.6%
- Canada 2.9%
- Other Europe 3.8%
- France 5.6%
- UK 8.5%
- USA 21.6%
- Caribbean 44.9%

ST LUCIA

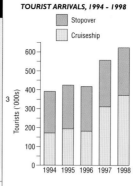

ST LUCIA

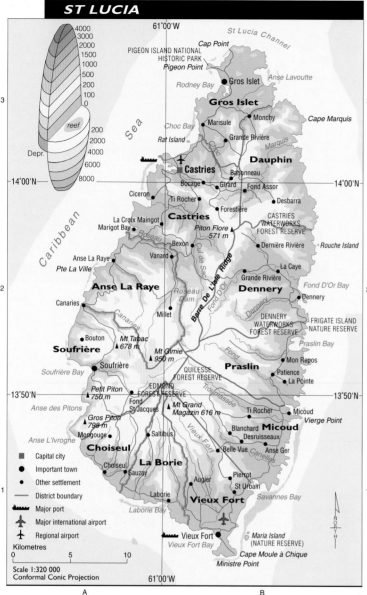

Capital city
Important town
Other settlement
District boundary
Major port
Major international airport
Regional airport

Kilometres
0   5   10

Scale 1:320 000
Conformal Conic Projection

TOURIST ARRIVALS, 1994 - 1998

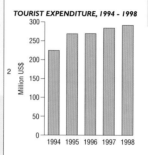

Stopover
Cruiseship

TOURIST EXPENDITURE, 1994 - 1998

Since they replaced sugar in the early 1960s, bananas have been the backbone of St Lucia's economy, but storm damage, drought, industrial unrest and falling market prices have conspired to make the future of the industry uncertain. From a high of 135 000 tonnes in 1992 production slumped to 65 000 tonnes in 1999, but despite that it is still the major export commodity. St Lucia's manufacturing sector was once the largest in the Windward Islands, but it too is on the decline and it is only tourism that has shown strong growth, making it now the most important sector of the economy.

KEY FACTS
Total area – 616 km²
Total population – 149 666
Population density – 243 people per km²
Capital city – Castries
Capital population – 55 000

ORIGIN OF TOURISTS, 1998

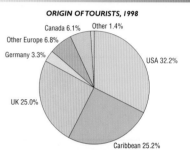

Canada 6.1%   Other 1.4%
Other Europe 6.8%
Germany 3.3%   USA 32.2%
UK 25.0%
Caribbean 25.2%

ECONOMIC ACTIVITY

BANANA PRODUCTION, 1995 - 1999

GROSS DOMESTIC PRODUCT BY ECONOMIC ACTIVITY, 1998

Other 4.9%
Electricity and water 4.1%   Transport and communications 17.3%
Manufacturing 5.3%
Real estate and housing 5.5%   Government services 14.1%
Construction 7.2%
Agriculture 7.5%
(Bananas 3.3%)   Wholesale and retail trade 13.2%
Banking and insurance 8.6%   Hotels and restaurants 12.3%

EXPORTS BY COMMODITY, 1999

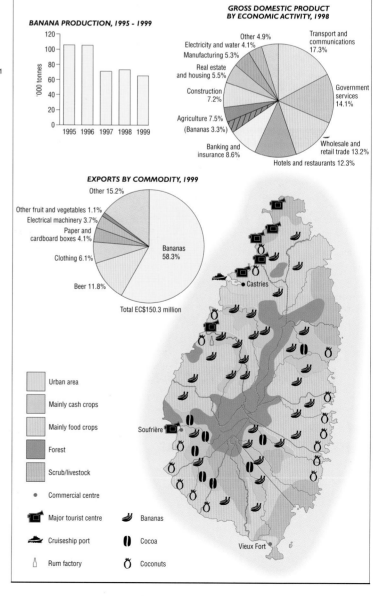

Other 15.2%
Other fruit and vegetables 1.1%
Electrical machinery 3.7%
Paper and cardboard boxes 4.1%   Bananas 58.3%
Clothing 6.1%
Beer 11.8%
Total EC$150.3 million

Urban area
Mainly cash crops
Mainly food crops
Forest
Scrub/livestock
Commercial centre
Major tourist centre   Bananas
Cruiseship port   Cocoa
Rum factory   Coconuts

ANNUAL RAINFALL

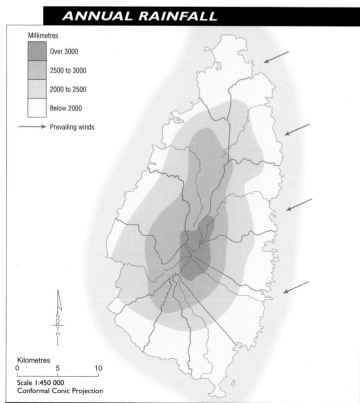

Millimetres
Over 3000
2500 to 3000
2000 to 2500
Below 2000
Prevailing winds

Kilometres
0   5   10

Scale 1:450 000
Conformal Conic Projection

ST VINCENT AND THE GRENADINES

ST VINCENT

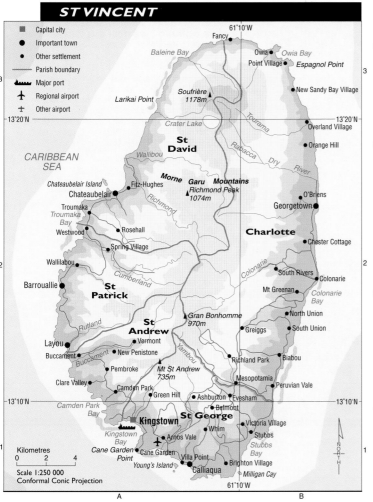

Capital city
Important town
Other settlement
Parish boundary
Major port
Regional airport
Other airport

Scale 1:250 000
Conformal Conic Projection

THE GRENADINES

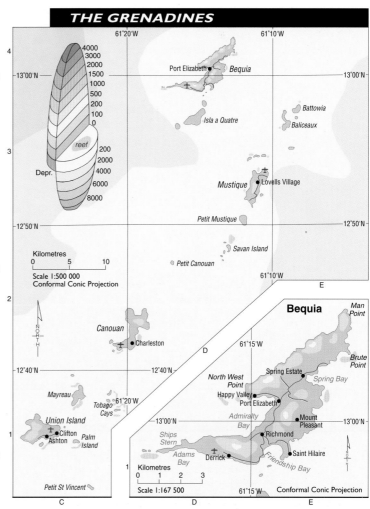

Scale 1:500 000
Conformal Conic Projection

Scale 1:167 500
Conformal Conic Projection

The economy of St Vincent and the Grenadines is largely dependent on the production of bananas, the export of which earnt EC$39 million in 1997 – well down from its high of EC$98 million in 1992. The dismantling of preferential trade arrangements under the Lomé Convention and falling world prices makes the future of the industry uncertain and there is a drive towards diversification into other crops. The islands have great potential for tourism, especially for sailing and upmarket tourism, and St Vincent in particular is working hard to develop its tourism infrastructure.

KEY FACTS

Total area – 389 km²
Total population – 111 224 (1997)
Population density – 286 people per km²
Capital city – Kingstown
Capital population – 27 384 (1997)
St Vincent population – 102 480 (1997)
The Grenadines population – 8 744 (1997)

ANNUAL RAINFALL

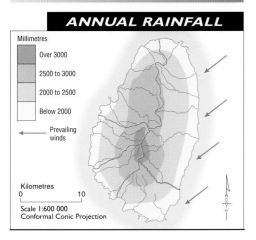

Millimetres
Over 3000
2500 to 3000
2000 to 2500
Below 2000
Prevailing winds

Kilometres
0   10
Scale 1:600 000
Conformal Conic Projection

ECONOMIC ACTIVITY

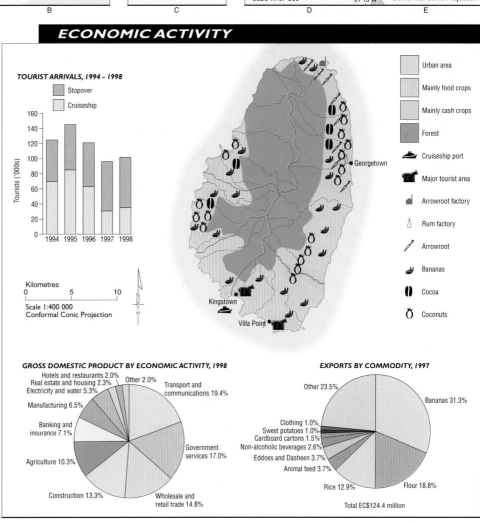

TOURIST ARRIVALS, 1994 - 1998
Stopover
Cruiseship
Tourists (000s)

Kilometres
0   5   10
Scale 1:400 000
Conformal Conic Projection

Urban area
Mainly food crops
Mainly cash crops
Forest
Cruiseship port
Major tourist area
Arrowroot factory
Rum factory
Arrowroot
Bananas
Cocoa
Coconuts

GROSS DOMESTIC PRODUCT BY ECONOMIC ACTIVITY, 1998

Hotels and restaurants 2.0%
Real estate and housing 2.3%
Electricity and water 5.3%
Other 2.0%
Transport and communications 19.4%
Manufacturing 6.5%
Banking and insurance 7.1%
Government services 17.0%
Agriculture 10.3%
Construction 13.3%
Wholesale and retail trade 14.8%

EXPORTS BY COMMODITY, 1997

Other 23.5%
Bananas 31.3%
Clothing 1.0%
Sweet potatoes 1.0%
Cardboard cartons 1.5%
Non-alcoholic beverages 2.6%
Eddoes and Dasheen 3.7%
Animal feed 3.7%
Rice 12.9%
Flour 18.8%
Total EC$124.4 million

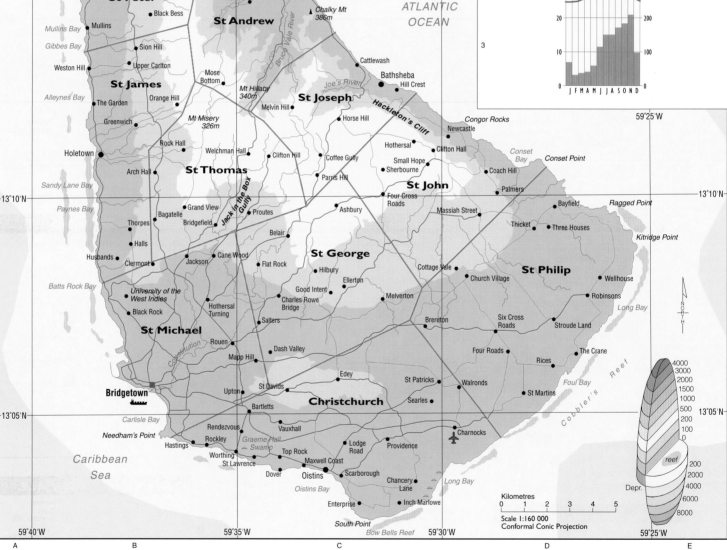

BARBADOS

Although once almost entirely dependent on sugar for export earnings, Barbados diversified its economy to the extent that for the last two decades it has relied equally on sugar, manufacturing and tourism to sustain the economy. With some instability in the manufacturing sector and continuing fluctuations in sugar production, the country has come to rely more and more on tourism. In 1998 over one million visitors contributed more than US$700 million to the economy, and much of the current investment is geared towards modernising the tourism infrastructure.

KEY FACTS
Total area – 430 km²
Total population – 266 800 (1998)
Population density – 620 people per km²
Capital city – Bridgetown
Capital population – 104 000

Legend:
- Capital city
- Important town
- Other settlement
- Parish boundary
- Main road
- Other road
- Major port
- Major international airport

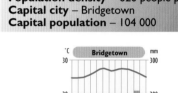

Bridgetown (climate chart)

Kilometres
0 1 2 3 4 5
Scale 1:160 000
Conformal Conic Projection

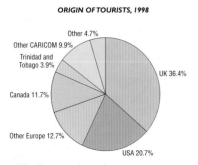

ORIGIN OF TOURISTS, 1998
- UK 36.4%
- USA 20.7%
- Other Europe 12.7%
- Canada 11.7%
- Other CARICOM 9.9%
- Trinidad and Tobago 3.9%
- Other 4.7%

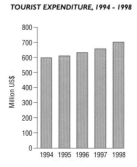

TOURIST EXPENDITURE, 1994 – 1998
Million US$
1994 1995 1996 1997 1998

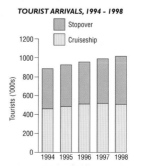

TOURIST ARRIVALS, 1994 – 1998
- Stopover
- Cruiseship
Tourists ('000s)
1994 1995 1996 1997 1998

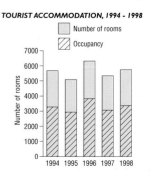

TOURIST ACCOMMODATION, 1994 – 1998
- Number of rooms
- Occupancy
Number of rooms
1994 1995 1996 1997 1998

ECONOMIC ACTIVITY

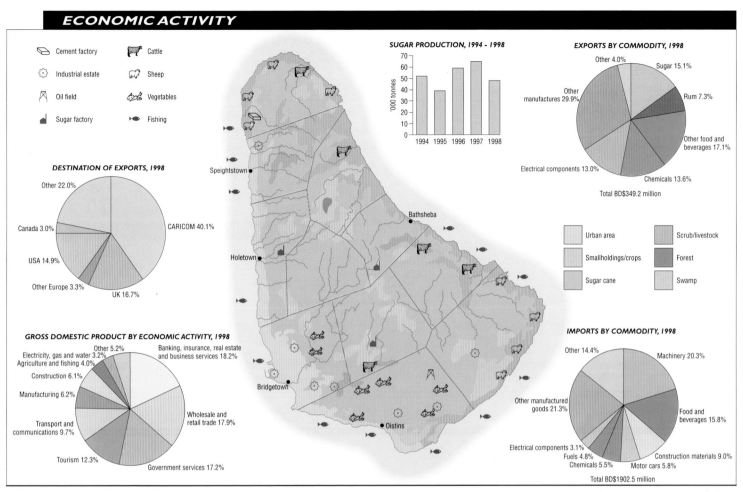

Cement factory
Industrial estate
Oil field
Sugar factory
Cattle
Sheep
Vegetables
Fishing

SUGAR PRODUCTION, 1994 - 1998

EXPORTS BY COMMODITY, 1998

Other 4.0%
Sugar 15.1%
Rum 7.3%
Other manufactures 29.9%
Other food and beverages 17.1%
Electrical components 13.0%
Chemicals 13.6%
Total BD$349.2 million

DESTINATION OF EXPORTS, 1998

Other 22.0%
Canada 3.0%
USA 14.9%
Other Europe 3.3%
UK 16.7%
CARICOM 40.1%

Urban area
Smallholdings/crops
Sugar cane
Scrub/livestock
Forest
Swamp

GROSS DOMESTIC PRODUCT BY ECONOMIC ACTIVITY, 1998

Other 5.2%
Electricity, gas and water 3.2%
Agriculture and fishing 4.0%
Construction 6.1%
Manufacturing 6.2%
Transport and communications 9.7%
Tourism 12.3%
Government services 17.2%
Banking, insurance, real estate and business services 18.2%
Wholesale and retail trade 17.9%

IMPORTS BY COMMODITY, 1998

Other 14.4%
Machinery 20.3%
Other manufactured goods 21.3%
Food and beverages 15.8%
Electrical components 3.1%
Fuels 4.8%
Chemicals 5.5%
Motor cars 5.8%
Construction materials 9.0%
Total BD$1902.5 million

TOURISM

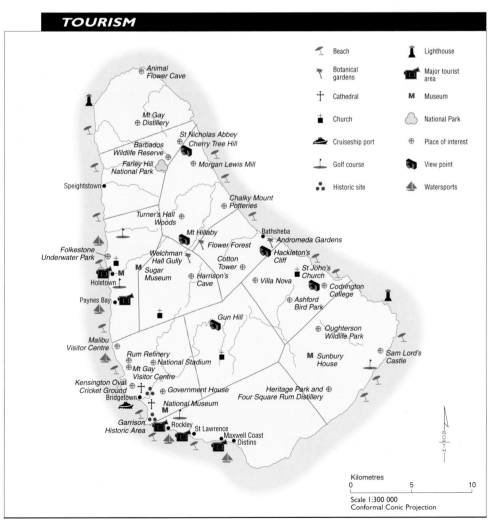

Beach
Botanical gardens
Cathedral
Church
Cruiseship port
Golf course
Historic site
Lighthouse
Major tourist area
Museum
National Park
Place of interest
View point
Watersports

Scale 1:300 000
Conformal Conic Projection

POPULATION

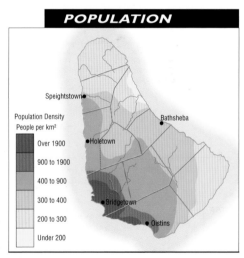

Population Density People per km²
Over 1900
900 to 1900
400 to 900
300 to 400
200 to 300
Under 200

ANNUAL RAINFALL

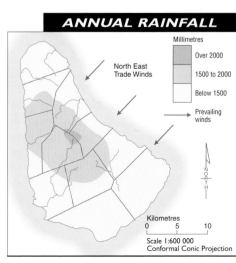

Millimetres
Over 2000
1500 to 2000
Below 1500
North East Trade Winds
Prevailing winds

Scale 1:600 000
Conformal Conic Projection

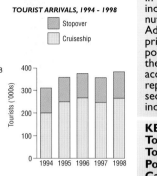

GRENADA

Capital city
Important town
Other settlement
Parish boundary
Major port
Regional airport
Other airport

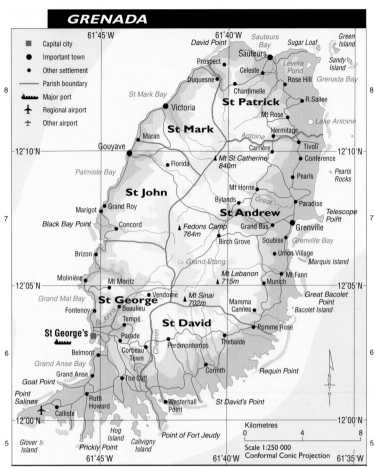

61°45'W   61°40'W

Sauteurs Bay
David Point   Sugar Loaf   Green Island
Prospect   Celeste   Sandy Island
Duquesne   Chantimelle   Rose Hill   Grenada Bay
St Mark Bay   Levera Pond
Victoria   St Patrick   R.Sailee
Maran   St Mark   Mt Rose
Gouyave   Antoine   Hermitage   Tivoli
Florida   Mt St Catherine 840m   Conference
Palmiste Bay   Carrière   Pearls   Pearls Rocks
St John   Mt Horne   Bylands   Paradise
Marigot   Grand Roy   St Andrew   Telescope Point
Black Bay Point   Concord   Fedons Camp 764m   Grand Bas   Grenville
Brizon   Birch Grove   Soubise   Grenville Bay
Molinière   Grand Etang   Union Village   Marquis Island
Mt Moritz   Mt Lebanon 715m   Mt Fann
Grand Mal Bay   Vendome   Mt Sinai 702m   Munich   Great Bacolet Point
St George   Beaulieu   Mamma Cannes   Bacolet Island
Fontenoy   Tempé   St David   Pomme Rose
St George's   Parade   Perdmontemps   Thebaide
Belmont   Corbeau Town   Chemin
Grand Anse Bay   Corinth   Requin Point
Grand Anse   The Cliff
Goat Point   Ruth Howard   Westerhall Point   St David's Point
Point Salines   Calliste
Hog Island   Point of Fort Jeudy
Glover Island   Prickly Point   Calivigny Island

12°10'N   12°05'N   12°00'N

Kilometres
0   4   8
Scale 1:250 000
Conformal Conic Projection

THE GRENADINES

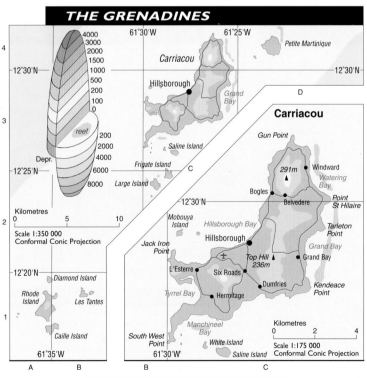

61°30'W   61°25'W
Petite Martinique
Carriacou
Hillsborough
Grand Bay
Saline Island
Frigate Island
Large Island
Diamond Island
Rhode Island   Les Tantes
Caille Island
South West Point   White Island   Saline Island

4000 3000 2000 1500 1000 500 200 100 0
reef
200 2000 4000 6000 8000
Depr.

Kilometres
0   5   10
Scale 1:350 000
Conformal Conic Projection

Carriacou

Gun Point
Windward
291m   Watering Bay
Bogles   Belvedere   Point St Hilaire
Mobouya Island   Tarleton Point
Hillsborough Bay   Hillsborough   Grand Bay
Jack Iron Point   Top Hill 236m   Grand Bay
L'Esterre   Six Roads   Dumfries
Tyrrel Bay   Hermitage   Kendeace Point
Manchineel Bay

Kilometres
0   2   4
Scale 1:175 000
Conformal Conic Projection

61°35'W   61°30'W

TOURIST ARRIVALS, 1994 - 1998

Stopover
Cruiseship

Tourists ('000s)
400
300
200
100
0
1994 1995 1996 1997 1998

In the past agriculture has been the major industry on Grenada with bananas, cocoa and nutmeg being the most important crops. Adverse weather conditions, international price fluctuations and, in the case of bananas, poor quality fruit, have badly hit this sector of the economy, but these three crops still account for over 40% of exports. Tourism is replacing agriculture as the most important sector of the economy and the growth of this industry is seen as the key to Grenada's future.

KEY FACTS
Total area – 344 km²
Total population – 99 500 (1997)
Population density – 289 people per km²
Capital city – St George's
Capital population – 7500

ANNUAL RAINFALL

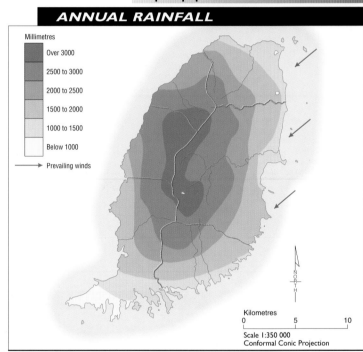

Millimetres
Over 3000
2500 to 3000
2000 to 2500
1500 to 2000
1000 to 1500
Below 1000

Prevailing winds

Kilometres
0   5   10
Scale 1:350 000
Conformal Conic Projection

ECONOMIC ACTIVITY

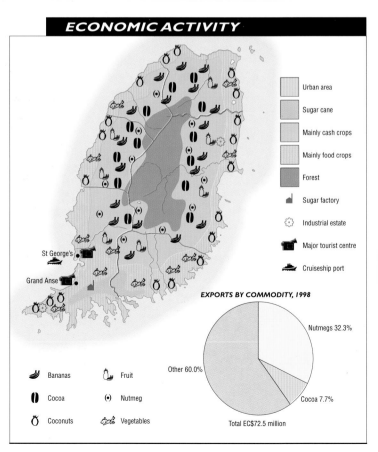

Urban area
Sugar cane
Mainly cash crops
Mainly food crops
Forest

Sugar factory
Industrial estate
Major tourist centre
Cruiseship port

St George's
Grand Anse

Bananas   Fruit
Cocoa   Nutmeg
Coconuts   Vegetables

GROSS DOMESTIC PRODUCT BY ECONOMIC ACTIVITY, 1998

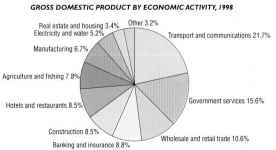

Other 3.2%
Real estate and housing 3.4%
Electricity and water 5.2%
Transport and communications 21.7%
Manufacturing 6.7%
Agriculture and fishing 7.8%
Government services 15.6%
Hotels and restaurants 8.5%
Construction 8.5%
Wholesale and retail trade 10.6%
Banking and insurance 8.8%

EXPORTS BY COMMODITY, 1998

Nutmegs 32.3%
Other 60.0%
Cocoa 7.7%
Total EC$72.5 million

80

The economy of Trinidad and Tobago is dominated by petroleum, which contributed over 28% of the country's GDP in 1997 and over 45% of foreign exchange earnings. Production began on land at the beginning of the 20th century and was boosted by discoveries in the Gulf of Paria, and again in the 1970s when both oil and natural gas were found off the east coast. 1998 saw the discovery of the largest oilfield in 25 years (see page 41 for a case study of the oil and gas industry in Trinidad and Tobago). Point Lisas is Trinidad's major industrial estate and has been undergoing substantial improvement and expansion. Petrochemicals are another important export and at Point Lisas there are five methanol plants, which reached record levels of production in 1997. Another major industry at Point Lisas is iron and steel with two plants in production and another three under construction. Tourism is the country's largest untapped resource, and largely focussed in Tobago. In recent years the government has been vigorously promoting this sector of the economy and a tourism development programme has been established to improve the tourist infrastructure.

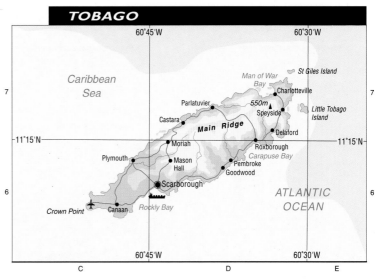

TOBAGO

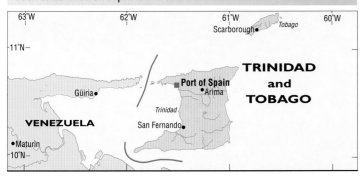

KEY FACTS
Total area – 5 128 km²
Total population – 1 274 800 (1997)
Population density – 249 people per km²
Capital city – Port of Spain
Capital population – 350 000

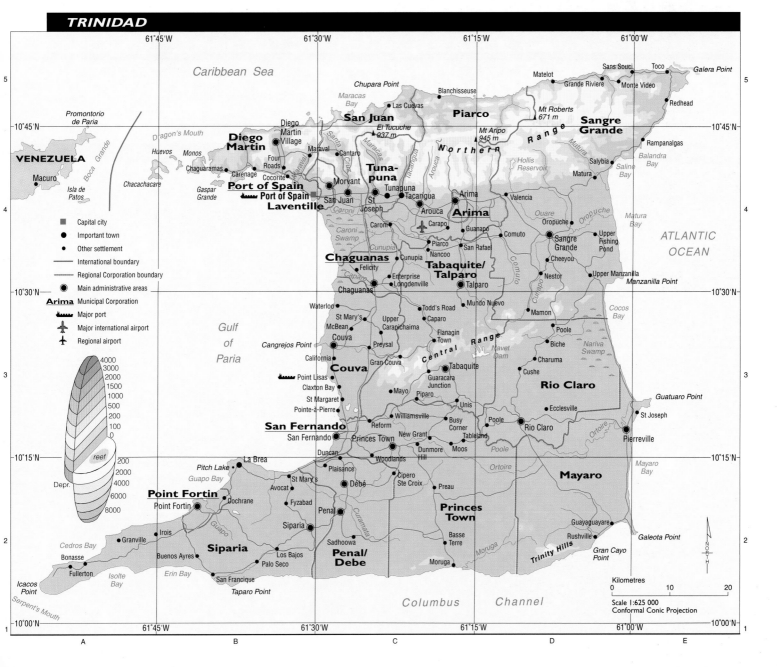

TRINIDAD

Scale 1:625 000
Conformal Conic Projection

TRINIDAD AND TOBAGO

TOURISM

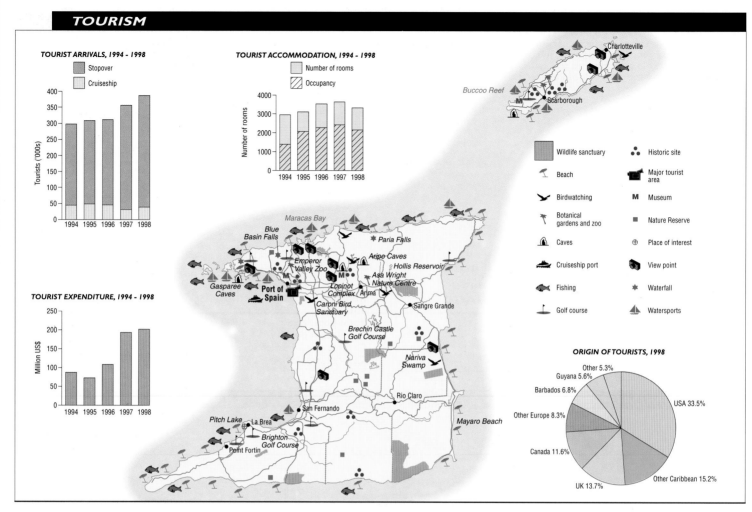

TOURIST ARRIVALS, 1994 - 1998

- Stopover
- Cruiseship

Tourists ('000s)

TOURIST ACCOMMODATION, 1994 - 1998

- Number of rooms
- Occupancy

Number of rooms

TOURIST EXPENDITURE, 1994 - 1998

Million US$

Key:
- Wildlife sanctuary
- Beach
- Birdwatching
- Botanical gardens and zoo
- Caves
- Cruiseship port
- Fishing
- Golf course
- Historic site
- Major tourist area
- M Museum
- Nature Reserve
- Place of interest
- View point
- Waterfall
- Watersports

Map labels:
Charlotteville, Buccoo Reef, Scarborough, Maracas Bay, Blue Basin Falls, Paria Falls, Emperor Valley Zoo, Aripo Caves, Hollis Reservoir, Asa Wright Nature Centre, Gasparee Caves, Lopinot Complex, Arima, Port of Spain, Caroni Bird Sanctuary, Sangre Grande, Brechin Castle Golf Course, Nariva Swamp, Rio Claro, San Fernando, Pitch Lake, La Brea, Brighton Golf Course, Point Fortin, Mayaro Beach

ORIGIN OF TOURISTS, 1998

- Other 5.3%
- Guyana 5.6%
- Barbados 6.8%
- Other Europe 8.3%
- Canada 11.6%
- UK 13.7%
- Other Caribbean 15.2%
- USA 33.5%

POPULATION

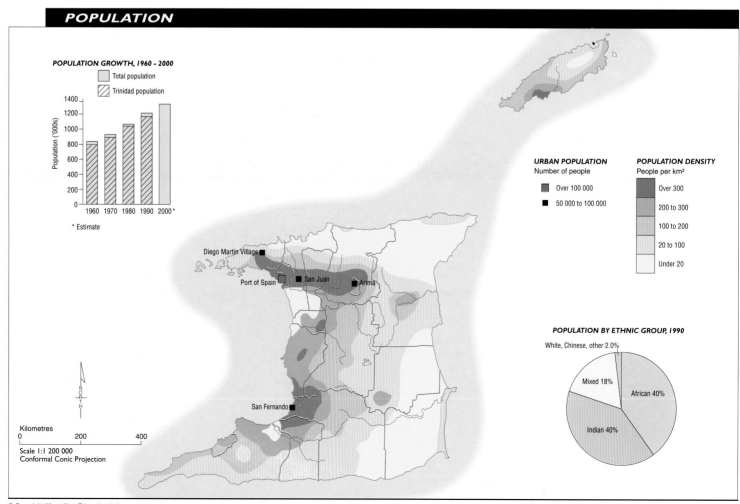

POPULATION GROWTH, 1960 - 2000

- Total population
- Trinidad population

Population ('000s)

1960 1970 1980 1990 2000*

* Estimate

URBAN POPULATION
Number of people
- Over 100 000
- 50 000 to 100 000

POPULATION DENSITY
People per km²
- Over 300
- 200 to 300
- 100 to 200
- 20 to 100
- Under 20

Map labels:
Diego Martin Village, Port of Spain, San Juan, Arima, San Fernando

POPULATION BY ETHNIC GROUP, 1990

- White, Chinese, other 2.0%
- Mixed 18%
- African 40%
- Indian 40%

Kilometres
0   200   400
Scale 1:1 200 000
Conformal Conic Projection

ECONOMIC ACTIVITY

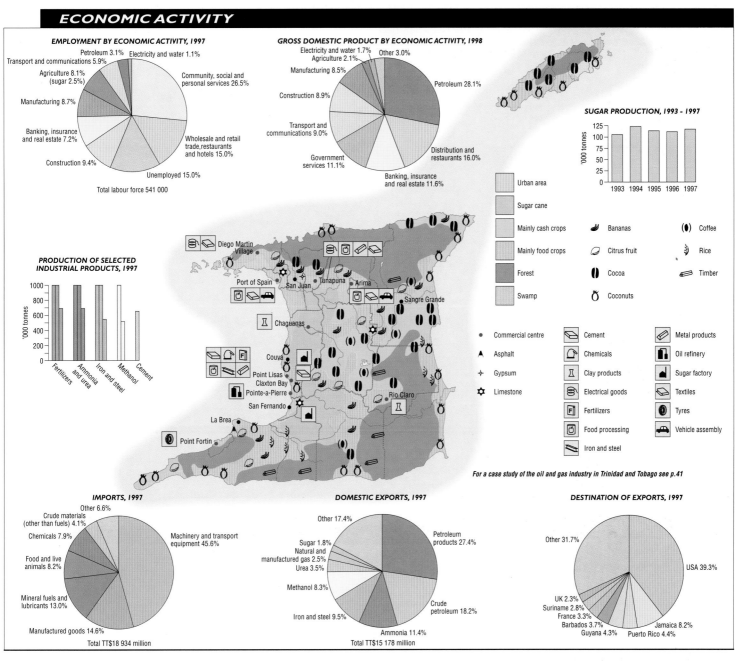

EMPLOYMENT BY ECONOMIC ACTIVITY, 1997

- Petroleum 3.1%
- Electricity and water 1.1%
- Transport and communications 5.9%
- Agriculture 8.1% (sugar 2.5%)
- Manufacturing 8.7%
- Banking, insurance and real estate 7.2%
- Construction 9.4%
- Community, social and personal services 26.5%
- Wholesale and retail trade, restaurants and hotels 15.0%
- Unemployed 15.0%

Total labour force 541 000

GROSS DOMESTIC PRODUCT BY ECONOMIC ACTIVITY, 1998

- Electricity and water 1.7%
- Other 3.0%
- Agriculture 2.1%
- Manufacturing 8.5%
- Construction 8.9%
- Transport and communications 9.0%
- Government services 11.1%
- Banking, insurance and real estate 11.6%
- Distribution and restaurants 16.0%
- Petroleum 28.1%

SUGAR PRODUCTION, 1993 - 1997

'000 tonnes — (bars for) 1993 1994 1995 1996 1997 (scale 0–125)

PRODUCTION OF SELECTED INDUSTRIAL PRODUCTS, 1997

'000 tonnes (scale 0–1000) — Fertilizers, Ammonia and urea, Iron and steel, Methanol, Cement

Map legend

- Urban area
- Sugar cane
- Mainly cash crops
- Mainly food crops
- Forest
- Swamp

- Bananas
- Citrus fruit
- Cocoa
- Coconuts
- Coffee
- Rice
- Timber

- Commercial centre
- Asphalt
- Gypsum
- Limestone

- Cement
- Chemicals
- Clay products
- Electrical goods
- Fertilizers
- Food processing
- Iron and steel

- Metal products
- Oil refinery
- Sugar factory
- Textiles
- Tyres
- Vehicle assembly

Map places: Diego Martin Village, Port of Spain, San Juan, Tunapuna, Arima, Sangre Grande, Chaguanas, Couva, Point Lisas, Claxton Bay, Pointe-a-Pierre, Rio Claro, San Fernando, La Brea, Point Fortin

For a case study of the oil and gas industry in Trinidad and Tobago see p.41

IMPORTS, 1997

- Other 6.6%
- Crude materials (other than fuels) 4.1%
- Chemicals 7.9%
- Food and live animals 8.2%
- Mineral fuels and lubricants 13.0%
- Manufactured goods 14.6%
- Machinery and transport equipment 45.6%

Total TT$18 934 million

DOMESTIC EXPORTS, 1997

- Other 17.4%
- Sugar 1.8%
- Natural and manufactured gas 2.5%
- Urea 3.5%
- Methanol 8.3%
- Iron and steel 9.5%
- Ammonia 11.4%
- Crude petroleum 18.2%
- Petroleum products 27.4%

Total TT$15 178 million

DESTINATION OF EXPORTS, 1997

- Other 31.7%
- USA 39.3%
- UK 2.3%
- Suriname 2.8%
- France 3.3%
- Barbados 3.7%
- Guyana 4.3%
- Puerto Rico 4.4%
- Jamaica 8.2%

ANNUAL RAINFALL

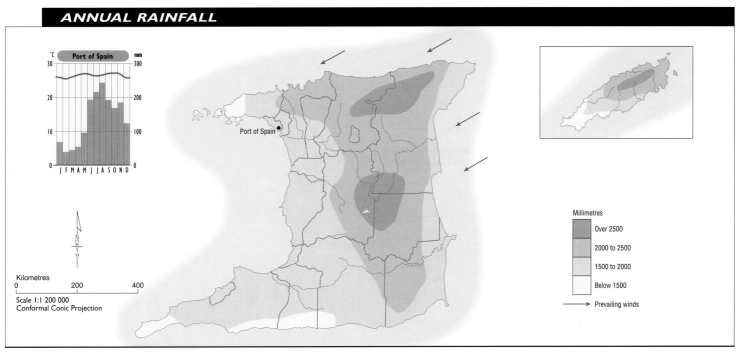

Port of Spain (climate graph, °C and mm, J F M A M J J A S O N D)

Port of Spain

Kilometres
0 — 200 — 400
Scale 1:1 200 000
Conformal Conic Projection

Millimetres
- Over 2500
- 2000 to 2500
- 1500 to 2000
- Below 1500
- → Prevailing winds

84

ST MARTIN, ST BARTHÉLEMY, SABA and ST EUSTATIUS

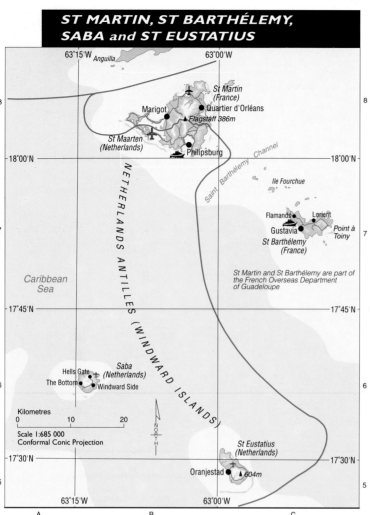

Anguilla

St Martin (France)
Marigot
Quartier d'Orléans
▲ Flagstaff 386m

St Maarten (Netherlands)
Philipsburg

Saint Barthélemy Channel

NETHERLANDS ANTILLES (WINDWARD ISLANDS)

Ile Fourchue

Flamands
Lorient
Gustavia
St Barthélemy (France)
Point à Toiny

St Martin and St Barthélemy are part of the French Overseas Department of Guadeloupe

Caribbean Sea

Hells Gate
The Bottom
Saba (Netherlands)
Windward Side

Kilometres
0   10   20
Scale 1:685 000
Conformal Conic Projection

St Eustatius (Netherlands)
Oranjestad   ▲604m

ST MARTIN/ST MAARTEN

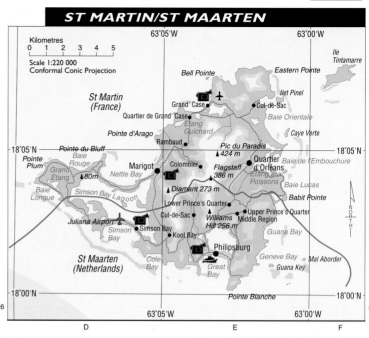

Kilometres
0 1 2 3 4 5
Scale 1:220 000
Conformal Conic Projection

St Martin (France)
Bell Pointe
Grand Case
Quartier de Grand Case
Eastern Pointe
Ilet Pinel
Cul-de-Sac
Baie Orientale
Caye Verte
Pointe d'Arago
Rambaud
Etang Guichard
Pic du Paradis ▲424 m

Pointe du Bluff
Pointe Plum
Baie Rouge
Grand Etang
Marigot
Nettle Bay
Colombier
Flagstaff 386 m
Quartier d'Orléans
Baie de l'Embouchure
Etang aux Poissons
Baie Lucas

Baie Longue
Simson Bay Lagoon
▲ Diamant 273 m
Lower Prince's Quarter
Cul-de-Sac
Williams Hill 256 m
Upper Prince's Quarter
Middle Region
Babit Pointe
Guana Bay

Juliana Airport
Simson Bay
Simson Bay
Kool Bay
Philipsburg
Geneve Bay
Mal Aborder
Guana Key

St Maarten (Netherlands)
Cole Bay
Great Bay
Pointe Blanche

Ile Tintamarre

KEY FACTS

Island	Area (km²)	Population		Population density (People per km²)
St Barthélemey (Fr)	21	5 043	(1990)	240
St Martin (Fr)	54	32 819	(1997)	608
St Maarten (Neths)	34	38 567	(1995)	1134
Saba (Neths)	13	1 200	(1995)	92
St Eustatius (Neths)	21	1 900	(1995)	90
Curaçao (Neths)	444	151 448	(1995)	341
Bonaire (Neths)	288	14 218	(1995)	49
Aruba (Neths)	193	83 651	(1995)	433

ST MAARTEN TOURIST ARRIVALS, 1994 - 1998

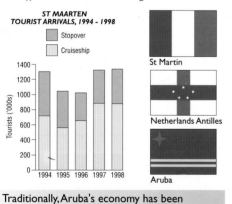

Stopover
Cruiseship

Tourists ('000s)
1400, 1200, 1000, 800, 600, 400, 200, 0
1994 1995 1996 1997 1998

St Martin
Netherlands Antilles
Aruba

Traditionally, Aruba's economy has been dependent on oil refining, although since the early 1980s tourism has overtaken refining and is now the main economic activity. The Netherlands Antilles' economy, like Aruba's, is service orientated with the main income coming from tourism and oil refining.

CURAÇAO

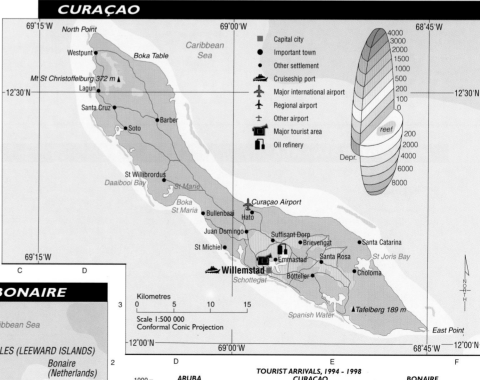

North Point
Westpunt
Boka Table
Caribbean Sea

Mt St Christoffelburg 372 m ▲
Lagun
Santa Cruz
Barber
Soto

St Willibrordus
Daaibooi Bay
St-Marie
Boka St Maria
Bullenbaai
Hato
Curaçao Airport

Juan Domingo
Suffisant Dorp
Brievengat
Santa Catarina
St Michiel
Emmastad
Santa Rosa
St Joris Bay
Willemstad
Bôttelier
Choloma
Schottegat

Kilometres
0   5   10   15
Scale 1:500 000
Conformal Conic Projection

Spanish Water
▲ Tafelberg 189 m
East Point

Capital city
Important town
Other settlement
Cruiseship port
Major international airport
Regional airport
Other airport
Major tourist area
Oil refinery

reef
Depr.
4000 3000 2000 1500 1000 500 200 100 0
200 2000 4000 6000 8000

ARUBA, CURAÇAO and BONAIRE

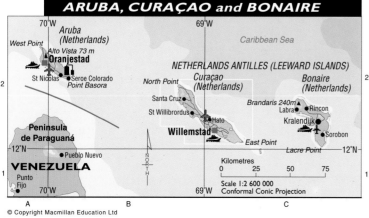

West Point
Aruba (Netherlands)
Alto Vista 73 m ▲
Oranjestad
St Nicolas
Seroe Colorado
Point Basora

Caribbean Sea

NETHERLANDS ANTILLES (LEEWARD ISLANDS)
North Point
Curaçao (Netherlands)
Santa Cruz
St Willibrordus
Hato
Willemstad
East Point

Bonaire (Netherlands)
Brandaris 240m ▲
Labra
Rincon
Kralendijk
Sorobon
Lacre Point

Peninsula de Paraguaná

VENEZUELA
Punto Fijo
Pueblo Nuevo

Kilometres
0   25   50   75
Scale 1:2 600 000
Conformal Conic Projection

TOURIST ARRIVALS, 1994 - 1998

ARUBA
Tourists ('000s)
1000, 800, 600, 400, 200
1994 1995 1996 1997 1998

CURAÇAO
Tourists ('000s)
600, 400, 200
1994 1995 1996 1997 1998

BONAIRE
Tourists ('000s)
400, 200
1994 1995 1996 1997 1998
Stopover
Cruiseship

GUYANA

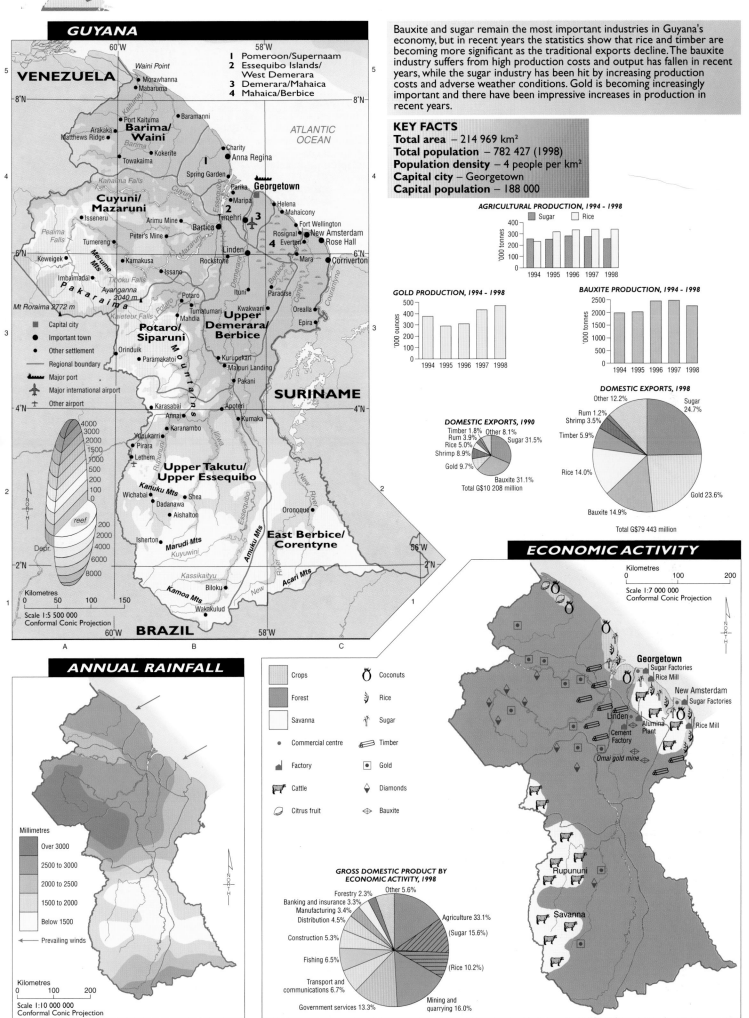

GUYANA

60°W 58°W

VENEZUELA

1 Pomeroon/Supernaam
2 Essequibo Islands/ West Demerara
3 Demerara/Mahaica
4 Mahaica/Berbice

Waini Point
Morawhanna
Mabaruma
Port Kaituma
Baramanni
Arakaka
Matthews Ridge
Barima/ Waini
Kokerite
Charity
Anna Regina
Towakaima
Spring Garden
Parika
Georgetown
Maripa
Helena
Mahaicony
Cuyuni/ Mazaruni
Isseneru
Arimu Mine
Timehri
Bartica
Fort Wellington
New Amsterdam
Peter's Mine
Tumereng
Rosignol
Everton
Rose Hall
Keweigek
Kamakusa
Linden
Rockstone
Mara
Corriverton
Imbaimadai
Issano
Ituni
Paradise
Mt Roraima 2772 m
Pakaraima
Potaro
Tumatumari
Kwakwani
Orealla
Mahdia
Upper Demerara/ Berbice
Epira

Potaro/ Siparuni

Orinduik
Paramakatoi
Kurupukari
Maipuri Landing
Pakani

SURINAME

Karasabai
Amaí
Apoteri
Karanambo
Kumaka
Yupukarri
Pirara
Lethem
Upper Takutu/ Upper Essequibo
Oronoque
Wichabai
Shea
Dadanawa
Aishalton
Isherton
Marudi Mts
Kanuku Mts
Kuyuwini
East Berbice/ Corentyne
Biloku
Kamoa Mts
Wakakulud
Acari Mts
Kassikaityu

BRAZIL

60°W 58°W

ATLANTIC OCEAN

Legend:
- Capital city
- Important town
- Other settlement
- Regional boundary
- Major port
- Major international airport
- Other airport

4000, 3000, 2000, 1500, 1000, 500, 200, 100, reef, 200, 2000, 4000, 6000, 8000
Depr.

Kilometres 0 50 100 150
Scale 1:5 500 000
Conformal Conic Projection

A B C

Bauxite and sugar remain the most important industries in Guyana's economy, but in recent years the statistics show that rice and timber are becoming more significant as the traditional exports decline. The bauxite industry suffers from high production costs and output has fallen in recent years, while the sugar industry has been hit by increasing production costs and adverse weather conditions. Gold is becoming increasingly important and there have been impressive increases in production in recent years.

KEY FACTS
Total area – 214 969 km²
Total population – 782 427 (1998)
Population density – 4 people per km²
Capital city – Georgetown
Capital population – 188 000

AGRICULTURAL PRODUCTION, 1994 - 1998
Sugar Rice
'000 tonnes
400, 300, 200, 100, 0
1994 1995 1996 1997 1998

GOLD PRODUCTION, 1994 - 1998
'000 ounces
500, 400, 300, 200, 100, 0
1994 1995 1996 1997 1998

BAUXITE PRODUCTION, 1994 - 1998
'000 tonnes
2500, 2000, 1500, 1000, 500, 0
1994 1995 1996 1997 1998

DOMESTIC EXPORTS, 1990
Timber 1.8% Other 8.1%
Rum 3.9% Sugar 31.5%
Rice 5.0%
Shrimp 8.9%
Gold 9.7%
Bauxite 31.1%
Total G$10 208 million

DOMESTIC EXPORTS, 1998
Other 12.2% Sugar 24.7%
Rum 1.2%
Shrimp 3.5%
Timber 5.9%
Rice 14.0%
Gold 23.6%
Bauxite 14.9%
Total G$79 443 million

ANNUAL RAINFALL

Millimetres
Over 3000
2500 to 3000
2000 to 2500
1500 to 2000
Below 1500
Prevailing winds

Kilometres 0 100 200
Scale 1:10 000 000
Conformal Conic Projection

Legend:
- Crops
- Forest
- Savanna
- Commercial centre
- Factory
- Cattle
- Citrus fruit
- Coconuts
- Rice
- Sugar
- Timber
- Gold
- Diamonds
- Bauxite

ECONOMIC ACTIVITY

Kilometres 0 100 200
Scale 1:7 000 000
Conformal Conic Projection

Georgetown
Sugar Factories
Rice Mill
New Amsterdam
Sugar Factories
Linden
Alumina Plant
Cement Factory
Rice Mill
Omai gold mine
Rupununi
Savanna

GROSS DOMESTIC PRODUCT BY ECONOMIC ACTIVITY, 1998
Forestry 2.3% Other 5.6%
Banking and insurance 3.3%
Manufacturing 3.4%
Distribution 4.5%
Agriculture 33.1%
(Sugar 15.6%)
Construction 5.3%
(Rice 10.2%)
Fishing 6.5%
Transport and communications 6.7%
Mining and quarrying 16.0%
Government services 13.3%

BELIZE

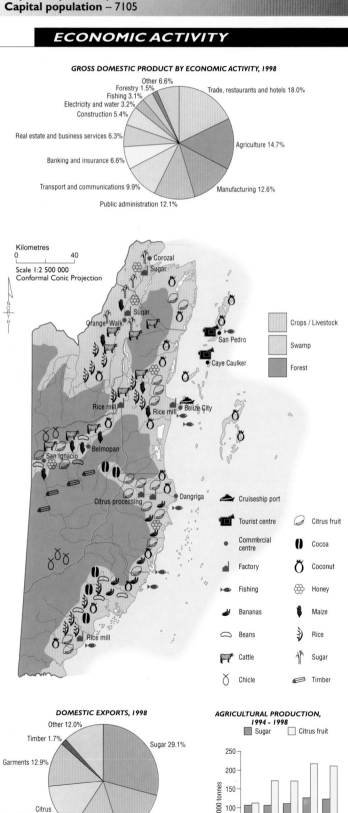

BELIZE

Capital city
Important town
Other settlement
District boundary
Major port
Major international airport
Other airport

MEXICO

Chan Chen
Patchacan
Corozal
Rocky Point
Libertad
Sarteneja
Louisville
Progresso
Buena Vista
Progresso Lagoon
San Estevan
Corozal
Deer Cay
Yo Creek
Orange Walk
Ambergris Cay
Carmelita
London
August Pine Ridge
San Pedro
Neustadt
Maskall
Rosita
San Felipe
Shipyard
Chicago
Orange Walk
Revenge Lagoon
Lucky Strike
New River Lagoon
Biscayne
Hick's Cays
Cedar Crossing
Sand Hill
Belize
Burmudian Landing
Ladyville
Rancho Dolores
Burrell Boom
Yalbac Hills
Hattieville
Belize City
Drowned Cays
Labouring Creek
Northern Lagoon
Turneffe Islands
Roaring Creek
Sapodilla Lagoon
Belmopan
Lighthouse Reef
Ontario
Caves Branch
Gales Point
Central Lagoon
San Ignacio
Over-the-Top Camp
Long Cay
Benque Viejo del Carman
Baldy Beacon 1020m
Southern Long Cay
Granite Cairn 860m
Pomona
Alta Vista
Dangriga
Cayo
Stann Creek
Glovers Reef
Vaca Plateau
Hopkins
Cockscomb Range
Victoria Peak 1120m
Middle Bank
Riversdale
Maya Mountains
Richardson Peak 1000m
Seine Bight
Placentia Cay
Big Creek
Silk Cays
Little Quartz Ridge
Medina Bank
Hellgate
Monkey River Town
Barrier Reef
Toledo
Big Fall
San Antonio
Ycacos Point
The Snake Cays
Laguna
Sapodilla Cays
Punta Gorda
Barranco
Gulf of Honduras
CARIBBEAN SEA
GUATEMALA
HONDURAS

Bahia Chetumal
Shipstern Lagoon
Bulkhead Reef
Northern Cay

Kilometres
0   20   40
Scale 1:2 100 000
Conformal Conic Projection

4000
3000
2000
1500
1000
500
200
100
reef
200
2000
4000
6000
8000
Depr.

Agriculture is the dominant sector of the Belize economy providing 71% of total foreign exchange earnings and employing 29% of the total labour force. Sugar is the most important crop and in 1997 a record production of 126 000 tonnes was achieved. Citrus fruit, which is used for processing into concentrate, and bananas, are also important export crops.

KEY FACTS
Total area – 22 965 km²
Total population – 238 500 (1998)
Population density – 10 people per km²
Capital city – Belmopan
Capital population – 7105

ECONOMIC ACTIVITY

GROSS DOMESTIC PRODUCT BY ECONOMIC ACTIVITY, 1998
Other 6.6%
Forestry 1.5%
Fishing 3.1%
Electricity and water 3.2%
Construction 5.4%
Real estate and business services 6.3%
Banking and insurance 6.6%
Transport and communications 9.9%
Public administration 12.1%
Trade, restaurants and hotels 18.0%
Agriculture 14.7%
Manufacturing 12.6%

Kilometres
0   40
Scale 1:2 500 000
Conformal Conic Projection

Crops / Livestock
Swamp
Forest

Corozal
Sugar
Orange Walk
Sugar
San Pedro
Caye Caulker
Rice mill
Rice mill
Belize City
Belmopan
San Ignacio
Citrus processing
Dangriga
Rice mill

Cruiseship port
Tourist centre
Commercial centre
Factory
Fishing
Bananas
Beans
Cattle
Chicle
Citrus fruit
Cocoa
Coconut
Honey
Maize
Rice
Sugar
Timber

DOMESTIC EXPORTS, 1998
Other 12.0%
Timber 1.7%
Garments 12.9%
Citrus concentrate 14.1%
Marine products 14.2%
Bananas 16.0%
Sugar 29.1%
Total BZ$306.1 million

AGRICULTURAL PRODUCTION, 1994 - 1998
Sugar
Citrus fruit

'000 tonnes
250
200
150
100
50
0
1994 1995 1996 1997 1998

ANNUAL RAINFALL

Millimetres
Over 4000
3500 to 4000
3000 to 3500
2500 to 3000
2000 to 2500
1500 to 2000
Below 1500

Prevailing winds

Kilometres
0   40
Scale 1:3 500 000
Conformal Conic Projection

KINGSTON, JAMAICA

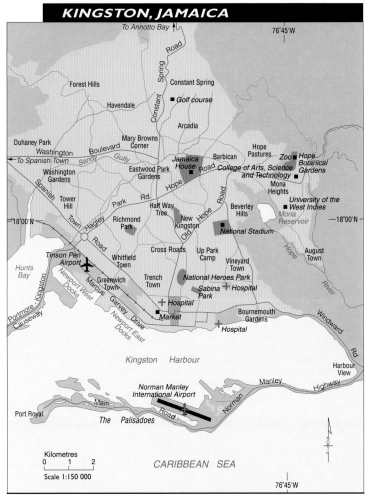

To Annotto Bay

76°45'W

Forest Hills
Havendale
Constant Spring
Golf course
Arcadia
Mary Browns Corner
Duhaney Park
Washington Boulevard
Hope Pastures
Hope Botanical Gardens
Zoo
Jamaica House
Barbican
College of Arts, Science and Technology
Eastwood Park Gardens
To Spanish Town
Washington Gardens
Mona Heights
Tower Hill
Half Way Tree
Richmond Park
New Kingston
Beverley Hills
Mona Reservoir
University of the West Indies
18°00'N
National Stadium
Cross Roads
Whitfield Town
Up Park Camp
Vineyard Town
August Town
Tinson Pen Airport
Greenwich Town
Trench Town
National Heroes Park
Sabina Park
Hospital
Hunts Bay
Newport West Docks
Newport East Docks
Market
Hospital
Bournemouth Gardens
Windward Rd
Harbour View
Portmore - Kingston Causeway
Kingston Harbour
Manley Highway
Norman Manley International Airport
Port Royal
Norman
The Palisadoes
Main Road

Kilometres
0 1 2
Scale 1:150 000

CARIBBEAN SEA

76°45'W

BRIDGETOWN, BARBADOS

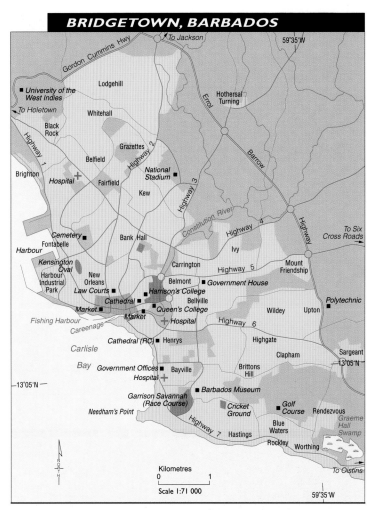

To Jackson
Gordon Cummins Hwy
59°35'W
University of the West Indies
Lodgehill
Hothersal Turning
Errol
To Holetown
Black Rock
Whitehall
Grazettes
Barrow
Highway 1
Brighton
Belfield
Fairfield
National Stadium
Hospital
Kew
Highway 3
To Six Cross Roads
Constitution River
Highway 4
Cemetery
Fontabelle
Bank Hall
Ivy
Mount Friendship
Harbour
Kensington Oval
Carrington
Highway 5
Polytechnic
Harbour Industrial Park
New Orleans
Belmont
Government House
Wildey
Upton
Law Courts
Harrison's College
Bellville
Fishing Harbour
Cathedral
Queen's College
Highway 6
Highgate
Market
Market
Hospital
Carlisle Bay
Cathedral (RC)
Henrys
Clapham
Sargeant
13°05'N
Government Offices
Bayville
Brittons Hill
Hospital
Barbados Museum
Graeme Hall Swamp
Garrison Savannah (Race Course)
Cricket Ground
Golf Course
Rendezvous
Needham's Point
Highway 7
Blue Waters
Hastings
Rockley
Worthing
Kilometres
0 1
Scale 1:71 000
To Oistins
59°35'W

PORT OF SPAIN, TRINIDAD

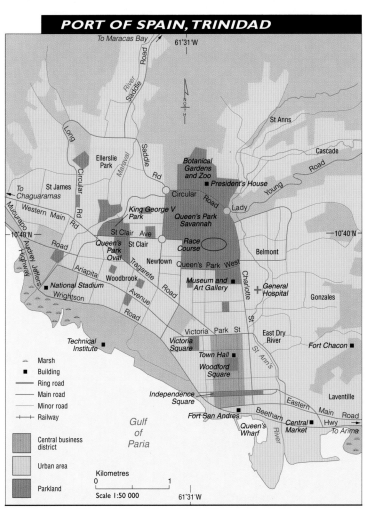

To Maracas Bay
61°31'W
River Saddle Road
St Anns
Long Circular
Ellerslie Park
Cascade
Botanical Gardens and Zoo
President's House
To Chaguaramas
St James
Saddle Rd
Circular Road
Young Road
Western Main Rd
King George V Park
Queen's Park Savannah
Lady
Race Course
Malvacapo Road
10°40'N
Queen's Park Oval
St Clair Ave
St Clair
Belmont
Aubrey Jefferson Highway
Ariapita
Newtown
Queen's Park West
Woodbrook
Avenue
National Stadium
Wrightson
Tragarete Road
Museum and Art Gallery
Charlotte St
General Hospital
Gonzales
Technical Institute
Victoria Park St
Victoria Square
East Dry River
Fort Chacon
Town Hall
Woodford Square
St Ann's
Independence Square
Eastern Main Road
Laventille
Fort San Andres
Central Market
To Arima
Queen's Wharf
Beetham
River
Gulf of Paria

Marsh
Building
Ring road
Main road
Minor road
Railway
Central business district
Urban area
Parkland

Kilometres
0 1
Scale 1:50 000
61°31'W

NASSAU, BAHAMAS

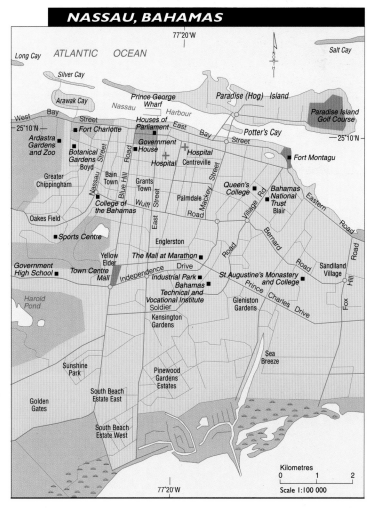

77°20'W
Long Cay
ATLANTIC OCEAN
Salt Cay
Silver Cay
Prince George Wharf
Paradise (Hog) Island
Arawak Cay
Nassau Harbour
Paradise Island Golf Course
West Bay
Street
Houses of Parliament
Bay Street
Potter's Cay
25°10'N
Fort Charlotte
Government House
Hospital
25°10'N
Ardastra Gardens and Zoo
Centreville
Fort Montagu
Botanical Gardens
Boyd
Bain Town
Hospital
Greater Chippingham
Blue Hill Road
Grants Town
Queen's College
Bahamas National Trust
Nassau Street
Wulff
Palmdale
Village Rd
Blair
Oakes Field
College of the Bahamas
Mackey Road
Eastern Road
Sports Centre
East Street
Englerston
Bernard Road
Sandiland Village
Government High School
Yellow Elder
Town Centre Mall
The Mall at Marathon
Drive
St Augustine's Monastery and College
Independence
Industrial Park
Prince Charles Drive
Harold Pond
Bahamas Technical and Vocational Institute
Soldier
Gleniston Gardens
Fox Hill
Kensington Gardens
Sunshine Park
Pinewood Gardens Estates
Sea Breeze
Golden Gates
South Beach Estate East
South Beach Estate West
Kilometres
0 1 2
Scale 1:100 000
77°20'W

Arizona

Santa Ana
Palm Springs
Escondido
San Diego
Tijuana
Mexicali
Ensenada
Yuma
San Luis
Peoria
Glendale
Chandler
Phoenix
Tucson
110°W
▲ Baldy Peak 3533 m
Albuquerque
Hereford
Canyon
Amarillo
Clovis
Plainview
Levelland
Lubbock
Brownfield
Lamesa
Altus
Vernon
Lawton
Oklahoma City
Ada
Duncan
Sherman

New Mexico

Casa Grande
Sierra Vista
Tombstone
Nogales
Cananea
Caborca
Las Cruces
Roswell
Alamogordo
Artesia
Hobbs
Andrews
Snyder
Abilene
Fort Worth
Cleburne
Dallas
Tyler

Muskogee
Jonesboro
Searcy
Fort Smith
Hot Springs
Arkadelphia
Arkansas
Little Rock
Pine Bluff

Tennes

Tullaho
Memphis
Forrest City
Clarksdale
Florence
Tupelo
Gac

San Felipe
Point Baja
30°N
Ciudad Juárez
El Paso
Kermit
Odessa
Midland
Pecos
Fort Stockton

Sierra Vista
Magdalena
Nuevo Casas Grandes

Hermosillo

Guaymas

Chihuahua

Delicias

Ciudad Camargo

Ojinaga
Presidio
Alpine
Sanderson
Del Rio
Amistad Reservoir
Eagle Pass
Piedras Negras
San Angelo
Brownwood
Hillsboro
Waco
Killeen
Bryan
Austin
Conroe
Crockett
Nacogdoches
McComb
Bogalusa
Laurel
Hattiesburg

Texas
Kerrville
San Antonio
Uvalde
Lockhart
Gonzales
Cuero
Victoria
Wharton
Houston
Galveston
Beaumont
Lake Charles
New Iberia
Houma
New Orleans

Mississippi
Alaba
Montgc
Fort Wa
Be
Mobile
Biloxi
Pascagoula

UNITED STATES OF AMERICA

Paris
Denton
Cleburne
Mansfield
Monroe
Alexandria
Baton Rouge
Louisiana

Shreveport
Jackson
Demopolis
Lake Providence

Birmi

Ciudad Obregón
Navojoa
San Ignacio
Santa Rosalía
Los Mochis
Topolobampo
Mocorito
Culiacán
Parral
Santa Bárbara
Monclova
Sabinas Hidalgo
Nueva Rosita
Falcón Reservoir
Nuevo Laredo
Laredo
Kingsville
Corpus Christi
Portland
Port Lavaca
Beeville
Bay City

Point Eugenia
Lower
California
Gulf of California
Western Sierra Madre

MEXICO
Torreón
Matamoros
Saltillo
Monterrey
Montemorelos
Linares
Reynosa
Harlingen
Brownsville
Matamoros
McAllen

GULF OF MEXICO

Tropic of Cancer
Lake Santiaguillo
Durango

Cape San Lucas
San José del Cabo
Mazatlán
Matehuala
Tula
Ciudad Victoria

Escuinapa
Acaponeta
Zacatecas
San Luis Potosí
Tampico

Tuxpan
Aguascalientes
Tepic
Marías Islands

20°N
Point Mita
León
Guadalajara
Irapuato
Madre
Querétaro
Poza Rica de Hidalgo
Mérida
Progreso
Tizimín
Puerto M
Ca
Ca

Cape Corrientes
Lake Chapala
Zamora
Ciudad Guzman
Uruapan
Colima
Morelia
Toluca
Mexico City
Jalapa Enríquez
Veracruz
Peto
Campeche
Bay of Campeche

Yucatán Peninsula
Champotón

Manzanillo
Lake Infiernillo
Popocatépetl 5452 m ▲
Citlaltépetl 5700 m ▲
Puebla
Orizaba
San Andrés Tuxtla
Cuernavaca
Iguala
Tehuacán
Terminos Lagoon
Chetumal

R
Chilpancingo
Coatzacoalcos
Villahermosa
Palenque

2
Southern Sierra Madre
Acapulco
Oaxaca de Juarez
Tuxtla Gutiérrez
Tehuantepec
Salina Cruz
Angostura Reservoir
Usumacinta
River
Flores
BELIZE
Belize City
Belmopan
Dangriga

Gulf of Tehuantepec
Gulf of Honduras
Puerto Barrios
La Ceiba
Cobán
Tajumulco 4220 m ▲
San Pedro Sula
Coma
Lake Izabal

Tapachula
Quezaltenango
Guatemala City
Santa
Ana
Santa Ana 2354 m ▲
Jutiapa
Sonsonate
San Salvador
Tegucigalpa
San Miguel

GUATEMALA
EL SALVADOR
Chinandega
León
Mana

Gulf of Fonseca

PACIFIC OCEAN
10°N

Population

- ■ Over 1 000 000
- ● 500 000 to 1 000 000
- ● 100 000 to 500 000
- • 50 000 to 100 000
- ○ Under 50 000

Monterrey, Mexico (climate graph)
°C / mm
30 / 300
20 / 200
10 / 100
0 / 0
J F M A M J J A S O N D

Elevation scale:
6000
5000
4000
3000
2000
1000
500
200
0
Depr.
200
2000
4000
6000
8000

Cocos Island (Costa Rica)

Kilometres
0   300   600
Scale 1:15 000 000
Conformal Conic Projection
NORTH

Lorries transporting sugar cane in Belize

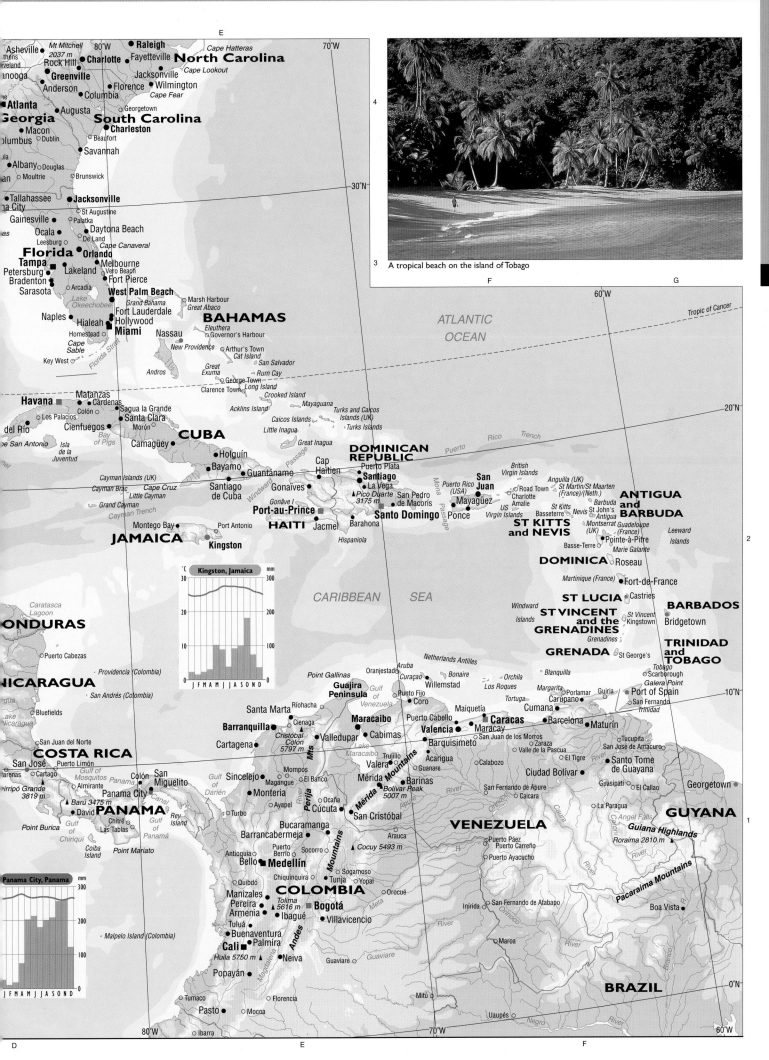

A tropical beach on the island of Tobago

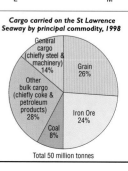

Population
- ■ Over 1 000 000
- ■ 500 000 to 1 000 000
- ● 100 000 to 500 000
- • 50 000 to 100 000
- ○ Under 50 000

Kilometres
0   500   1000

Scale 1:40 000 000
Azimuthal Equal Area Projection

FACT FILE

Land area – Largest country Canada (9 976 139 km²); smallest country St Kitts and Nevis (267 km²). Highest point - Mt McKinley, USA (6194m).
Population – United States 265.8 million (largest); St Kitts and Nevis 43 000 (smallest); largest city Mexico City in Mexico (22.9 million).
Life expectancy – Canada 79 years (longest); Haiti 58 years (shortest).
Economic development (GDP per capita) – United States US$24 279 (richest); Haiti US$490 (poorest).
The Great Lakes system – Five large interconnected inland bodies of fresh water drain into the St Lawrence River and then into the Atlantic Ocean. The largest, Lake Superior (82 413 km²), is the second largest lake in the world.

The Great Lakes/St Lawrence Seaway system – Finished in 1959, this system stretches from the Atlantic Ocean to Duluth on Lake Superior, a distance of more than 3 700 kilometres (or 8.5 sailing days). It has 245 750 km² of navigable waters and has fifteen major international ports and fifty smaller regional ports. The seaway operates from March to late December (during winter, ice makes it impossible to navigate) and in 1998 carried fifty million tonnes of cargo.

Cargo carried on the St Lawrence Seaway by principal commodity, 1998

- General cargo (chiefly steel & machinery) 14%
- Grain 26%
- Other bulk cargo (chiefly coke & petroleum products) 28%
- Iron Ore 24%
- Coal 8%

Total 50 million tonnes

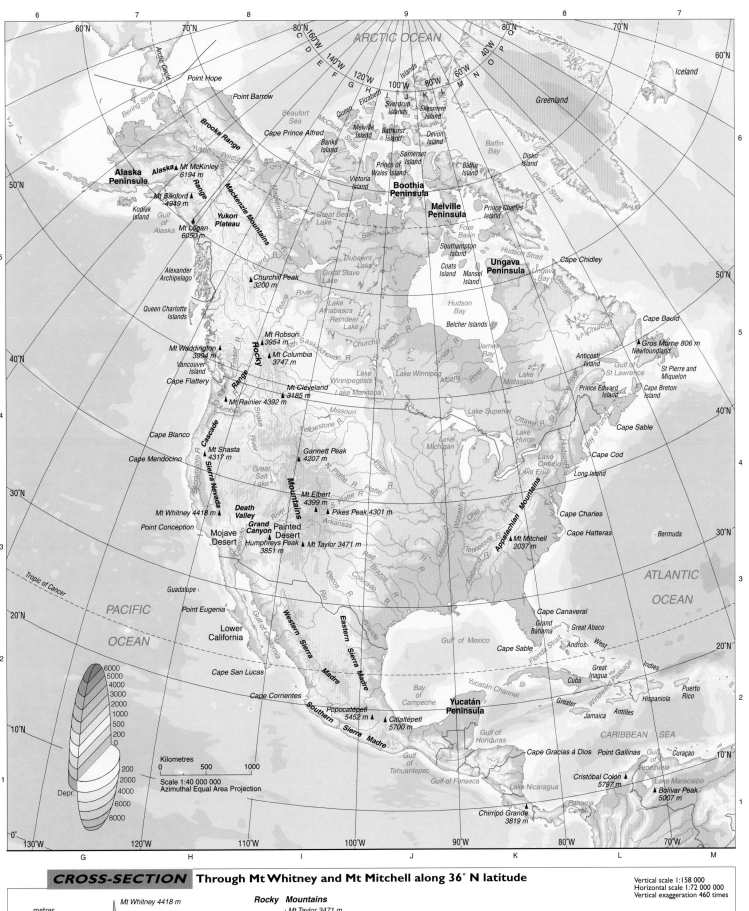

ARCTIC OCEAN

Iceland

Greenland

Point Hope
Point Barrow

Beaufort Sea
Cape Prince Alfred
Banks Island
Melville Island
Bathurst Island
Queen Elizabeth Islands
Sverdrup Islands
Ellesmere Island
Devon Island

Brooks Range

Alaska Peninsula
Alaska ▲ Mt McKinley 6194 m
Range
Mt Sanford ▲ 4949 m
Kodiak Island
Gulf of Alaska
Mt Logan 6050 m

Mackenzie Mountains
Yukon Plateau

Victoria Island
Prince of Wales Island
Somerset Island
Boothia Peninsula
Baffin Island
Baffin Bay
Disko Island

Great Bear Lake
Melville Peninsula
Prince Charles Island
Foxe Basin
Southampton Island
Coats Island
Mansel Island
Ungava Peninsula
Hudson Strait
Ungava Bay
Cape Chidley

Alexander Archipelago
▲ Churchill Peak 3200 m
Great Slave Lake
Dubawnt Lake
Hudson Bay
Belcher Islands

Queen Charlotte Islands
Lake Athabasca
Reindeer Lake

Cape Bauld
Gros Morne 806 m ▲ Newfoundland
Anticosti Island
Gulf of St Lawrence
St Pierre and Miquelon
Cape Breton Island
Prince Edward Island

Mt Waddington ▲ 3994 m
Vancouver Island
Cape Flattery
Mt Robson ▲ 3954 m
Mt Columbia ▲ 3747 m
Rocky Range
James Bay
Lake Mistassini

Cape Blanco
Mt Cleveland ▲ 3185 m
▲ Mt Rainier 4392 m
Cascade
Lake Winnipeg
Lake Superior
Lake Huron
Cape Sable
Bay of Fundy

Cape Mendocino
Mt Shasta ▲ 4317 m
Sierra Nevada
Gannett Peak ▲ 4207 m
Great Salt Lake
Lake Michigan
Lake Ontario
Lake Erie
Long Island
Cape Cod

Mt Whitney 4418 m ▲
Death Valley
Mt Elbert ▲ 4399 m
▲ Pikes Peak 4301 m
Mountains
Appalachian Mountains
Cape Charles

Point Conception
Mojave Desert
Grand Canyon
Painted Desert
Humphreys Peak ▲ 3851 m
▲ Mt Taylor 3471 m
▲ Mt Mitchell 2037 m
Cape Hatteras
Bermuda

Guadalupe
Tropic of Cancer
ATLANTIC OCEAN

PACIFIC OCEAN

Point Eugenia
Lower California
Western Sierra Madre
Eastern Sierra Madre
Cape Canaveral
Grand Bahama
Great Abaco
Cape Sable
Gulf of Mexico
West Indies
Andros
Cuba

Cape San Lucas
Cape Corrientes
Southern Sierra Madre
Popocatépetl 5452 m ▲
▲ Citlaltépetl 5700 m
Yucatán Peninsula
Bay of Campeche
Yucatán Channel
Great Inagua
Windward Passage
Hispaniola
Puerto Rico
Greater Antilles
Jamaica

Gulf of Honduras
CARIBBEAN SEA

Cape Gracias á Dios
Point Gallinas
Gulf of Venezuela
Curaçao

Gulf of Tehuantepec
Lake Nicaragua
Gulf of Fonseca
Panama Canal
Cristóbal Colón ▲ 5797 m
Bolívar Peak ▲ 5007 m
Lake Maracaibo

Chirripó Grande ▲ 3819 m

Kilometres
0   500   1000
Scale 1:40 000 000
Azimuthal Equal Area Projection

6000
5000
4000
3000
2000
1000
500
200
0
Depr.
200
1000
2000
4000
6000
8000

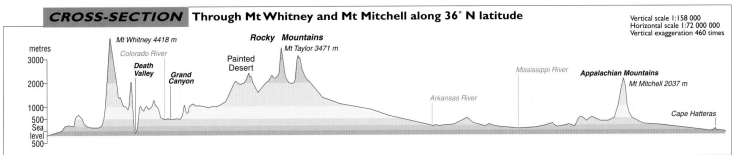

CROSS-SECTION Through Mt Whitney and Mt Mitchell along 36° N latitude

Vertical scale 1:158 000
Horizontal scale 1:72 000 000
Vertical exaggeration 460 times

metres
3000
2000
1000
500
Sea level
500

Mt Whitney 4418 m
Colorado River
Death Valley
Grand Canyon
Painted Desert
Rocky Mountains
Mt Taylor 3471 m
Mississippi River
Arkansas River
Appalachian Mountains
Mt Mitchell 2037 m
Cape Hatteras

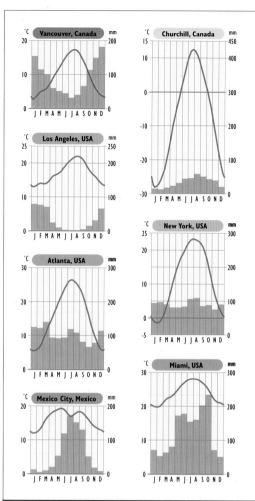

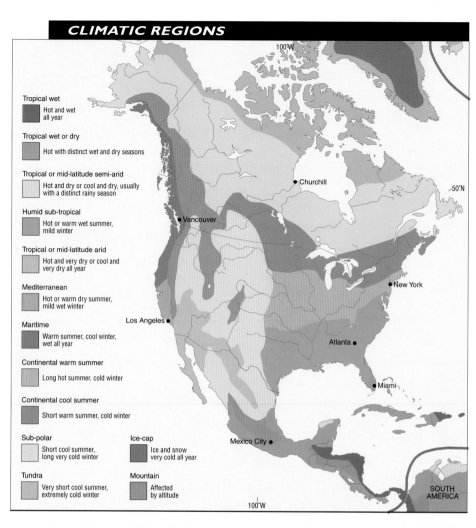

CLIMATIC REGIONS

Tropical wet
Hot and wet
all year

Tropical wet or dry
Hot with distinct wet and dry seasons

Tropical or mid-latitude semi-arid
Hot and dry or cool and dry, usually
with a distinct rainy season

Humid sub-tropical
Hot or warm wet summer,
mild winter

Tropical or mid-latitude arid
Hot and very dry or cool and
very dry all year

Mediterranean
Hot or warm dry summer,
mild wet winter

Maritime
Warm summer, cool winter,
wet all year

Continental warm summer
Long hot summer, cold winter

Continental cool summer
Short warm summer, cold winter

Sub-polar
Short cool summer,
long very cold winter

Ice-cap
Ice and snow
very cold all year

Tundra
Very short cool summer,
extremely cold winter

Mountain
Affected
by altitude

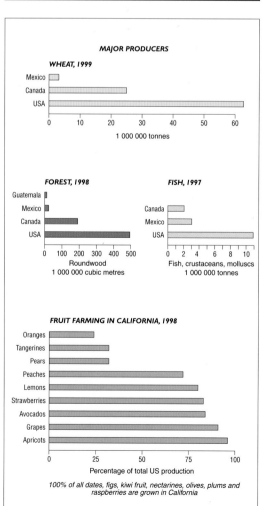

MAJOR PRODUCERS

WHEAT, 1999
1 000 000 tonnes

FOREST, 1998
Roundwood
1 000 000 cubic metres

FISH, 1997
Fish, crustaceans, molluscs
1 000 000 tonnes

FRUIT FARMING IN CALIFORNIA, 1998
Percentage of total US production

*100% of all dates, figs, kiwi fruit, nectarines, olives, plums and
raspberries are grown in California*

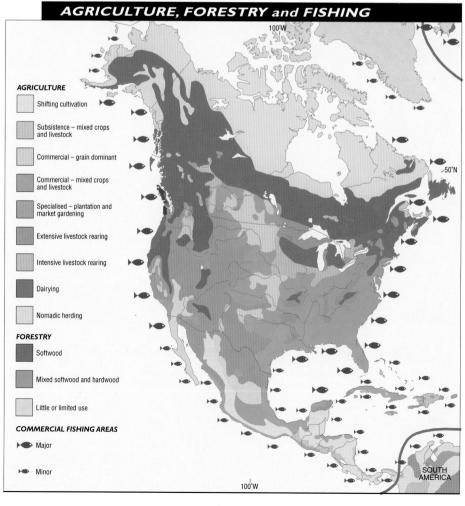

AGRICULTURE, FORESTRY and FISHING

AGRICULTURE

Shifting cultivation

Subsistence – mixed crops
and livestock

Commercial – grain dominant

Commercial – mixed crops
and livestock

Specialised – plantation and
market gardening

Extensive livestock rearing

Intensive livestock rearing

Dairying

Nomadic herding

FORESTRY

Softwood

Mixed softwood and hardwood

Little or limited use

COMMERCIAL FISHING AREAS

Major

Minor

MINERALS, ENERGY and INDUSTRY

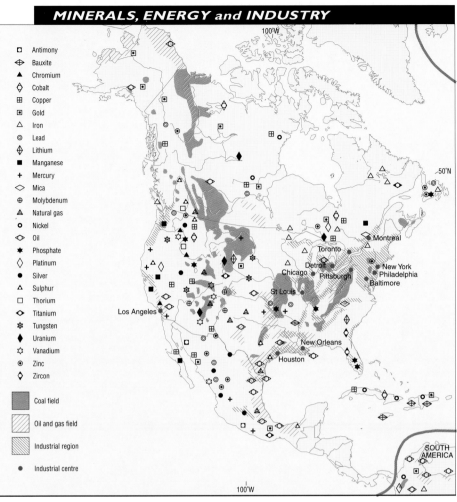

Antimony
Bauxite
Chromium
Cobalt
Copper
Gold
Iron
Lead
Lithium
Manganese
Mercury
Mica
Molybdenum
Natural gas
Nickel
Oil
Phosphate
Platinum
Silver
Sulphur
Thorium
Titanium
Tungsten
Uranium
Vanadium
Zinc
Zircon

Coal field
Oil and gas field
Industrial region
Industrial centre

MAJOR PRODUCERS

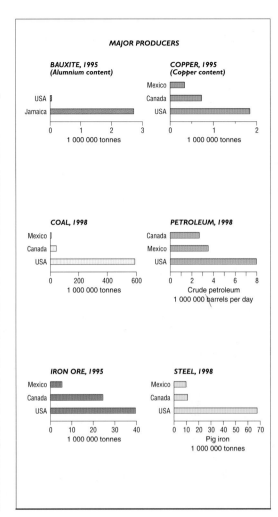

BAUXITE, 1995 (Alumnium content)
COPPER, 1995 (Copper content)
COAL, 1998
PETROLEUM, 1998
IRON ORE, 1995
STEEL, 1998

POPULATION

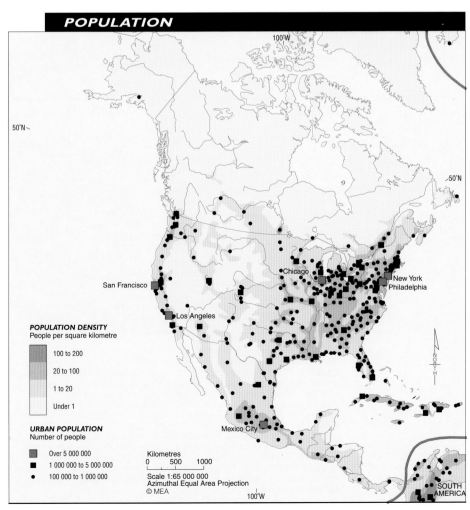

POPULATION DENSITY
People per square kilometre
100 to 200
20 to 100
1 to 20
Under 1

URBAN POPULATION
Number of people
Over 5 000 000
1 000 000 to 5 000 000
100 000 to 1 000 000

Scale 1:65 000 000
Azimuthal Equal Area Projection
© MEA

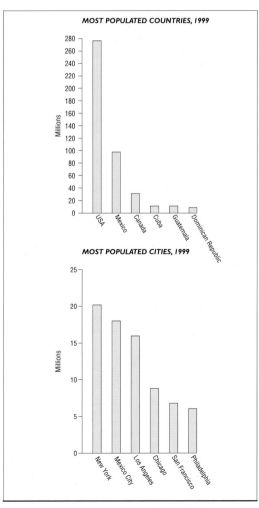

MOST POPULATED COUNTRIES, 1999

MOST POPULATED CITIES, 1999

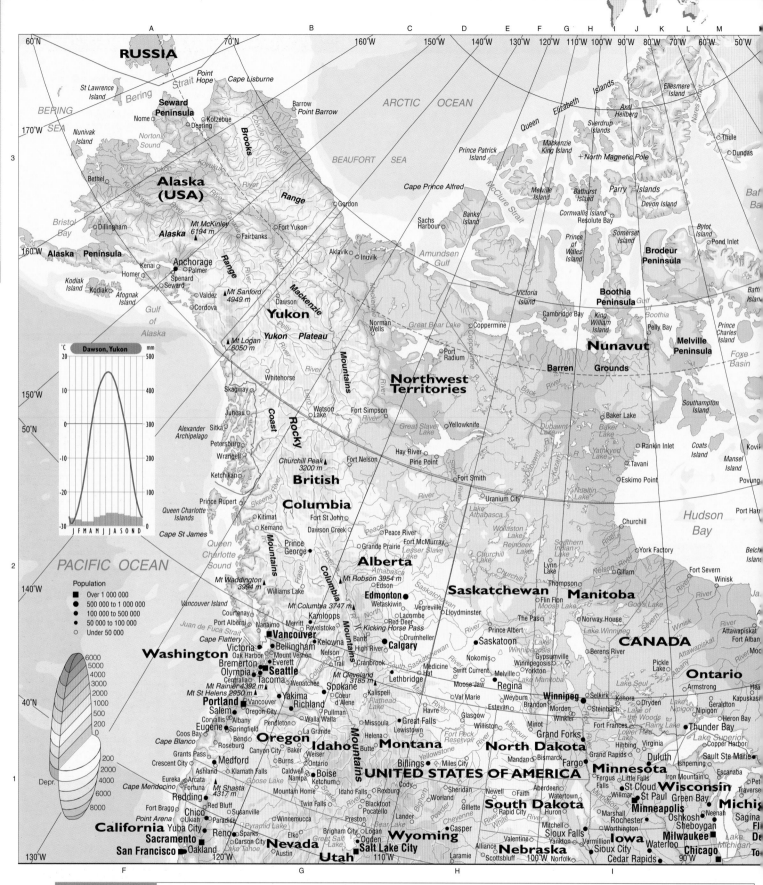

Climate graph: **Dawson, Yukon**

FACT FILE

Land area – 9 976 139 km². Highest point is Mt Logan (6050 metres)
Population – 30 million
Capital city – Ottawa
Largest cities – Toronto (3.9 million), Montréal (3.1 million), Vancouver (1.6 million)
Major exports – Newsprint, wood, motor cars and components, wheat, petroleum, minerals, telecommunications equipment and livestock.
The Territory of Nunavut – Nunavut means 'our land' and is the name given to the ancestral home of the indigenous Inuit. The Nunavut Land Claim Agreement of 1992 between the Inuit and the Canadian government provided for the establishment in 1999 of the new Territory of Nunavut – 350 000 km² of Inuit land – with clear rules on the ownership and control of land resources in the territory (see map opposite).

The Québec separatists

Canada is a country with strong British and French influences. Both languages are officially recognised and people are encouraged to become bilingual. Québec has long been a centre of French nationalism which has been growing since 1976 when moves were made for Québec to secede from Canada. The decentralisation of federal powers to provide more autonomy for Québec was seen as a means of settling relations between Québec and the government in Ottawa. However, this did not occur. In 1994, in local elections, the separatist party gained power and forced a referendum. In late 1995, the referendum was held but the separatist move was narrowly defeated. While Canada remains united, the referendum loss was considered not so great as to suffocate the forces of separatism. Another referendum is likely in the future.

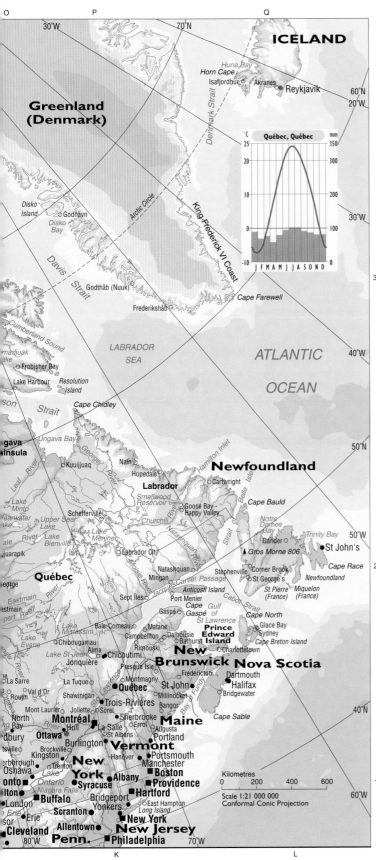

ICELAND

Huna Bay
Horn Cape
Isafjordbur   Akranes
Reykjavik   60°N
20°W

Greenland
(Denmark)

30°W
70°N

Denmark Strait

King Frederick VI Coast

Disko
Island   Godhavn
Disko
Bay

Arctic Circle

30°W

Davis Strait

Godthåb (Nuuk)

Cape Farewell

Frederikshåb

Cumberland Sound

madjuak ake
Frobisher Bay

Lake Harbour   Resolution
Island

Strait

Cape Chidley

LABRADOR
SEA

ATLANTIC

OCEAN

40°W

gava
insula

Ungava Bay

Leaf River

George River

Kuujjuaq   Nain
Hopedale

50°N

Newfoundland

Labrador   Cartwright

Schefferville   Smallwood
Reservoir   Goose Bay-
Happy Valley   Cape Bauld

Churchill River   Notre
Dame
Bay

Lake
Minto

Upper Seal
Lake

Lake
Menihec

Labrador City   Gander   Trinity Bay

ale
River   Lake
Bienville   Natashquan River   Grös Morne 806   St John's   50°W

jjuarapik

Natashquan   Stephenville   Corner Brook
Mingan   Jacques-Cartier Passage   St George's   Newfoundland

Québec   Sept Îles   Anticosti Island   St Pierre   Miquelon
(France)   (France)

Eastmain
River   Moisie River   Port Menier
Gaspé   Cape   Gulf
Gaspé   of
St Lawrence   Cape North

stmain
pert River   Matane   Glace Bay
Baie-Comeau   Sydney
Campbellton   Prince   Cape Breton Island

Lake
Mistassini   Chibougamau   Dalhousie   Edward
Rimouski   Island

Lake
Evans   Alma   Chicoutimi   Bathurst   Charlottetown

Lake St-Jean   Jonquière   New   Nova Scotia
Presque Isle   Fredericton   Brunswick

La Sarre   St Lawrence River   Montmagny   Dartmouth
Val d'Or   St John   Halifax

North   La Tuque   Québec   Millinocket   Bridgewater
dbury   Shawinigan   Trois-Rivières   Bangor

Mont Laurier   Joliette   Sherbrooke   Maine   Cape Sable
Sorel   Errol

Montréal   La Salle   Augusta

Ottawa   Hull   St Albans   Portland   40°N
Brockville   Burlington   Hanover
Kingston   Vermont   Portsmouth
Trenton   New   Manchester
Oshawa   York   Boston
nto   Lake   Albany   Syracuse   Providence   1
lton   Ontario   Hartford
London   Niagara Falls   Buffalo   Bridgeport   East Hampton   60°W
Scranton   Yonkers   Long Island
Erie   New York   70°W
Cleveland   Allentown   New Jersey
Penn.   Philadelphia

Québec, Québec
°C   mm
25 ████████████ 350
20 ████████████ 300
█████████████████ 250
10 ████████████ 200
0   ████████████ 100
-10 ████████████ 0
    J F M A M J J A S O N D

Kilometres
0   200   400   600
Scale 1:21 000 000
Conformal Conic Projection

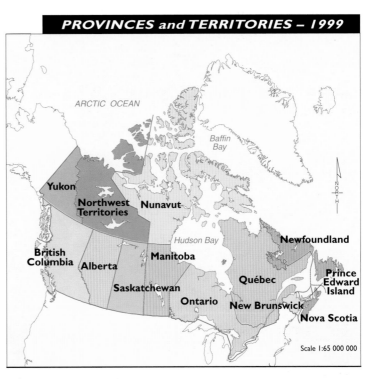

ARCTIC OCEAN

Baffin
Bay

NORTH

Yukon

Northwest
Territories   Nunavut

British
Columbia   Alberta   Manitoba   Newfoundland

Saskatchewan   Hudson Bay   Québec   Prince
Edward
Island

Ontario   New Brunswick

Nova Scotia

Scale 1:65 000 000

Floating logs in a storage area on a river in Québec Province

Wheat being harvested on the Canadian prairies

Niagara Falls between Lake Ontario and Lake Erie on the Canadian – USA border

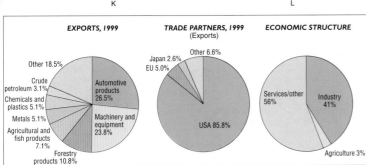

EXPORTS, 1999

Other 18.5%
Crude
petroleum 3.1%
Chemicals and
plastics 5.1%
Metals 5.1%
Agricultural and
fish products
7.1%
Forestry
products 10.8%
Automotive
products
26.5%
Machinery and
equipment
23.8%

TRADE PARTNERS, 1999
(Exports)

Japan 2.6%   Other 6.6%
EU 5.0%
USA 85.8%

ECONOMIC STRUCTURE

Services/other
56%
Industry
41%
Agriculture 3%

Salt Lake City, Utah

PACIFIC OCEAN

Population
- ■ Over 1 000 000
- ■ 500 000 to 1 000 000
- ● 100 000 to 500 000
- • 50 000 to 100 000
- ○ Under 50 000

Kilometres
0   150   300
Scale 1:12 000 000
Conformal Conic Projection

For Alaska see page 94

Hawaii
Kauai
Niihau
Oahu Kaneohe
Kailua
Honolulu
Molokai
Lanai
Wailuku Kahului Maui
Kahoolawe
Mauna Kea 4205 m
Hawaii
Hilo
Scale 1:12 000 000

Juan de Fuca Strait
Cape Flattery
Nanaimo
Langley
Vancouver
Kelowna
Victoria
Bellingham
Anacortes
Oak Harbor
Mount Vernon
Everett
Bremerton
Tacoma
Seattle
Olympia
Mt Rainier 4392 m
Longview
Wenatchee
Spokane
Coeur d'Alene
Kelso
St Helens
Washington
Yakima
Mt St Helens 2950 m
Hillsboro
Portland
Oregon City
Richland
Tigard
Columbia
Pullman
Moscow
Lewiston
Salem
Hermiston
Pendleton
Walla Walla
La Grande
Newport
Corvallis
Albany
Eugene
Springfield
Cottage Grove
Bend
Oregon
Baker
Coos Bay
Roseburg
Canyon City
Cape Blanco
Grants Pass
Medford
Burns
Weiser
Ontario
Crescent City
Ashland
Klamath Falls
Caldwell
Nampa
Boise
Ketchum
Upper Klamath Lake
Idaho
Goose Lake
Mountain Home
Twin Falls
Burley

Kelowna
High River
Penticton
Alberta
Nelson
Kimberley
Fernie
Cranbrook
Trail
Franklin D. Roosevelt Lake
Pend Oreille Lake
Mt Cleveland 3185 m
Kalispell
Flathead Lake
Missoula
Anaconda
Butte
Three Forks
Bozeman
Montana
Livingston
Granite Peak 3901 m
Yellowstone Lake
Rexburg
Idaho Falls
Blackfoot
Pocatello
Grand Teton 4196 m
Gannett Peak 4207 m

Nanaimo
Nokomis
Winnipegosis
Gyp
Manito
Swift Current
Moose Jaw
Regina
Lake Manitob
Portage la Pr
Medicine Hat
Taber
Lethbridge
Havre
Glasgow
Great Falls
Lewistown
Fort Peck Reservoir
South Saskatchewan
Saskatchewan
Val Marie
Weyburn
Estevan
Brandon
Williston
Minot
Devils Lake
North Dakota
Dickinson
Bismarck
Jamestown
Mandan
Lake Sakakawea
Miles City
Billings
Cloud Peak 4016 m
Sheridan
Gillette
Newell
Faith
South Dakota
Aberdee
Oahe Reservoir
Pierre
Rapid City
Lake Sharpe
Black Hills
Lake Francis Case

Mt Shasta 4317 m
California
Eureka
Arcata
Cape Mendocino
Fortuna
Redding
Red Bluff
Fort Bragg
Chico
Point Arena
Ukiah
Yuba City
Nevada
Susanville
Winnemucca
Humboldt River
Pyramid Lake
Elko
Reno
Fallon
Lake Tahoe
Santa Rosa
Napa
Sacramento
Shoshone Mountains
Austin
Hawthorne
Arc Dome 3593 m
Ely
McGill
Eureka
Preston
Logan
Bear Lake
Brigham City
Rock Springs
Green River
Ogden
Bountiful
Great Salt Lake
Salt Lake City
Murray
Orem
Provo
Duchesne
Price
Wyoming
Lander
Casper
Rawlins
Laramie
Cheyenne

San Rafael
Oakland
San Francisco
Stockton
San Jose
Modesto
Santa Cruz
Turlock
Merced
Monterey Bay
Madera
Monterey
Fresno
Salinas
Hanford
Mt Whitney 4418 m
Tulare
Paso Robles
Atascadero
Delano
San Luis Obispo
Santa Maria
Lompoc
Bakersfield
Point Conception
Santa Barbara
Ventura
Oxnard
Pasadena
Los Angeles
San Bernardino
Long Beach
Anaheim
Santa Ana
Palm Springs
Oceanside
Carlsbad
Escondido
El Cajon
San Diego
Chula Vista
Tijuana
Mexicali

Sierra Nevada
Coaldale
Warm Springs
Goldfield
Ridgecrest
Death Valley
Las Vegas
Henderson
Lake Mead
Boulder City
Barstow
Lake Havasu City
Pioche
Cedar City
Washington
St George
Richfield
Monroe
Delano Peak 3710 m
Utah
Green River
Grand Junction
Aspen
Mt Elbert 4399 m
Montrose
Colorado
Canon City
Cortez
Mt Wilson 4342 m
Durango
Alamosa
Blanca Peak 4364 m
Trinidad
Raton
Fort Collins
Greeley
Loveland
Longmont
Platte
Boulder
Englewood
Denver
Pikes Peak 4301 m
Colorado Springs
Pueblo
La Junta
Lamar
Craig
Duchesne

Fort Collins
Loveland
Greeley
Sterling
McCook
Hastings
Nebraska
North Platte
Scottsbluff
Alliance
Valentine
Niobrara
Kansas
Goodland
Dodge City
Liberal
Hutchins

Grand Canyon
Colorado Plateau
Humphreys Peak 3851 m
Flagstaff
Arizona
Prescott
Wickenburg
Peoria
Holbrook
Gallup
Mt Taylor 3471 m
Springerville
Baldy Peak 3533 m
Phoenix
Glendale
Chandler
Florence
Ajo
Casa Grande
Gila Bend
Yuma
San Luis
Morenci
Silver City
Los Alamos
Espanola
Santa Fe
Las Vegas
Albuquerque
Belen
Socorro
Magdalena
New Mexico
Deming
Las Cruces
Lordsburg
Tombstone
Paradise Valley
Tucson
Sierra Vista
Nogales
Nogales
Cananea
Agua Prieta
Nuevo Casas Grandes
Ciudad Juárez
El Paso
Kermit

Dalhart
Perryton
Pampa
Amarillo
Oklahoma C
Oklahoma
Canyon
Hereford
Clovis
Plainview
Portales
Levelland
Roswell
Lubbock
Brownfield
Artesia
Hobbs
Lamesa
Carlsbad
Snyder
Sweetwater
Andrews
Pecos
Midland
Odessa
San Angelo
Texas
Fort Stockton
Alpine
Sanderson
Del Rio
Eagle Pass
Piedras Negras
San Antonio
Kerrville
Round Roc
Austin
Killeen
Tucumcari
Vaughn
Clovis
Portales
Lawton
Vernon
Wichita Falls
Abilene
Stepher
Fort Wo
Brownwood

Guymon
Woodward
Enid
Nor
Borger
Dumas
Pecos
MEXICO
Hermosillo
Guaymas
San Felipe
Caborca
Magdalena
Nogales
Nuevo Casas Grandes
Chihuahua
Delicias
Ojinaga
Ciudad Camargo
Parral
Santa Bárbara
Hidalgo del Parral
Topolobampo
Mocorito
Ciudad Obregón
Navojoa
Guerrero
Nuevo Laredo
Laredo
Monclova
Sabinas Hidalgo
McAllen
Reynosa
Monterrey
Saltillo
Torreón
Matamoros
Brownsvi
Matamor
Montemorelos
Linares
Culiacán
La Paz
Durango

Ensenada
Point Baja
Cedros Island
Point Eugenia
San Ignacio
Santa Rosalía
Carmen Island
Gulf of California
San José Island
Western Sierra Madre
Eastern Sierra Madre
Lower California

Copyright Macmillan Education Ltd

Population
- ■ Over 1 000 000
- ● 500 000 to 1 000 000
- ● 100 000 to 500 000
- • 50 000 to 100 000
- ○ Under 50 000

Kilometres
0   400   800   1200

Scale 1: 38 000 000
Azimuthal Equal Area Projection
© MEA

FACT FILE

Land area – Largest country Brazil (8 511 996 km²); smallest Trinidad and Tobago (5128 km²). Highest point is Aconcagua in Argentina (6960 metres).
Population – Brazil 164.4 million (largest); Trinidad and Tobago 1.3 million (smallest); largest city São Paulo 20 million.
Life expectancy – Chile 75 years (longest); Bolivia 61 years (shortest).
Economic development (GDP per capita) – Uruguay US$4174 (richest); Bolivia US$762 (poorest).
Portuguese and Spanish influence – Most of the countries of South America were colonised by Spain or Portugal. Although now independent, these countries still retain much of their Spanish and Portuguese influence, especially in their architecture.

Forest Depletion

The Amazon Basin, which covers an area of about six million km², contains the largest continuous area of dense tropical rainforest and the largest and most diverse plant and animal life in the world. Because of its sheer size, the Amazon rainforest exerts a major influence on world climatic patterns. Over the past twenty years there has been large-scale clearing of rainforest to make way for cropland and pastures, and for increasing logging activities. This landcover conversion is commonly called *tropical deforestation*.
The forests of the Amazon are being depleted at a rate which has alarmed environmentalists and brought protests to the Brazilian government. In addition, large numbers of forest Indians have been displaced by forest clearing.

SOUTH AMERICA

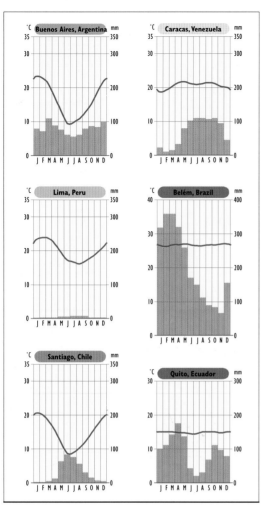

Buenos Aires, Argentina

Caracas, Venezuela

Lima, Peru

Belém, Brazil

Santiago, Chile

Quito, Ecuador

CLIMATIC REGIONS

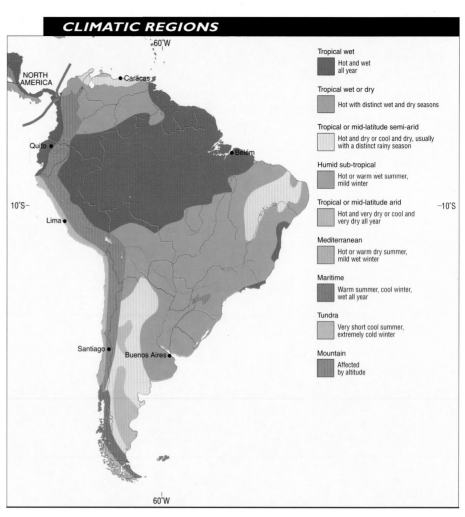

Tropical wet
Hot and wet all year

Tropical wet or dry
Hot with distinct wet and dry seasons

Tropical or mid-latitude semi-arid
Hot and dry or cool and dry, usually with a distinct rainy season

Humid sub-tropical
Hot or warm wet summer, mild winter

Tropical or mid-latitude arid
Hot and very dry or cool and very dry all year

Mediterranean
Hot or warm dry summer, mild wet winter

Maritime
Warm summer, cool winter, wet all year

Tundra
Very short cool summer, extremely cold winter

Mountain
Affected by altitude

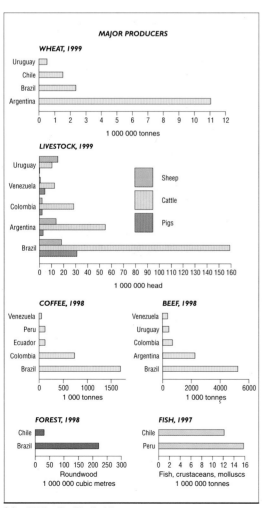

MAJOR PRODUCERS

WHEAT, 1999

Uruguay
Chile
Brazil
Argentina

1 000 000 tonnes

LIVESTOCK, 1999

Uruguay
Venezuela
Colombia
Argentina
Brazil

Sheep
Cattle
Pigs

1 000 000 head

COFFEE, 1998

Venezuela
Peru
Ecuador
Colombia
Brazil

1 000 tonnes

BEEF, 1998

Venezuela
Uruguay
Colombia
Argentina
Brazil

1 000 tonnes

FOREST, 1998

Chile
Brazil

Roundwood
1 000 000 cubic metres

FISH, 1997

Chile
Peru

Fish, crustaceans, molluscs
1 000 000 tonnes

AGRICULTURE, FORESTRY and FISHING

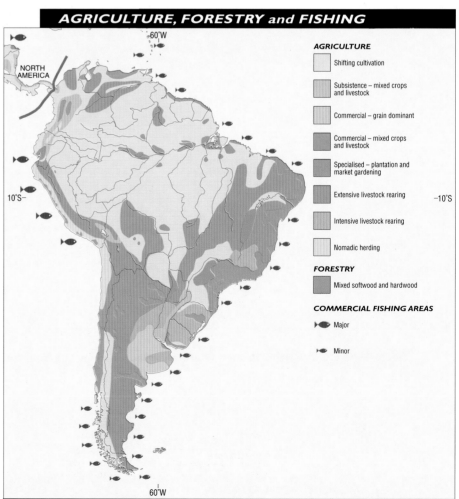

AGRICULTURE

Shifting cultivation

Subsistence – mixed crops and livestock

Commercial – grain dominant

Commercial – mixed crops and livestock

Specialised – plantation and market gardening

Extensive livestock rearing

Intensive livestock rearing

Nomadic herding

FORESTRY

Mixed softwood and hardwood

COMMERCIAL FISHING AREAS

Major

Minor

MINERALS, ENERGY and INDUSTRY

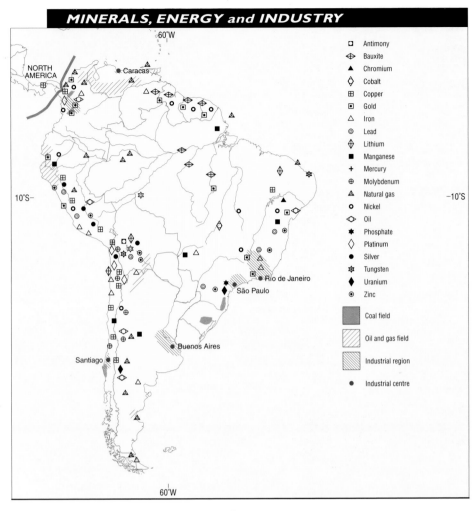

Antimony
Bauxite
Chromium
Cobalt
Copper
Gold
Iron
Lead
Lithium
Manganese
Mercury
Molybdenum
Natural gas
Nickel
Oil
Phosphate
Platinum
Silver
Tungsten
Uranium
Zinc

Coal field
Oil and gas field
Industrial region
Industrial centre

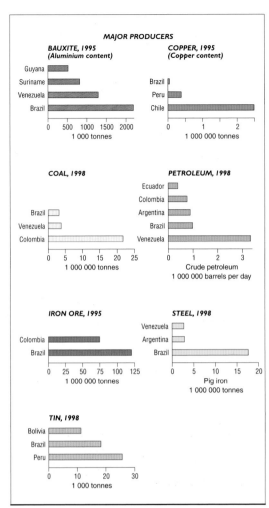

MAJOR PRODUCERS

POPULATION

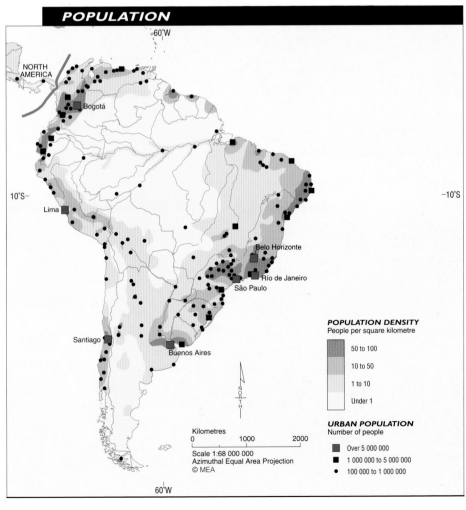

POPULATION DENSITY
People per square kilometre

50 to 100
10 to 50
1 to 10
Under 1

URBAN POPULATION
Number of people
Over 5 000 000
1 000 000 to 5 000 000
100 000 to 1 000 000

Kilometres
0   1000   2000
Scale 1:68 000 000
Azimuthal Equal Area Projection
© MEA

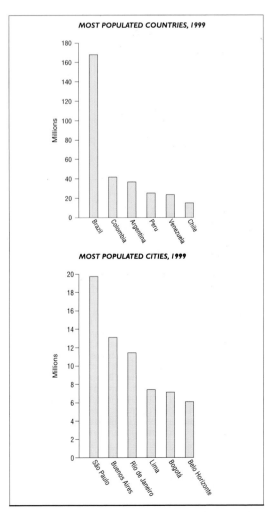

MOST POPULATED COUNTRIES, 1999

MOST POPULATED CITIES, 1999

FACT FILE

European Union

The European Union (EU) is a political association of 15 member countries joined together for their mutual benefit. In 1951, following the devastation of World War II, Belgium, France, West Germany, Italy, Luxembourg and the Netherlands formed the European Coal and Steel Community with the aim of ensuring peace by cooperating in trade matters. In 1957, under the Treaty of Rome, these same countries formed the European Economic Community (EEC) or Common Market. Trade among member countries was stimulated by the abolition of customs duties and the introduction of the freedom of movement for persons, goods and capital between the countries. With an enlarged market for goods and services, member countries experienced high growth rates and rising living standards. Other European countries then applied to join and in 1973 Great Britain, Denmark and Ireland were admitted. Greece joined in 1981, followed by Spain and Portugal in 1986. The countries of Europe moved even closer towards political unity with the signing of the Maastricht Treaty in 1993, creating the EU. The EU covered foreign affairs, security and judicial concerns, and gave EEC citizens the right to stand for elections for the European Parliament which began in 1994. Monetary union, which would bring about a single currency, is a longer-term aim of the EU. The members of the EU in 2000 were Austria, Belgium, Denmark, Finland, France, Germany, Greece, Ireland, Italy, Luxembourg, the Netherlands, Portugal, Spain, Sweden and the United Kingdom. Associate membership agreements have been signed by Bulgaria, the Czech Republic, Hungary, Poland, Romania and Slovakia. Norway and Switzerland rejected membership.

EUROPEAN UNION

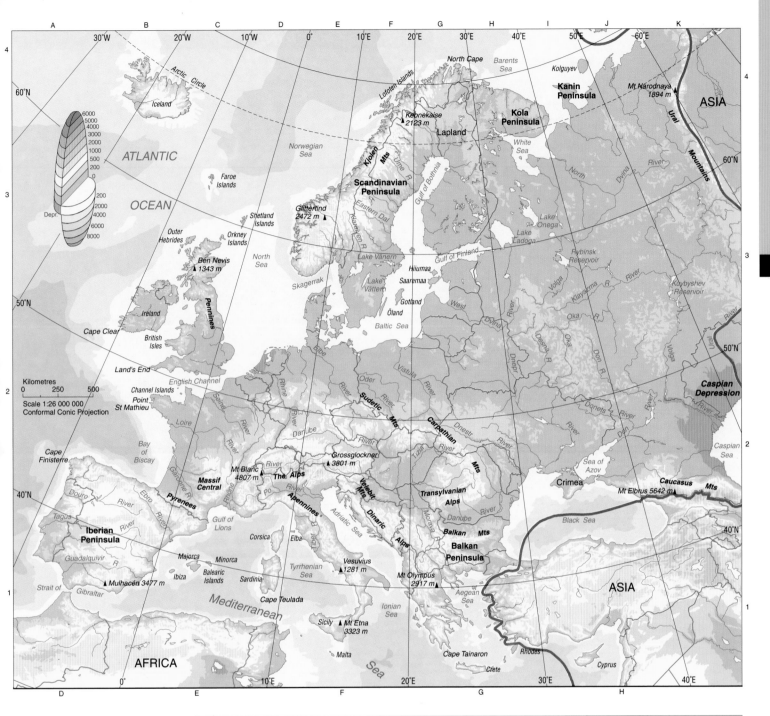

CROSS-SECTION Through the Pyrenees and Mt Elbrus along 43° North

metres
Vertical scale 1:275 000
Horizontal scale 1:28 500 000
Vertical exaggeration 104 times

5000
4000
3000
2000
1000
500
Sea level
2000

Ebro River — Pyrenees — Garonne River — Gulf of Lions

Apennines / Tiber River

Dinaric Alps — Morava River

Black Sea

Caucasus Mts — Mt Elbrus — Caspian Depression

SPAIN | **FRANCE** | **ITALY** | **YUGOSLAVIA** | **BULGARIA** | **GEORGIA** | **RUSSIA**

FACT FILE

Land area – Largest country, excluding Russia which straddles both Europe and Asia, is France (547 026 km²); smallest country Vatican City (44 ha). Highest point is Mt Elbrus in Russia (5642 metres)
Population – Germany 81.8 million (largest); Vatican City 1000 (smallest); largest city Paris (9.3 million)
Life expectancy – Sweden 79 years (longest); Latvia 69 years (shortest)
Economic development (GDP per capita) – Luxembourg US$39 850 (richest); Albania US$330 (poorest)
Channel tunnel – Linking the UK with France the 50 kilometre train tunnel was completed in 1994 and is the longest in Europe.

Airports – Europe's busiest is Heathrow, London with 451 371 aircraft movements in 1998, followed by Charles de Gaulle, Paris with 416 227.
Tourism in Switzerland – During the summer, visitors to Switzerland enjoy the lake resorts and walking in the mountains, while in the winter, skiing is the major attraction. Tourism is an important part of the economy, bringing in revenue and providing jobs, especially in the hotel and restaurant industries.
Receipts from tourism, 1996 – US$7277 million;
Expenditure on tourism, 1996 – US$6121 million
Profit from tourism, 1996 – US$1156 million
Number of tourists, 1996 – 6.74 million
Number of overnight stays, 1996 – 67 117 000
Number of beds available, 1996 – 1 075 000

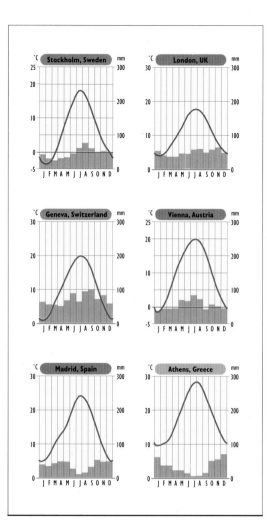

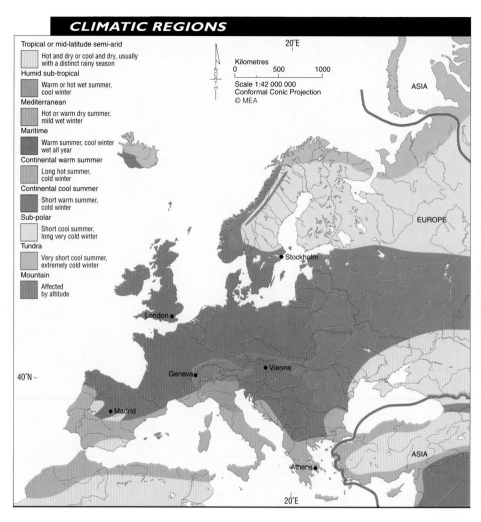

CLIMATIC REGIONS

Tropical or mid-latitude semi-arid
Hot and dry or cool and dry, usually with a distinct rainy season

Humid sub-tropical
Warm or hot wet summer, cool winter

Mediterranean
Hot or warm dry summer, mild wet winter

Maritime
Warm summer, cool winter wet all year

Continental warm summer
Long hot summer, cold winter

Continental cool summer
Short warm summer, cold winter

Sub-polar
Short cool summer, long very cold winter

Tundra
Very short cool summer, extremely cold winter

Mountain
Affected by altitude

20°E

Kilometres
0   500   1000

Scale 1:42 000 000
Conformal Conic Projection
© MEA

ASIA

EUROPE

Stockholm

London

Vienna

Geneva

40°N

Madrid

ASIA

Athens

20°E

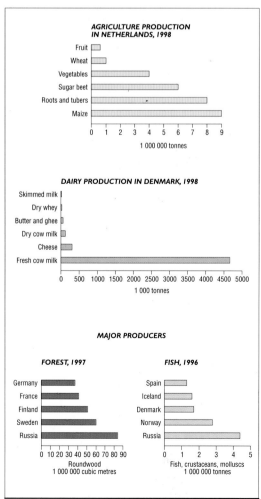

AGRICULTURE PRODUCTION IN NETHERLANDS, 1998

Fruit
Wheat
Vegetables
Sugar beet
Roots and tubers
Maize

0 1 2 3 4 5 6 7 8 9

1 000 000 tonnes

DAIRY PRODUCTION IN DENMARK, 1998

Skimmed milk
Dry whey
Butter and ghee
Dry cow milk
Cheese
Fresh cow milk

0 500 1000 1500 2000 2500 3000 3500 4000 4500 5000

1 000 tonnes

MAJOR PRODUCERS

FOREST, 1997

Germany
France
Finland
Sweden
Russia

0 10 20 30 40 50 60 70 80 90
Roundwood
1 000 000 cubic metres

FISH, 1996

Spain
Iceland
Denmark
Norway
Russia

0 1 2 3 4 5
Fish, crustaceans, molluscs
1 000 000 tonnes

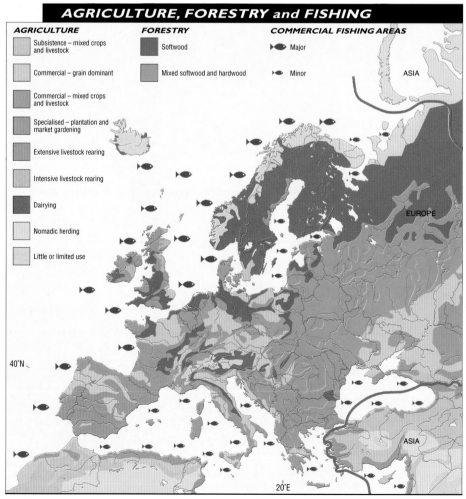

AGRICULTURE, FORESTRY and FISHING

AGRICULTURE

Subsistence – mixed crops and livestock

Commercial – grain dominant

Commercial – mixed crops and livestock

Specialised – plantation and market gardening

Extensive livestock rearing

Intensive livestock rearing

Dairying

Nomadic herding

Little or limited use

FORESTRY

Softwood

Mixed softwood and hardwood

COMMERCIAL FISHING AREAS

Major

Minor

ASIA

EUROPE

40°N

ASIA

20°E

MINERALS, ENERGY and INDUSTRY

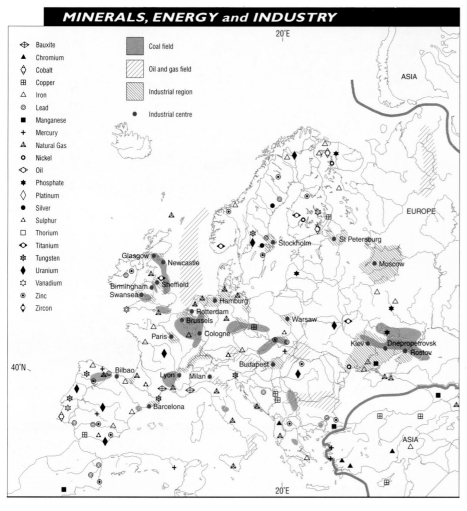

Bauxite
Chromium
Cobalt
Copper
Iron
Lead
Manganese
Mercury
Natural Gas
Nickel
Oil
Phosphate
Platinum
Silver
Sulphur
Thorium
Titanium
Tungsten
Uranium
Vanadium
Zinc
Zircon

Coal field
Oil and gas field
Industrial region
Industrial centre

Glasgow, Newcastle, Birmingham, Sheffield, Swansea, Hamburg, Rotterdam, Brussels, Paris, Cologne, Lyon, Milan, Barcelona, Bilbao, Stockholm, St Petersburg, Moscow, Warsaw, Budapest, Kiev, Dnepropetrovsk, Rostov

ASIA, EUROPE

MAJOR PRODUCERS

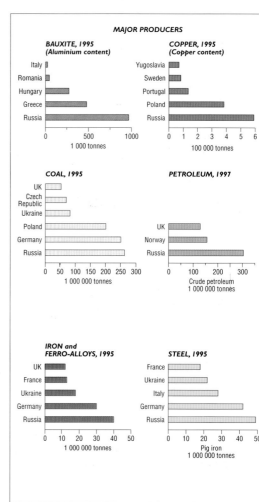

BAUXITE, 1995 (Aluminium content)
Italy, Romania, Hungary, Greece, Russia
1 000 tonnes

COPPER, 1995 (Copper content)
Yugoslavia, Sweden, Portugal, Poland, Russia
100 000 tonnes

COAL, 1995
UK, Czech Republic, Ukraine, Poland, Germany, Russia
1 000 000 tonnes

PETROLEUM, 1997
UK, Norway, Russia
Crude petroleum 1 000 000 tonnes

IRON and FERRO-ALLOYS, 1995
UK, France, Ukraine, Germany, Russia
1 000 000 tonnes

STEEL, 1995
France, Ukraine, Italy, Germany, Russia
Pig iron 1 000 000 tonnes

POPULATION

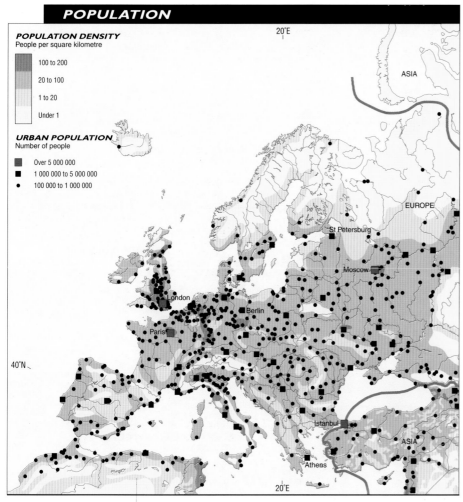

POPULATION DENSITY
People per square kilometre
100 to 200
20 to 100
1 to 20
Under 1

URBAN POPULATION
Number of people
Over 5 000 000
1 000 000 to 5 000 000
100 000 to 1 000 000

St Petersburg, Moscow, London, Paris, Berlin, Istanbul, Athens, ASIA, EUROPE

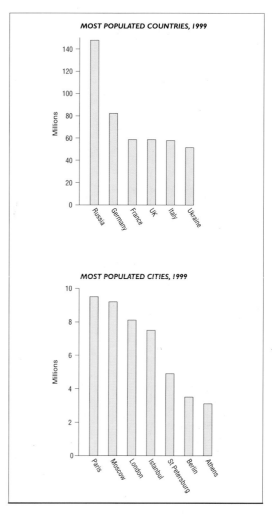

MOST POPULATED COUNTRIES, 1999
Millions
Russia, Germany, France, UK, Italy, Ukraine

MOST POPULATED CITIES, 1999
Millions
Paris, Moscow, London, Istanbul, St Petersburg, Berlin, Athens

Aurland fjord in Norway

°C **Vilnius, Lithuania** mm

°C **Dublin, Ireland** mm

Population
■ Over 1 000 000
● 500 000 to 1 000 000
● 100 000 to 500 000
● 50 000 to 100 000
○ Under 50 000

Kilometres
0   100   200   300

Scale 1:8 500 000
Conformal Conic Projection

Scandinavian
Peninsula

*Norwegian
Sea*

Namsos
Steinkjer
Levanger Verdal
Stjørdal
Trondheim
Östersund
Kristiansund
Molde
Ålesund
Ørsta
NORWAY
▲ Glittertind 2472 m

Shetland
Islands

Lillehammer Hamar
Aurland   Elverum   Mora
Voss   Gjøvik   Bor
Bergen   Lud

Oslo ▪ Lillestrøm
Kongsberg Drammen   Arvika
Notodden   Karlstad   Öre
Haugesund   Horten Moss   Kristine
Skien Sarpsborg
Stavanger Porsgrunn
Sandnes   Kragerø   Lake
Vänern
Egersund   Arendal   Vänersborg
Grimstad   Uddevalla   Trollhättan
Kristiansand   Lake Vättern
Mandal   Skagerrak   Skagen   Göteborg
Molndal   Hus
Hirtshals   Borås   Jönköp
Hjørring   Frederikshavn   Värnamo
Thisted   Älborg   Falkenberg   Vä
Halmstad
Lemvig   Skive   Randers
Herning   Silkeborg   Grenå   Ängelholm
Ringkøbing   Hässle
DENMARK   Århus   Helsingør Helsingbor
Esbjerg   Kolding   Fredericia   Copenhag
Ribe   Assens   Odense   Malmö
Hadersløv   Naestved   Trelleborg
Svendborg   Rør
Flensburg   Nykøbing
Husum   Schleswig   Sass
Rendsburg   Kiel   Rostock   Stralsund
Greifsw
Brunsbüttelkoog   Neumünster   Swinoujscie
Hamburg   Lübeck   Anklam
Wilhelmshaven   Bremerhaven   Schwerin
Harlingen   Emden   Oldenburg   Lüneburg   Waren   Neustrelitz   Szczec
Den Helder   Groningen   Bremen   Soltau   Uelzen   Wittenberge   Schwed
Alkmaar   Assen   Eberswalde
NETHERLANDS   Emmen   Nienburg   Celle   Wolfsburg
Haarlem   Amsterdam   Minden   Hannover   Magdeburg   Berlin
The Hague   Utrecht   Enschede   Salzgitter   Halberstadt   Potsda
Rotterdam   Münster   Paderborn   Göttingen   Dessau   Wittenberg   Luckenw   Cottb
Breda   Wesel   Dortmund   Kassel   Aschersleben   Torgau
Flushing   Den Bosch   Duisburg   Essen   Halle   Leipzig   Dresden
Ostend   Eindhoven   Düsseldorf   Eisenach   Erfurt   Jena   Gera   Chemnit
Brugge   Ghent   Mechelen   Cologne   Gotha
Dunkirk   Antwerp   Bonn   Zwickau   Plauen   Pragu
Calais   Lille   Brussels   Liège   GERMANY   Hof   Cheb
Boulogne   Charleroi   Koblenz   Coburg   Louny
Lens   BELGIUM   LUXEMBOURG   Frankfurt   Bamberg   Weiden   Plze
Abbeville   Cambrai   Bastogne   Mainz   Darmstadt   Marianske La
Cherbourg   Dieppe   Amiens   St Quentin   Arlon   Würzburg   Weiden   Domazlice
Le Havre   Rouen   Beauvais   Laon   Luxembourg   Mannheim   Heidelberg   Erlangen   Cham
Compiègne   Verdun   Metz   Saarbrücken   Heilbronn   Nuremberg   Pise
St Lô   Caen   Évreux   Reims   Thionville   Karlsruhe   Regensburg   Ceske Budejo
Granville   Argentan   Épernay   Nancy   Pforzheim   Stuttgart   Ingolstadt   Passau   Ce
Avranches   Mantes-la-Jolie   Châlons   Bar-le-Duc   Strasbourg   Reutlingen   Ulm   Landshut
Fougères   Paris   St Dizier   Nancy   Augsburg   Braunau
Trappes   Versailles   Chartres   Sens   Chaumont   Épinal   Colmar   Sigmaringen   Munich   Salz
Rennes   Alençon   Melun   Freiburg   Memmingen   Bad Ischl
Laval   Le Mans   Troyes   Langres   Mulhouse   Ravensburg
Vannes   Châteaudun   Auxerre   Basel   Friedrichshafen   AUSTR
Châteaubriant   Orléans   Montbéliard   Zürich   Innsbruck   Grossglock
St Nazaire   Angers   Blois   Gien   Besançon   Olten   Solothurn   LIECHTENSTEIN   3801 m
Nantes   Tours   Vierzon   Dijon   Biel   Lucerne   Spittal
Cholet   Saumur   Vendôme   Autun   Bern   SWITZERLAND   Merano
Bourges   Nevers   Dole   Lausanne   Bolzano   Klagen
FRANCE   Moulins   Lons-le-Saunier   Solothurn   ITALY
La Roche-sur-Yon   Châtellerault   Châteauroux   Macon   Bourg-en-Bresse   Geneva   Trento   Belluno
Les Sables d'Olonne   Parthenay   Poitiers   Vichy   Roanne   Annecy   Lugano   Sondrio   Udin
Niort   Montluçon   Digoin   Matterhorn 4478 m   Varese
La Rochelle   Thiers   Mt Blanc 4807 m   Riva   Rovereto
Rochefort   Gueret   Limoges   Clermont-Ferrand   Lyon   Annecy
Saintes   Digoin
Cognac   Angoulême   Périgueux   Tulle

10°W   5°W   0°   5°E   10°E

Orkney
Islands
Thurso
Outer
Hebrides
Fraserburgh
Elgin
Inverness   Peterhead
Fort William   Scotland   Aberdeen
Ben Nevis   Forfar   Montrose
1343 m   Perth   Arbroath
Dundee
Greenock   Stirling   Kirkcaldy
Glasgow   Edinburgh
Kilmarnock
Coleraine   Ayr   Berwick-upon-Tweed
Londonderry   Northern   Hawick
Ireland   Stranraer   Dumfries   UNITED
Belfast   Carlisle   KINGDOM
Newtownabbey   Workington   Newcastle-upon-Tyne
Armagh   Portadown   Durham
Sligo   Enniskillen   Newry   Middlesbrough
REPUBLIC   Dundalk   Kendal   Stockton-on-Tees
OF IRELAND   Drogheda   Douglas   Lancaster   Scarborough
Galway   Irish   Blackpool   York   Bridlington
Sea   Blackburn   Hull
Dublin   Liverpool   Leeds
Ennis   Dun Laoghaire   Bray   Manchester   Sheffield
Limerick   Carlow   Chester   Stoke-on-Trent
Tralee   Newcastle-under-Lyme   Derby   Nottingham
Waterford   Stafford
Cape Clear   Cork   Wales   Dudley   Birmingham   England
Peterborough
Milford Haven   Carmarthen   Northampton   Norwich
Pembroke   Gloucester   Milton Keynes
ATLANTIC OCEAN   Swansea   Newport   Oxford   Ipswich
Cardiff   London
Bristol   Bath   Basildon
Barnstaple   Salisbury   Canterbury
Taunton   Southampton   Dover
St Ives   Exeter   Bournemouth   Portsmouth   Brighton
Penzance   Bodmin   Torbay
Land's End   Plymouth

Channel Islands (U.K.)
Brest   Lannion   St Lô
Point St Mathieu   Morlaix   Caen
Douarnenez   St Brieuc
Quimper   Dinan
Rennes   Laval

Pennines
Wharfe R.

River

Severn R.

River Thames R.

English Channel

Shannon R.
Barrow R.

Loire R.

Rhine R.
Elbe R.

Danube R.

R.

Seine

North
Sea

Atlantic Ocean

Depr

6000
5000
4000
3000
2000
1000
500
200
0

200
2000
4000
6000
8000

Bay of
Biscay

ATLANTIC OCEAN

Scale 1:11 000 000
Conformal Conic Projection

Kilometres
0   100   200   300

Population
■ Over 1 000 000
■ 500 000 to 1 000 000
● 100 000 to 500 000
• 50 000 to 100 000
○ Under 50 000

Depr.

UNITED KINGDOM

Cardiff Newport Ipswich Lowestoft Groningen Emmen New Brandenburg
Bristol Oxford London NETHERLANDS Bremen Wittenberge
Hartland Point Reading Southend-on-Sea The Hague Amsterdam Hannover Wolfsburg
Bodmin Salisbury Utrecht Osnabrück Hildesheim Brunswick
Land's End Exeter Southampton Rotterdam Arnhem Münster Magdeburg
Lizard Point Plymouth Portsmouth Breda Den Bosch Essen Dortmund GERMANY
Torbay Brighton Calais Antwerp Duisburg Düsseldorf Göttingen
Bournemouth Strait of Dover Lille BELGIUM Brussels Cologne Bonn Kassel
English Channel Boulogne Ghent Charleroi Aachen Koblenz Erfurt
Cape La Hague Dieppe Lens St Quentin LUXEMBOURG Wiesbaden Coburg
Cherbourg Le Havre Caen Rouen Luxembourg Mainz Frankfurt
Channel Islands (UK) Seine Bay Amiens Reims Thionville Saarbrücken Darmstadt Karlovy Vary
Guernsey Jersey St Lô Normandy Argenteuil Metz Speyer Mannheim Heidelberg
Point St Mathieu Brest St Malo Évreux Mantes-la-Jolie Trappes Paris Nancy Karlsruhe Heilbronn Nuremberg
Douarnenez Dinan Fougères Chartres Châlons-sur-Marne Épinal Pforzheim Stuttgart Regensburg
Quimper St Brieuc Laval Le Mans Fontainebleau Lunéville Colmar Reutlingen Ingolstadt
Lorient Rennes Châteaudun Sens Troyes Chaumont Langres Mulhouse Freiburg Ulm Augsburg
Vannes Châteaubriant Angers Orléans Auxerre Romilly Basel Bern Munich
Belle Island St Nazaire Saumur Thouars Gien Clamecy Dijon Besançon Zürich LIECHTENSTEIN
Noirmoutier Island Nantes Tours Poitiers Bourges Autun Chalon-sur-Saône Olten Biel Vaduz Innsbruck AUSTRIA
La Roche-sur-Yon Parthenay Châteauroux Nevers Mâcon Thiers Lausanne Lucerne Wildspitze 3774 m
Les Sables d'Olonne Niort Indre River Limoges Roanne Lyon Geneva SWITZERLAND Bolzano SLOVENIA
Ré Island La Rochelle Angoulême Guéret Clermont-Ferrand Mt Blanc 4807 m Annecy The Alps Matterhorn Bernina 4049 m Trento Klagenfurt
Oléron Island Royan Saintes Tulle St Etienne Voiron Chambéry 4478 m Lugano Bergamo Udine
Bay of Biscay Pauillac Périgueux Massif Central Valence Grenoble Romans-sur-Isère Biella Novara Monza Brescia Vicenza Venice
Bordeaux Bergerac Lot River Cahors Millau Alès Montélimar Gap Alessandria Turin Milan Verona Padua
Cape Ortegal Mimizan Marmande Agen Montauban Orange Digne Acqui Mondovi Cuneo Piacenza Parma Modena Ferrara Bologna
La Coruña El Ferrol Cape Peñas Gulf of Gascony Condom Villefranche-de-Rouergue Avignon Aix-en-Provence Cannes Nice Genoa Rapallo La Spezia Ravenna Rimini
Cape Finisterre Ribadeo Gijón Llanes Santander Mont-de-Marsan Tarbes Castres Béziers Nîmes Marseille Toulon MONACO Livorno Pisa Forlì SAN MARINO
Santiago de Compostela La Estrada Lugo Oviedo Mieres Torrelavega Reinosa Laredo Bayonne Lourdes Montpellier La Seyne Ligurian Sea Florence Prato
Pontevedra Orense León Bilbao Guernica San Sebastián Pau Foix Sète Cape Corse Cecina Siena Arezzo
Vigo Ponferrada Cantabrian Mountains Irún Pamplona Pamiers Perpignan La Seyne Bastia Elba Grosseto Perugia Foligno Terni
Viana do Castelo Astorga Benavente Vitoria Miranda de Ebro Huesca Andorra-la-Vella ANDORRA Berga Ripoll Figueras Ajaccio Corte Orbetello Viterbo
Braga Verín Chaves Zamora Burgos Logroño Calahorra Tarazona Zaragoza Lérida Vic Girona Mt Cinto 2710 m Corsica Porto Vecchio Orvieto ITALY Rome
Oporto Esla River Valladolid Palencia Soria Calatayud Belchite Sabadell Palamós Cape Negro Strait of Bonifacio Sartène Anzio
PORTUGAL Douro River Medina del Campo Segovia Ávila Almazán Caspe Tarragona Badalona Porto Torres Sassari Velletri Sora
Viseu Salamanca Guadarrama Range Madrid Alcalá de Henares Montalbán Barcelona Olbia Latina Terracina
Coimbra Leiria Ledesma Garrovillas Colmenar Viejo Tarancón Teruel Tortosa Mt Cinto Iglesias Cape Circeo Caserta
Covilhã Castelo Branco Cáceres Talavera de la Reina Toledo Cuenca Vinaroz Castelló de la Plana Oristano Sardinia Cape Carbonara Naples
Torres Vedras Santarém SPAIN Villacañas Requena Valencia Sant' Antioco Marmora 1834 m Vesuvius 1281 m
Sintra Almada Mt Ossa 649 m Badajoz Mérida Ciudad Real Daimiel Liria Sagunto Lanusei Cagliari Salerno
Lisbon Manassas Évora Olivenza Castuera Pozoblanco Alcaraz Albacete Gulf of Valencia Pollença Minorca Tyrrhenian Sea
Cape Roca Beja Moura Llerena Puertollano Alcázar Gandía Majorca Mahón
Cape St Vincent Monchique 902 m Serpa Barrancos Zafra Córdoba Linares Hellín Alcoy Cape Nao Palma Felanitx
Sines Faro Portimão Sierra Morena Seville Jaén Villena Alcoy Ibiza Llucmajor Balearic Islands Cape Spartivento
Huelva Utrera Marchena Morón de la Frontera Caravaca Elche Alicante Ibiza
Guadalquivir River Sierra Nevada Granada Lorca Murcia Mediterranean Sea
Sanlúcar de Barrameda Cádiz Jerez de la Frontera Ronda Alora Mulhacén 3477 m Vera Cartagena
Cape Trafalgar Algeciras Málaga Motril Aguilas
Gibraltar (UK) Almería
Tangier Strait of Gibraltar Cape Gata
Tetouan Ceuta Xauen 2170 m
Ksar-el-Kebir Asilah
Souk el Arba du Rharb Hussein-Dey Algiers Tizi Ouzou Palermo
Kenitra Quezzane Targuist Melilla (Sp) Oran Mostaganem Ech Cheliff Blida Bejaïa Skikda Annaba Bizerte Cape Blanc Marsala Sicily Termini Mt Etna 3323 m
Rabat Salé Sidi Kacem Nador Berkane Mohammadia Relizane Medea Berrouaghia Sétif Constantine Mateur Gulf of Tunis Castelvetrano Sciacca Catania Siracusa
Casablanca Moulay Idriss Aknoul Sidi Bel Abbès Ksar-el-Boukhari Bordj Bou Arreridj Aïn M'Lila Souk Ahras Mejez el Bab Tunis Agrigento Ragusa
Khemisset Fès Taza Maghnia Nédroma Tiaret Mahdia M'Sila Ouenza Aïn Beïda Zaghouan Pantelleria Licata Gela
Settat Meknès Azrou Oujda Ghriss Frenda Bordj Omar Driss Batna Siliana Gulf of Hammamet
Khouribga Sefrou Guercif Ojerada Saïda Aïn Oussera Lake el Hodna Kairouan Sousse Gozo
Beni Mellal Bedeau Berguent Marhoum Djelfa Biskra Tébessa El Djem MALTA
Demnate Mecheria El Aricha Le Kreider Saharan Atlas El Djem Sfax
MOROCCO Atlas Mountains Moulouya Lake Ech Chergui El Bayadh Aflou Ouled Djellal TUNISIA Maharès
ALGERIA Laghouat Lake Melrhir Gafsa Cékhira
Ouargla El Oued Nefta El Hamma Gulf of Gabès Zarzis
Touggourt El Djerid Gabès
Ghadames Daraj Tripoli Al Khums Misratah
Az Zawiyah Nalut Yafran Tarhunah Awbari Desert

FRANCE **SPAIN** **ITALY** **Rome** **ANDORRA** **MONACO** **MALTA** **ALGERIA** **TUNISIA** **MOROCCO**

Rome, Italy

°C mm
35 350
30 300
25 250
20 200
15 150
10 100
5 50
J F M A M J J A S O N D

The Greek island of Santorini in the Aegean Sea

© Copyright Macmillan Education Ltd

Istanbul, Turkey

AFRICA Political

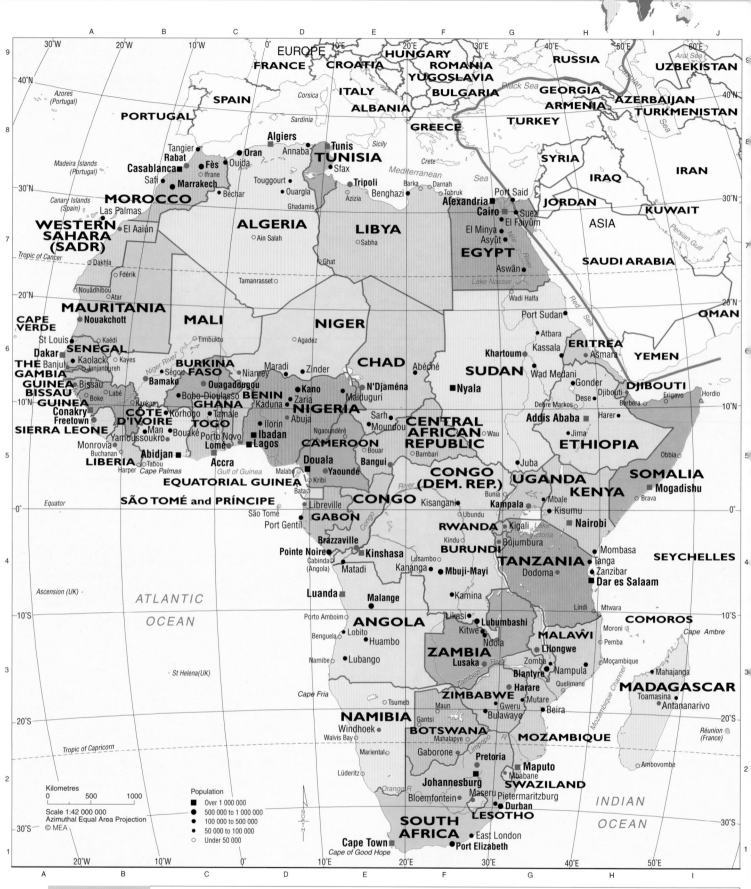

FACT FILE

Land area – Largest country Sudan (2 505 813 km²); smallest country Seychelles (455 km²). Highest point is Mt Kilimanjaro in Tanzania (5895m)

Population – Nigeria 118 million (largest); Seychelles 78 000 (smallest); largest city Lagos in Nigeria (10.3 million)

Life expectancy – Tunisia 73 years (longest); Malawî 36 years (shortest)

Economic development (GDP per capita) – Seychelles US$7272 (richest); São Tomé and Príncipe US$36 (poorest)

One country's three capitals – South Africa has three different capital cities; Cape Town (legislative), Pretoria (administrative), and Bloemfontein (judicial)

Organisation of African Unity – The OAU was formed in 1963 by thirty two independent African states and has its headquarters in Addis Ababa. Every African country is a member, with the exception of Morocco, which resigned in 1984 following the recognition of the Sahrawi Arab Democratic Republic (Western Sahara) as a member state. The main aims of the OAU are to provide unity and solidarity between its members, to eliminate colonialism in Africa, and to promote international co-operation. The Assembly of Heads of State and Government meets annually to co-ordinate policies on political, economic, cultural, health, scientific and defence issues.

© Copyright Macmillan Education Ltd

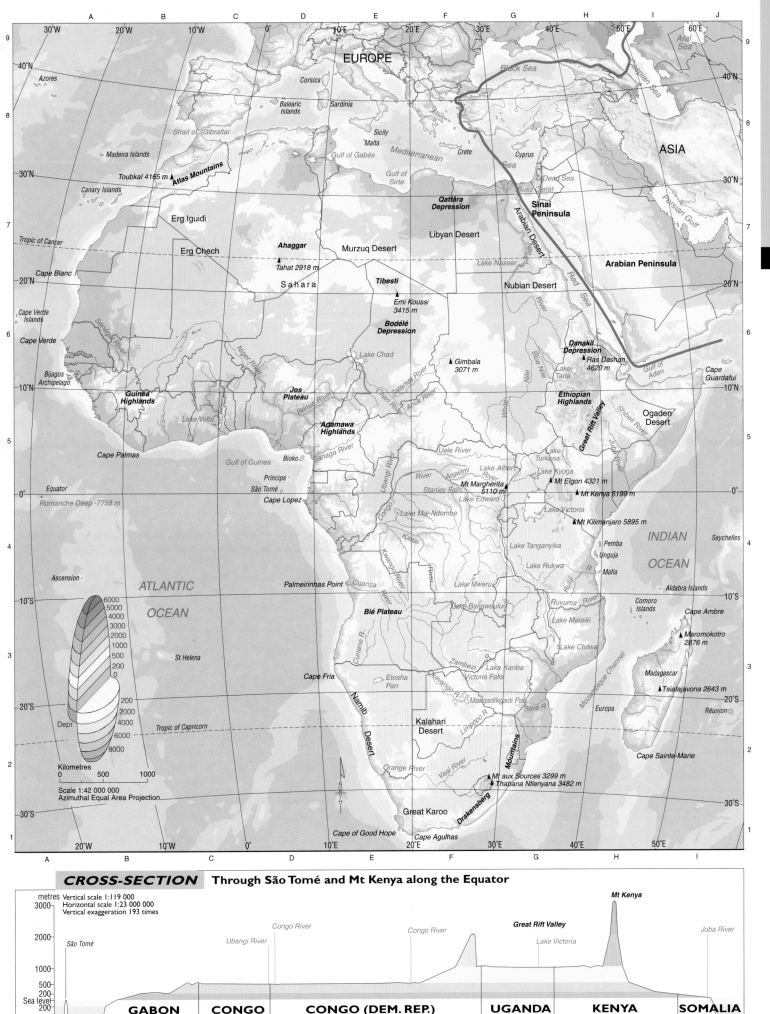

9 8 7 6 5 4 3 2 1

A   B   C   D   E   F   G   H   I   J

30°W   20°W   10°W   0°   10°E   20°E   30°E   40°E   50°E   60°E

EUROPE

ASIA

Azores
40°N
Corsica
Black Sea
Aral Sea
40°N

Madeira Islands
Balearic Islands
Sardinia
Caspian Sea

30°N
Strait of Gibraltar
Sicily
Malta
Mediterranean Sea
Crete
Cyprus
Dead Sea
30°N
Toubkal 4165 m ▲ Atlas Mountains
Gulf of Gabès
Gulf of Sirte
Qattâra Depression
Suez Canal
Sinai Peninsula

Canary Islands

Tropic of Cancer
Erg Iguidi
Libyan Desert
Arabian Desert
Persian Gulf

Erg Chech
Ahaggar
Murzuq Desert
Lake Nasser
Arabian Peninsula

Cape Blanc
20°N
Tahat 2918 m ▲
Sahara
Tibesti
Nubian Desert
Red Sea
20°N

Cape Verde Islands
Emi Koussi 3415 m ▲
Danakil Depression

Cape Verde
Bodélé Depression
Lake Chad
Gimbala 3071 m ▲
Ras Dashan 4620 m ▲
Cape Guardafui

Bijagos Archipelago
10°N
Guinea Highlands
Jos Plateau
Niger River
Benue River
Ethiopian Highlands
Great Rift Valley
Ogaden Desert
10°N
Lake Volta
Adamawa Highlands
Chari River
Aouk River
Salamat River
Lake Tana
Shibeli River
Blue Nile
White Nile

Cape Palmas
Gulf of Guinea
Bioko
Sanaga River
Uele River
Lake Turkana
Juba River

Equator
0°
Príncipe
São Tomé
Cape Lopez
Ubangi River
Aruwimi River
Stanley Falls
Mt Margherita 5110 m ▲
Lake Albert
Lake Kyoga
Mt Elgon 4321 m ▲
Mt Kenya 5199 m ▲
0°
Romanche Deep -7758 m
Congo River
Lake Mai-Ndombe
Lake Edward
Lake Victoria
Mt Kilimanjaro 5895 m ▲
INDIAN OCEAN
Seychelles

Ascension
ATLANTIC
Kasai River
Lake Tanganyika
Pemba
Unguja

OCEAN
Kwango River
Mafia

10°S
Palmeirinhas Point
Cuanza
Lake Bangweulu
Lake Rukwa
Lake Mweru
Ruvuma River
Comoro Islands
Cape Ambre
10°S
St Helena
Bié Plateau
Cunene R.
Lake Malawi
Rufiji R.
Aldabra Islands
Maromokotro 2876 m ▲

Cape Fria
Etosha Pan
Okavango R.
Zambezi R.
Lake Kariba
Victoria Falls
Lake Chilwa
Mozambique Channel
Madagascar
Tsiafajavona 2643 m ▲

20°S
Namib Desert
Makgadikgadi Pan
Save R.
Europa
Réunion
20°S
Kalahari Desert
Limpopo R.
Tropic of Capricorn

Orange River
Vaal River
Drakensberg Mountains
Mt aux Sources 3299 m ▲
Thabana Ntlenyana 3482 m ▲
Cape Sainte-Marie

30°S
Great Karoo
30°S
Cape of Good Hope
Cape Agulhas

20°W   10°W   0°   10°E   20°E   30°E   40°E   50°E

metres
6000 5000 4000 3000 2000 1000 500 200 0

200 1000 2000 4000 6000 8000
Depr.

Kilometres
0   500   1000

Scale 1:42 000 000
Azimuthal Equal Area Projection

NORTH

CROSS-SECTION   Through São Tomé and Mt Kenya along the Equator

metres   Vertical scale 1:119 000
3000   Horizontal scale 1:23 000 000
Vertical exaggeration 193 times

Mt Kenya

2000
São Tomé
Congo River
Congo River
Great Rift Valley
Juba River

1000
Ubangi River
Lake Victoria

500
200
Sea level
200

GABON   **CONGO**   **CONGO (DEM. REP.)**   **UGANDA**   **KENYA**   **SOMALIA**

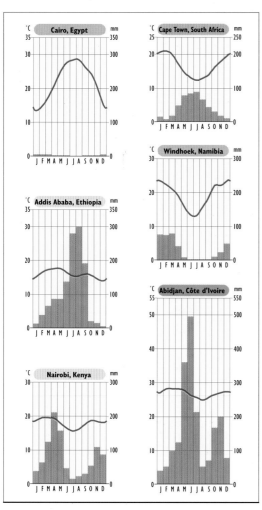

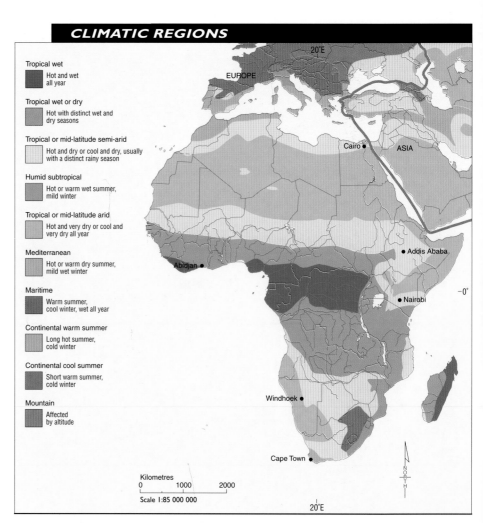

CLIMATIC REGIONS

Tropical wet
Hot and wet all year

Tropical wet or dry
Hot with distinct wet and dry seasons

Tropical or mid-latitude semi-arid
Hot and dry or cool and dry, usually with a distinct rainy season

Humid subtropical
Hot or warm wet summer, mild winter

Tropical or mid-latitude arid
Hot and very dry or cool and very dry all year

Mediterranean
Hot or warm dry summer, mild wet winter

Maritime
Warm summer, cool winter, wet all year

Continental warm summer
Long hot summer, cold winter

Continental cool summer
Short warm summer, cold winter

Mountain
Affected by altitude

Kilometres
0   1000   2000
Scale 1:85 000 000

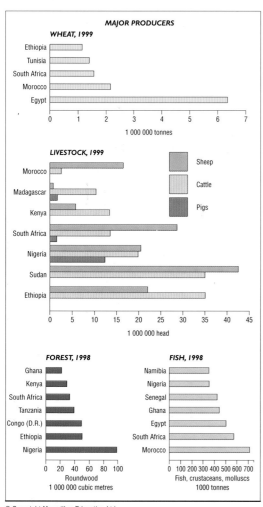

MAJOR PRODUCERS

WHEAT, 1999

1 000 000 tonnes

LIVESTOCK, 1999

Sheep
Cattle
Pigs

1 000 000 head

FOREST, 1998

Roundwood
1 000 000 cubic metres

FISH, 1998

Fish, crustaceans, molluscs
1000 tonnes

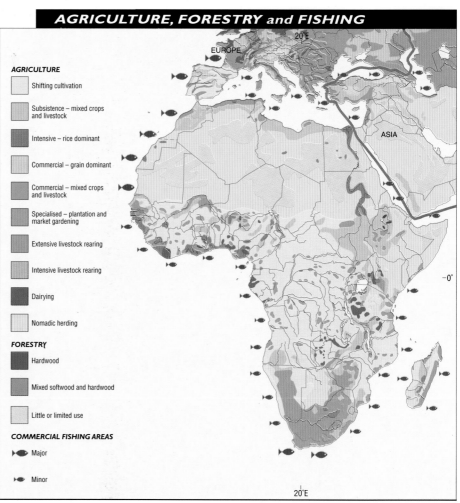

AGRICULTURE, FORESTRY and FISHING

AGRICULTURE

Shifting cultivation

Subsistence – mixed crops and livestock

Intensive – rice dominant

Commercial – grain dominant

Commercial – mixed crops and livestock

Specialised – plantation and market gardening

Extensive livestock rearing

Intensive livestock rearing

Dairying

Nomadic herding

FORESTRY

Hardwood

Mixed softwood and hardwood

Little or limited use

COMMERCIAL FISHING AREAS

Major

Minor

MINERALS, ENERGY and INDUSTRY

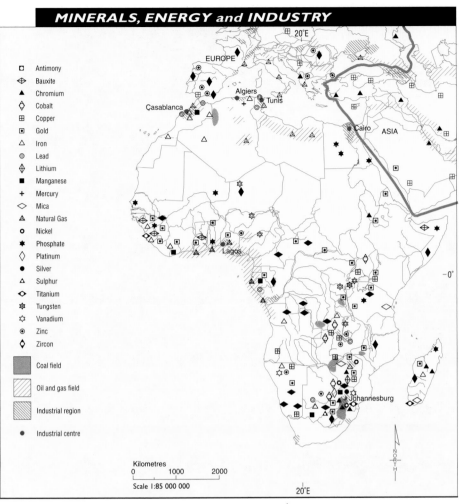

Legend:
- ☐ Antimony
- ◈ Bauxite
- ▲ Chromium
- ◇ Cobalt
- ⊞ Copper
- ⊡ Gold
- △ Iron
- ◉ Lead
- ⊕ Lithium
- ■ Manganese
- + Mercury
- ◇ Mica
- △ Natural Gas
- ○ Nickel
- ✶ Phosphate
- ◇ Platinum
- ● Silver
- △ Sulphur
- ◇ Titanium
- ✸ Tungsten
- ✩ Vanadium
- ⊙ Zinc
- ◇ Zircon

- Coal field
- Oil and gas field
- Industrial region
- ● Industrial centre

Kilometres
0   1000   2000
Scale 1:85 000 000

MAJOR PRODUCERS

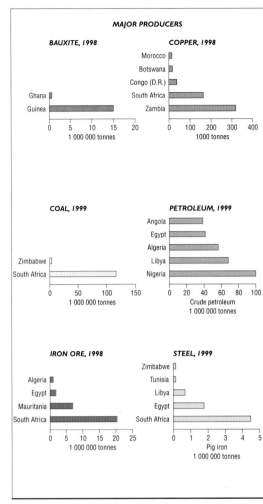

BAUXITE, 1998

Ghana
Guinea

0 5 10 15 20
1 000 000 tonnes

COPPER, 1998

Morocco
Botswana
Congo (D.R.)
South Africa
Zambia

0 100 200 300 400
1000 tonnes

COAL, 1999

Zimbabwe
South Africa

0 50 100 150
1 000 000 tonnes

PETROLEUM, 1999

Angola
Egypt
Algeria
Libya
Nigeria

0 20 40 60 80 100
Crude petroleum
1 000 000 tonnes

IRON ORE, 1998

Algeria
Egypt
Mauritania
South Africa

0 5 10 15 20 25
1 000 000 tonnes

STEEL, 1999

Zimbabwe
Tunisia
Libya
Egypt
South Africa

0 1 2 3 4 5
Pig iron
1 000 000 tonnes

POPULATION

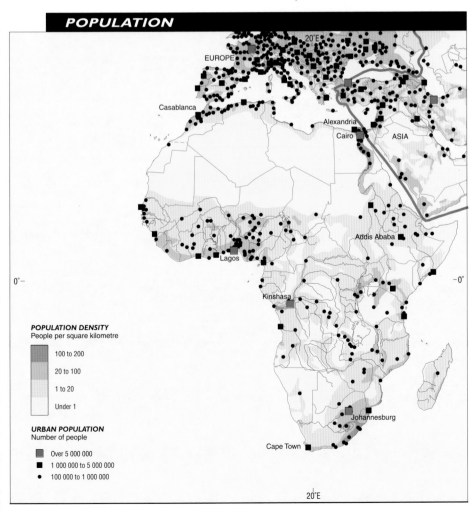

POPULATION DENSITY
People per square kilometre
- 100 to 200
- 20 to 100
- 1 to 20
- Under 1

URBAN POPULATION
Number of people
- ■ Over 5 000 000
- ■ 1 000 000 to 5 000 000
- ● 100 000 to 1 000 000

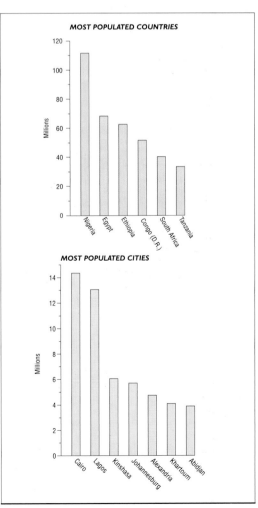

MOST POPULATED COUNTRIES

Millions
120
100
80
60
40
20
0

Nigeria, Egypt, Ethiopia, Congo (D.R.), South Africa, Tanzania

MOST POPULATED CITIES

Millions
14
12
10
8
6
4
2
0

Cairo, Lagos, Kinshasa, Johannesburg, Alexandria, Khartoum, Abidjan

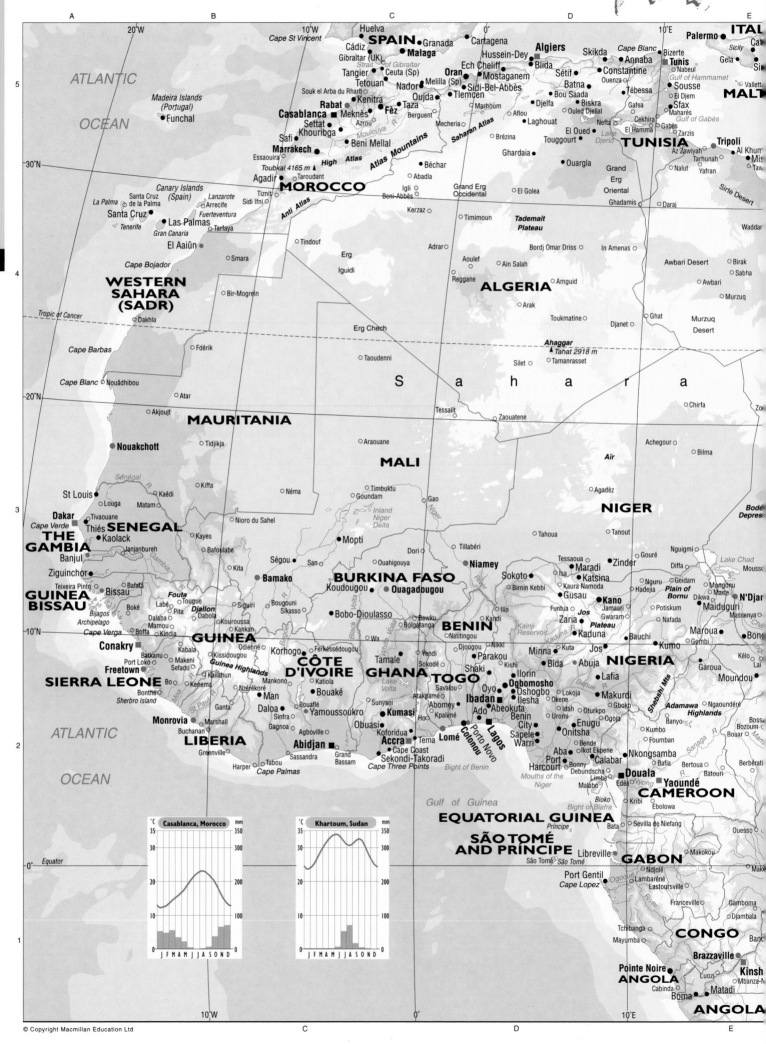

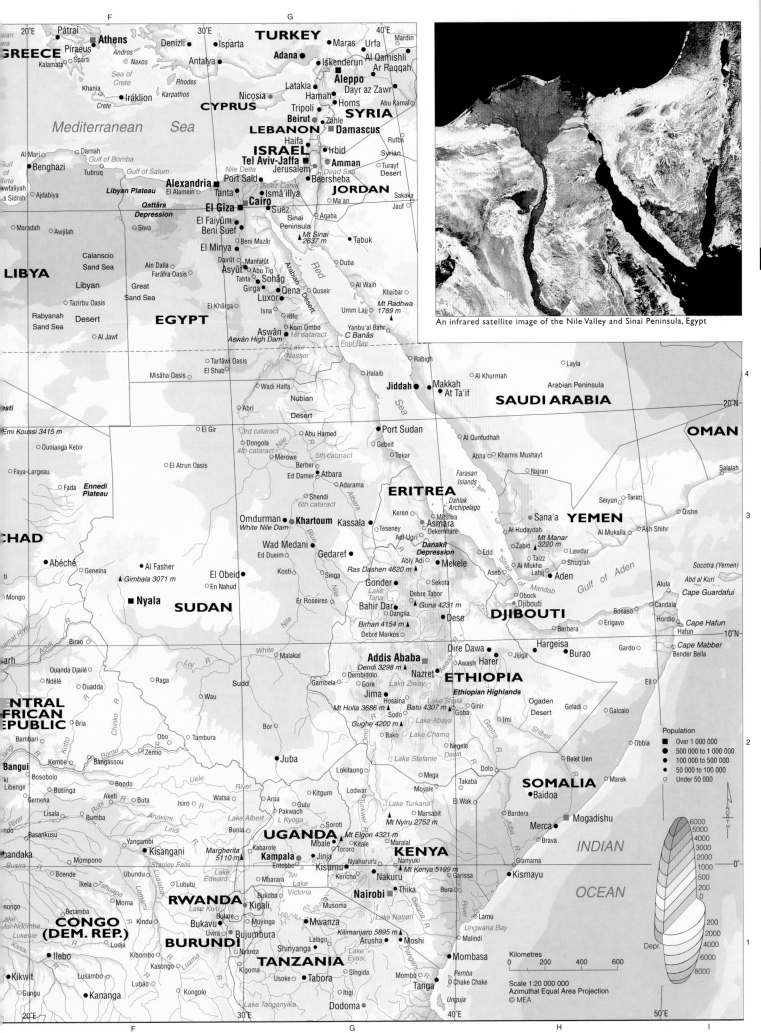

An infrared satellite image of the Nile Valley and Sinai Peninsula, Egypt

SOUTHERN AFRICA

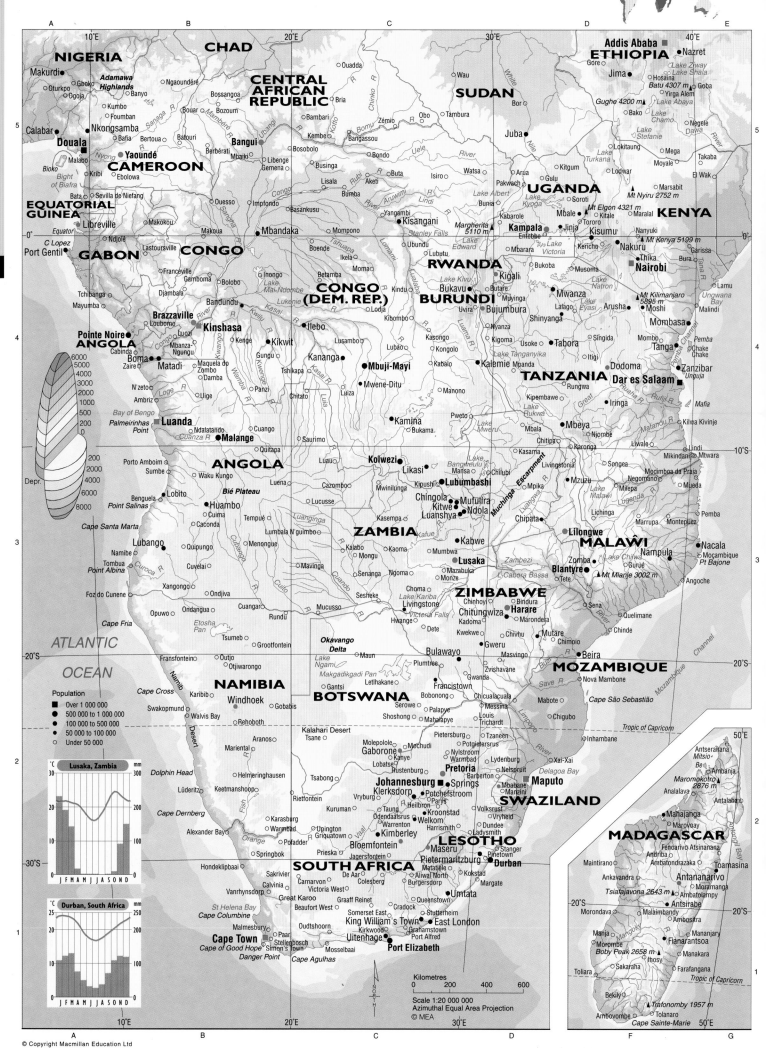

NIGERIA
Makurdi
Oturkpo
Gboko
Ogoja
Kumbo
Adamawa
Highlands
Banyo
Foumban
Nkongsamba
Bafia
Bertoua
Bangui
Berbérati
Mbaiki
Calabar
Douala
Malabo
Bioko
Kribi
Ebolowa
Yaoundé
Bight
of Biafra
CAMEROON

CHAD

**CENTRAL
AFRICAN
REPUBLIC**
Ngaoundéré
Bossangoa
Bouar
Bozoum
Bria
Bambari
Ouadda
Obo

SUDAN
Wau
Bor
Juba

Ngbémé
Lisala
Aketi
Buta
Isiro
Watsa
Arua
Gulu
Kitgum
Lokitaung
Mega
Takaba

ETHIOPIA
Addis Ababa
Nazret
Gore
Jima
Lake Ziway
Lake Shala
Batu 4307 m
Goba
Gughe 4200 m
Bako
Lake
Chamo
Negele
Dawa

KENYA
Mt Elgon 4321 m
Kitale
Tororo
Marsabit
Mbale
Soroti
Kabarole
Kampala
Jinja
Kisumu
Nanyuki
Mt Kenya 5199 m
Garissa
Bura
Lamu

**EQUATORIAL
GUINEA**
Bata
Sevilla de Niefang
Libreville
Equator
C Lopez
Port Gentil
GABON
Ndjolé
Lastoursville
Franceville
Tchibanga
Mayumba

CONGO
Makokou
Makoua
Ouesso
Impfondo
Mbandaka
Basankusu
Gamboma
Bolobo
Djambala
Brazzaville
Loubomo
Pointe Noire
Luozi
ANGOLA
Cabinda
Boma
Zaire
Matadi
N'zeto
Ambriz

**CONGO
(DEM. REP.)**
Kisangani
Stanley Falls
Yangambi
Bumba
Businga
Basankusu
Boende
Ikela
Betamba
Lake
Mai-Ndombe
Inongo
Bandundu
Kinshasa
Kenge
Kikwit
Ilebo
Lusambo
Kananga
Mbuji-Mayi
Mwene-Ditu
Tshikapa
Luiza
Chitato

Lubutu
Ubundu
Kindu
Kibombo
Kasongo
Kongolo
Kabalo
Kalemie
Manono
Kamina
Bukama

RWANDA
Kigali
Butare
BURUNDI
Bujumbura
Uvira
Nyanza
Kigoma
Muyinga
Lake Kivu
Bukavu
Lake Edward
Bunia

UGANDA
Lake Albert
Pakwach
Lake Kyoga
Entebbe
Lake Victoria
Mbarara
Margherita 5110 m
Keri cho
Nakuru
Thika
Nairobi
Bukoba
Musoma
Mwanza
Mt Kilimanjaro 5895 m
Moshi
Arusha
Shinyanga
Singida
Tabora
Usoke
Mombo
Mombasa
Pemba
Chake Chake
Zanzibar
Unguja

TANZANIA
Dodoma
Dar es Salaam
Rungwa
Iringa
Kipembawe
Mpanda
Mbeya
Njombe
Mbala
Chitipa
Karonga
Mzuzu
Lichinga

MALAWI
Lilongwe
Zomba
Blantyre
Tete
Mt Mlanje 3002 m
Gurué
Nampula
Nacala
Pt Bajone
Moçambique
Angoche
Pemba
Mueda
Mocimboa da Praia
Negomano
Milepa

Lake
Tanganyika
Lake Mweru
Lake Bangweulu
Lake Malawi
Lake Rukwa

ANGOLA
Palmeirinhas
Point
Luanda
Ndalatando
Cuango
Malange
Quitapa
Saurimo
Luau
Luena
Porto Amboim
Sumbe
Waku Kungo
Bié Plateau
Benguela
Lobito
Point Salinas
Huambo
Cuima
Tempué
Caconda
Menongue
Cuito
Lumbala N'guimbo
Cazombo
Lucusse
Mavinga

Cape Santa Marta
Lubango
Quipungo
Namibe
Tombua
Cuvelai
Point Albina
Xangongo
Ondjiva
Foz do Cunene
Opuwo
Ondangua
Cape Fria
Rundu

ZAMBIA
Kolwezi
Likasi
Lubumbashi
Chingola
Mufulira
Kitwe
Ndola
Luanshya
Kabwe
Lusaka
Kalabo
Mongu
Kaoma
Mumbwa
Monze
Mazabuka
Senanga
Ngoma
Choma
Kasama
Mpika
Chipata

ZIMBABWE
Lake Kariba
Livingstone
Victoria Falls
Hwange
Dete
Chinhoyi
Bindura
Chitungwiza
Harare
Marondera
Kadoma
Kwekwe
Chivhu
Mutare
Gweru
Masvingo
Bulawayo
Plumtree
Zvishavane
Gwanda

MOZAMBIQUE
Chipata
Tete
Cabora Bassa
Sena
Chinde
Quelimane
Chimoio
Beira
Nova Mambone
Cape São Sebastião
Inhambane

NAMIBIA
Fransfontein
Outjo
Otjiwarongo
Etosha
Pan
Tsumeb
Grootfontein
Okavango
Delta
Maun
Lake
Ngami
Makgadikgadi Pan
Cape Cross
Karibib
Windhoek
Gobabis
Swakopmund
Walvis Bay
Rehoboth

BOTSWANA
Gantsi
Tsane
Letlhakane
Francistown
Bobonong
Chicualacuala
Mabote
Chigubo

Mariental
Helmeringhausen
Tsabong
Aranos
Molepolole
Mochudi
Gaborone
Kanye
Lobatse
Serowe
Palapye
Mahalapye
Shoshong

SOUTH AFRICA
Pietersburg
Potgietersrus
Nylstroom
Warmbad
Lydenburg
Xai-Xai
Messina
Louis
Trichardt
Tzaneen
Nelspruit
Rustenburg
Pretoria
Johannesburg
Springs
Klerksdorp
Potchefstroom
Heilbron
Parys
Vryburg
Taung
Kuruman
Odendaalsrus
Kroonstad
Welkom
Harrismith
Warrenton
Kimberley
Bloemfontein
Griquatown
Prieska

MAPUTO
SWAZILAND
Mbabane
Manzini
Barberton
Delagoa Bay
Volksrust
Vryheid
Dundee
Ladysmith
LESOTHO
Maseru
Stanger
Pinetown
Durban
Pietermaritzburg
Matatiele
Kokstad
Margate
Kirkwood
Port Alfred
Grahamstown
East London
Stutterheim
Umtata

MADAGASCAR
Antseranana
Mitsio
Be
Ambanja
Maromokotro 2876 m
Analalava
Antalaha
Mahajanga
Marovoay
Andriba
Ambatondrazaka
Toamasina
Maintirano
Antananarivo
Moramanga
Ambatolampy
Antsirabe
Tsiafajavona 2643 m
Maevatanana
Morondava
Malaimbandy
Ambositra
Manja
Morombe
Mananjary
Boby Peak 2658 m
Fianarantsoa
Ihosy
Manakara
Bekily
Trafonomby 1957 m
Tolanaro
Ambovombe
Cape Sainte-Marie
Sakaraha
Toliara

**ATLANTIC
OCEAN**

Population
- ■ Over 1 000 000
- ● 500 000 to 1 000 000
- ● 100 000 to 500 000
- ● 50 000 to 100 000
- ○ Under 50 000

Lusaka, Zambia

Durban, South Africa

Tropic of Capricorn

Kilometres
0   200   400   600

Scale 1:20 000 000
Azimuthal Equal Area Projection
© MEA

© Copyright Macmillan Education Ltd

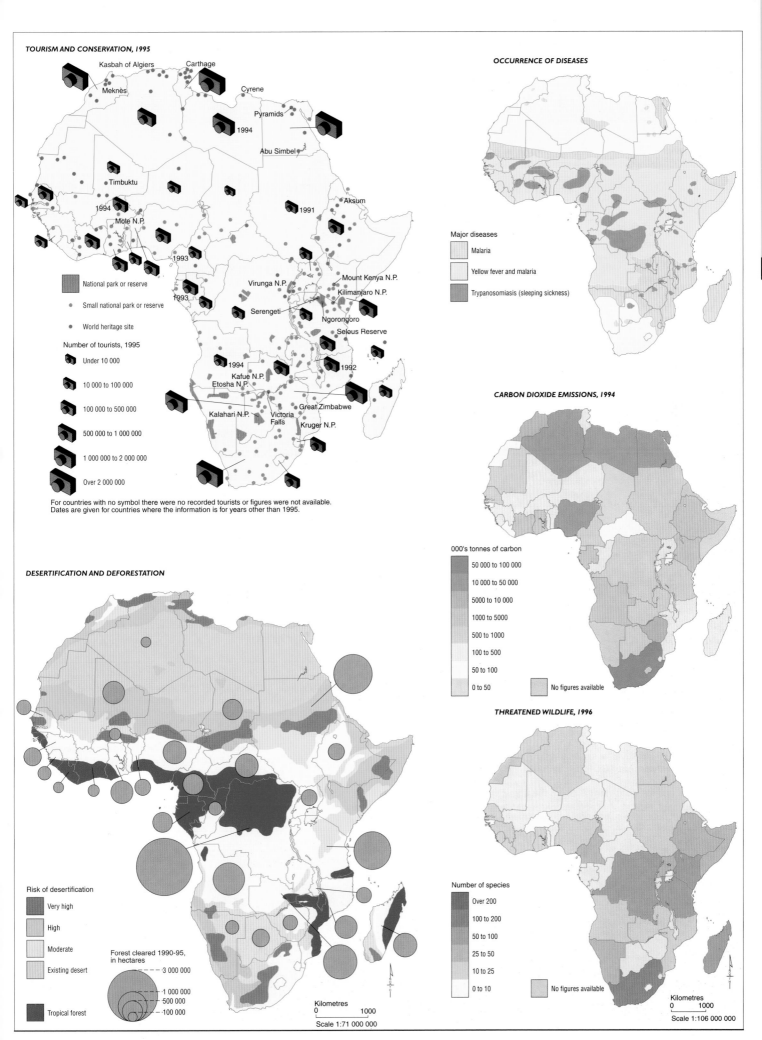

TOURISM AND CONSERVATION, 1995

Kasbah of Algiers
Carthage
Meknès
Cyrene
Pyramids
1994
Abu Simbel
Timbuktu
Aksum
1994
Mole N.P.
1991
1993
Mount Kenya N.P.
Virunga N.P.
Kilimanjaro N.P.
1993
Serengeti
Ngorongoro
Selous Reserve
1994
Kafue N.P.
1992
Etosha N.P.
Great Zimbabwe
Kalahari N.P.
Victoria Falls
Kruger N.P.

National park or reserve

Small national park or reserve

World heritage site

Number of tourists, 1995

Under 10 000

10 000 to 100 000

100 000 to 500 000

500 000 to 1 000 000

1 000 000 to 2 000 000

Over 2 000 000

For countries with no symbol there were no recorded tourists or figures were not available.
Dates are given for countries where the information is for years other than 1995.

DESERTIFICATION AND DEFORESTATION

Risk of desertification

Very high

High

Moderate

Existing desert

Forest cleared 1990-95, in hectares
3 000 000
1 000 000
500 000
100 000

Tropical forest

Kilometres
0   1000
Scale 1:71 000 000

OCCURRENCE OF DISEASES

Major diseases

Malaria

Yellow fever and malaria

Trypanosomiasis (sleeping sickness)

CARBON DIOXIDE EMISSIONS, 1994

000's tonnes of carbon

50 000 to 100 000

10 000 to 50 000

5000 to 10 000

1000 to 5000

500 to 1000

100 to 500

50 to 100

0 to 50

No figures available

THREATENED WILDLIFE, 1996

Number of species

Over 200

100 to 200

50 to 100

25 to 50

10 to 25

0 to 10

No figures available

Kilometres
0   1000
Scale 1:106 000 000

117

Kilometres
0   500   1000
Scale 1:42 000 000
Azimuthal Equal Area Projection
© MEA

Population
■ Over 1 000 000
● 500 000 to 1 000 000
• 100 000 to 500 000
• 50 000 to 100 000
○ Under 50 000

FACT FILE

Land area – Largest country China (9 572 900 km²); smallest country Maldives (298 km²). Highest point is Mt Everest in Nepal (8848 metres)
Population – China 1234.3 million (largest) and Maldives 298 000 (smallest), largest city Tokyo in Japan (23.4 million)
Life expectancy – Japan 80 years (longest); Afghanistan 43 years (shortest)
Economic development (GDP per capita) – Japan US$33 667 (richest); Nepal US$180 (poorest)
The world's largest continent – Asia is the largest continent in the world with a total land area of 43 608 000 km². It is also the world's most densely populated continent, with a total population estimated at 3513.2 million people

The Seikan tunnel – Completed in 1988, it is the longest in the world at 54 kilometres and links the two Japanese islands of Hokkaido and Honshu.
Airports – Asia's busiest – Tokyo's Haneda with 236 428 aircraft movements in 1988. Second busiest – Bangkok with 178 458 aircraft movements.
Indonesia – Comprises over 13 000 islands. Achieved independence from the Netherlands in 1947 and later embarked on a policy of confrontation against the newly formed Federation of Malaysia. More recent disputes have occurred between the Indonesian Government and the people in Irian Jaya & East Timor.
Malaysia – The Federation of Malaysia came into being in 1963, consisting of the Malay Peninsula, Singapore and the former colonies of North Borneo (Sarawak and Sabah). In 1965, **Singapore** seceded from Malaysia and is now an independent country.

The Ganges in central India is the Hindu's most sacred river

Hong Kong is a major manufacturing centre

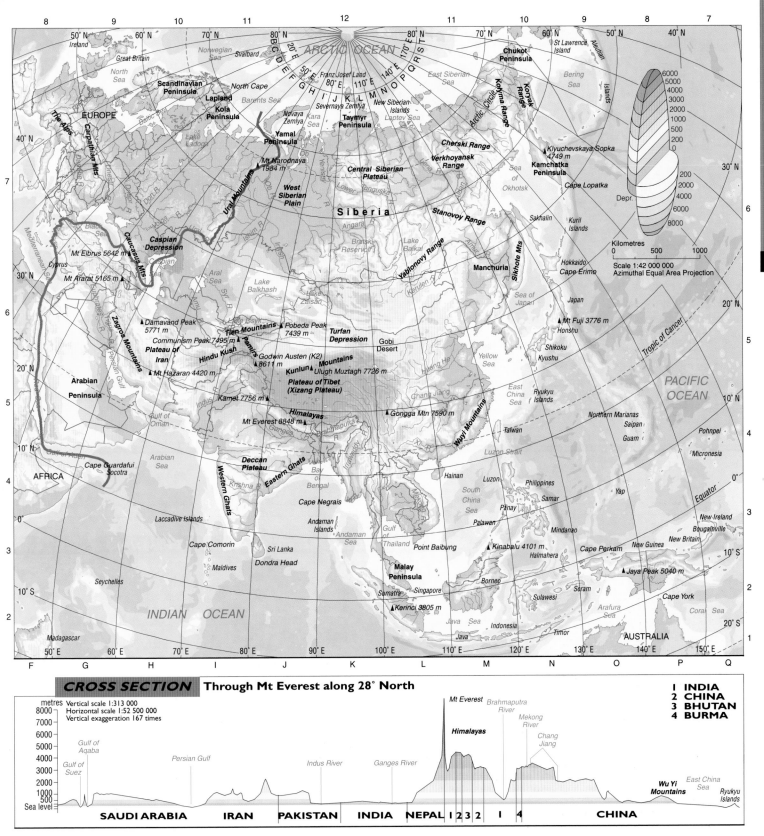

CROSS SECTION — Through Mt Everest along 28° North

metres Vertical scale 1:313 000
Horizontal scale 1:52 500 000
Vertical exaggeration 167 times

1 INDIA
2 CHINA
3 BHUTAN
4 BURMA

SAUDI ARABIA   IRAN   PAKISTAN   INDIA   NEPAL 1 2 3 2   1   4   CHINA

Mount Fuji (a dormant volcano in Japan) with a high-speed train in the foreground

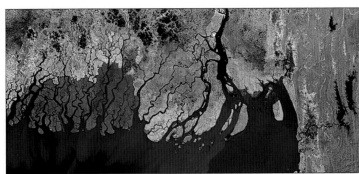

View from space of the Ganges River Delta, Bangladesh

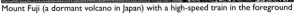

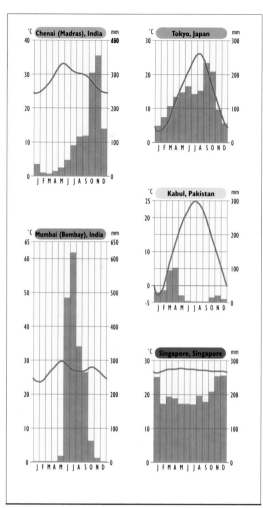

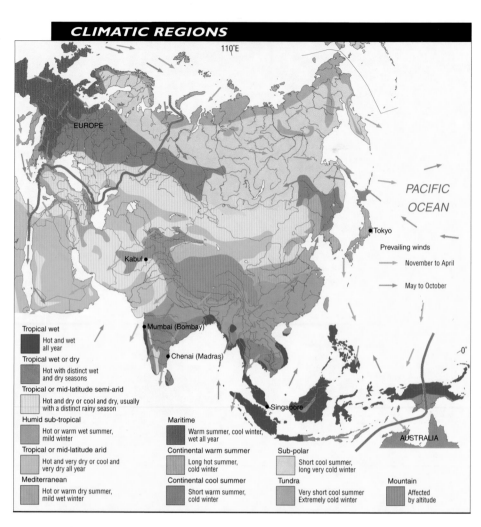

CLIMATIC REGIONS

110°E

EUROPE

PACIFIC OCEAN

Tokyo

Prevailing winds

→ November to April

→ May to October

Kabul

Mumbai (Bombay)

Chenai (Madras)

Singapore

AUSTRALIA

Tropical wet
- Hot and wet all year

Tropical wet or dry
- Hot with distinct wet and dry seasons

Tropical or mid-latitude semi-arid
- Hot and dry or cool and dry, usually with a distinct rainy season

Humid sub-tropical
- Hot or warm wet summer, mild winter

Tropical or mid-latitude arid
- Hot and very dry or cool and very dry all year

Mediterranean
- Hot or warm dry summer, mild wet winter

Maritime
- Warm summer, cool winter, wet all year

Continental warm summer
- Long hot summer, cold winter

Continental cool summer
- Short warm summer, cold winter

Sub-polar
- Short cool summer, long very cold winter

Tundra
- Very short cool summer Extremely cold winter

Mountain
- Affected by altitude

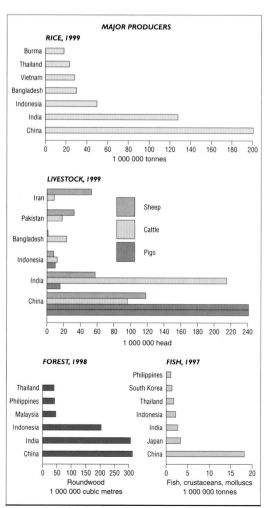

MAJOR PRODUCERS

RICE, 1999
Burma, Thailand, Vietnam, Bangladesh, Indonesia, India, China
0 20 40 60 80 100 120 140 160 180 200
1 000 000 tonnes

LIVESTOCK, 1999
Iran, Pakistan, Bangladesh, Indonesia, India, China
0 20 40 60 80 100 120 140 160 180 200 220 240
1 000 000 head

- Sheep
- Cattle
- Pigs

FOREST, 1998
Thailand, Philippines, Malaysia, Indonesia, India, China
0 50 100 150 200 250 300
Roundwood
1 000 000 cubic metres

FISH, 1997
Philippines, South Korea, Thailand, Indonesia, India, Japan, China
0 5 10 15 20
Fish, crustaceans, molluscs
1 000 000 tonnes

AGRICULTURE, FORESTRY and FISHING

110°E

EUROPE

PACIFIC OCEAN

AUSTRALIA

AGRICULTURE
- Shifting cultivation
- Subsistence – mixed crops and livestock
- Intensive – rice dominant
- Commercial – grain dominant
- Commercial – mixed crops and livestock
- Specialised – plantation and market gardening
- Extensive livestock rearing
- Intensive livestock rearing
- Dairying
- Nomadic herding
- Little or limited use

FORESTRY
- Softwood
- Mixed softwood and hardwood

COMMERCIAL FISHING
- Major
- Minor

MINERALS, ENERGY and INDUSTRY

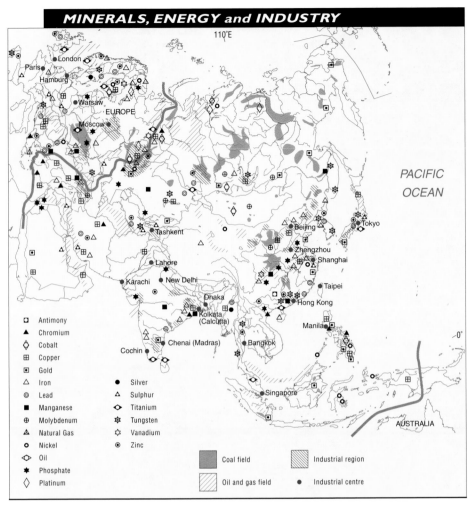

110°E

EUROPE

PACIFIC OCEAN

Paris
London
Hamburg
Warsaw
Moscow
Tashkent
Lahore
Karachi
New Delhi
Dhaka
Cochin
Chenai (Madras)
Beijing
Zhengzhou
Shanghai
Taipei
Kolkata (Calcutta)
Hong Kong
Manila
Bangkok
Singapore
Tokyo

AUSTRALIA

0°

☐ Antimony	
▲ Chromium	
◇ Cobalt	
⊞ Copper	
⊡ Gold	
△ Iron	● Silver
◎ Lead	△ Sulphur
■ Manganese	◇ Titanium
⊕ Molybdenum	✲ Tungsten
⬠ Natural Gas	✩ Vanadium
○ Nickel	⊙ Zinc
◇ Oil	
✶ Phosphate	
◇ Platinum	

▨	Coal field	▧	Industrial region
▨	Oil and gas field	●	Industrial centre

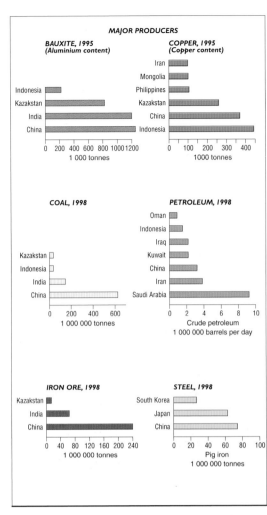

MAJOR PRODUCERS

BAUXITE, 1995
(Aluminium content)

Indonesia
Kazakstan
India
China

0 200 400 600 800 1000 1200
1 000 tonnes

COPPER, 1995
(Copper content)

Iran
Mongolia
Philippines
Kazakstan
China
Indonesia

0 100 200 300 400
1000 tonnes

COAL, 1998

Kazakstan
Indonesia
India
China

0 200 400 600
1 000 000 tonnes

PETROLEUM, 1998

Oman
Indonesia
Iraq
Kuwait
China
Iran
Saudi Arabia

0 2 4 6 8 10
Crude petroleum
1 000 000 barrels per day

IRON ORE, 1998

Kazakstan
India
China

0 40 80 120 160 200 240
1 000 000 tonnes

STEEL, 1998

South Korea
Japan
China

0 20 40 60 80 100
Pig iron
1 000 000 tonnes

POPULATION

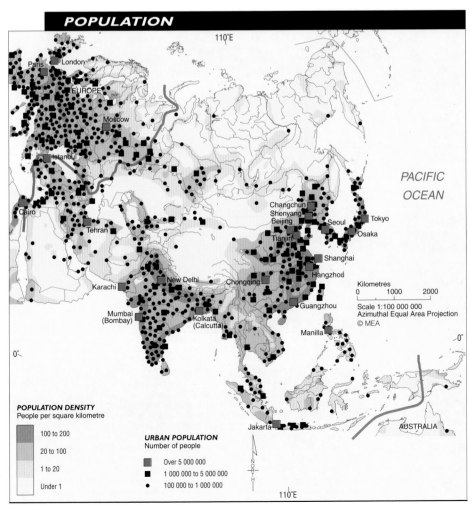

110°E

EUROPE

PACIFIC OCEAN

Paris
London
Moscow
Istanbul
Cairo
Tehran
Karachi
New Delhi
Mumbai (Bombay)
Kolkata (Calcutta)
Changchun
Shenyang
Beijing
Tianjin
Seoul
Tokyo
Osaka
Shanghai
Hangzhou
Chongqing
Guangzhou
Manila
Jakarta

Kilometres
0 1000 2000

Scale 1:100 000 000
Azimuthal Equal Area Projection
© MEA

0°

AUSTRALIA

110°E

POPULATION DENSITY
People per square kilometre

	100 to 200
	20 to 100
	1 to 20
	Under 1

URBAN POPULATION
Number of people

▪	Over 5 000 000
■	1 000 000 to 5 000 000
•	100 000 to 1 000 000

NORTH

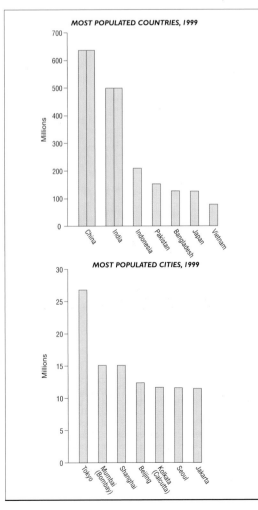

MOST POPULATED COUNTRIES, 1999

Millions
700
600
500
400
300
200
100
0

China
India
Indonesia
Pakistan
Bangladesh
Japan
Vietnam

MOST POPULATED CITIES, 1999

Millions
30
25
20
15
10
5
0

Tokyo
Mumbai (Bombay)
Shanghai
Beijing
Kolkata (Calcutta)
Seoul
Jakarta

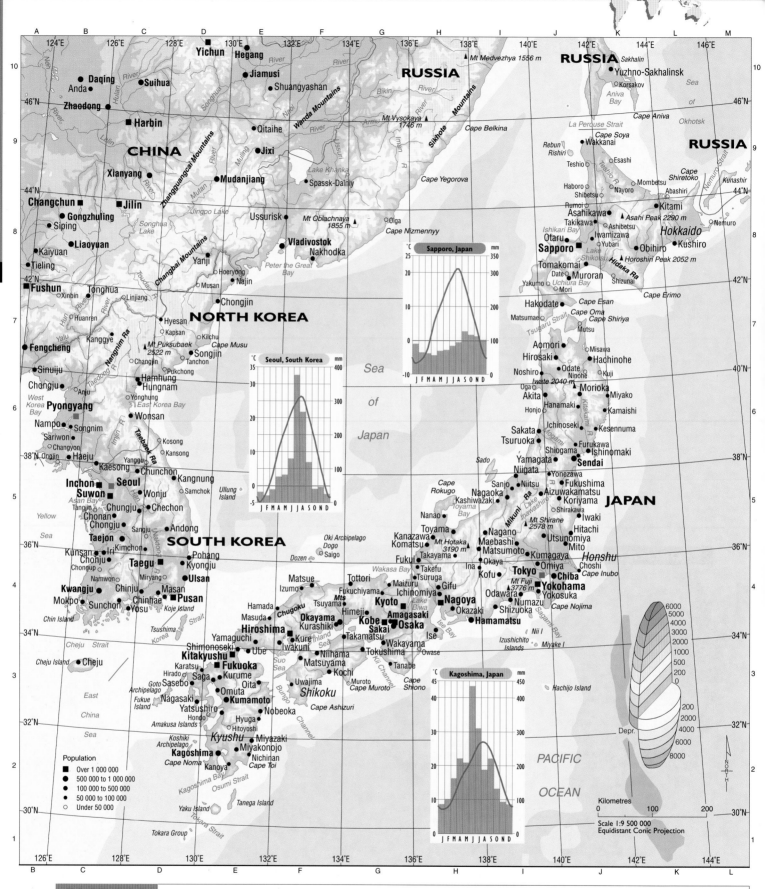

Population

- ■ Over 1 000 000
- ● 500 000 to 1 000 000
- ● 100 000 to 500 000
- • 50 000 to 100 000
- ○ Under 50 000

Scale 1:9 500 000
Equidistant Conic Projection

Kilometres
0   100   200

FACT FILE

Japan – Land area 377 727 km²; population 125.4 million; capital city Tokyo; largest cities Tokyo, Yokohama, Osaka, Nagoya, Sapporo, Kobe, Kyoto

Republic of Korea (South Korea) – Land area 99 263 km², separated from North Korea by a demilitarised zone of 1262 km²; population 45.4 million; capital city Seoul; largest cities Seoul, Pusan, Taegu, Inchon

People's Democratic Republic of Korea (North Korea) – Land area 122 762 km²; population 24.3 million; capital city Pyongyang; largest cities Pyongyang, Chongjin, Nampo, Sinuiju

Two Koreas – Following World War II Soviet forces occupied northern Korea (north of the 38th parallel) and established the pro-communist People's Democratic Republic of Korea in 1948. US forces occupied the land to the south, which became the Republic of Korea. After the Korean War (1950–53) the two countries were formally separated by a demilitarised zone at the 38th parallel.

The Industrial Giants – Japan and South Korea have both experienced phenomenal growth in their manufacturing industries. Over the past 50 years, both countries have embarked on ambitious programmes of industrialisation based on the importation of raw materials such as coal, iron ore and oil. Industry is founded on giant corporate groups of companies (known as *keiretsu* in Japan and *chaebol* in South Korea). Manufacturing in both Japan and South Korea has moved from light to heavy industry concentrated mainly in oil, petro-chemicals, iron and steel, machinery, ship-building and motor vehicles. Japan is now the world's leading producer of motor vehicles, making in excess of 16 million annually. South Korea produces more than 2 million motor vehicles annually.

CLIMATIC REGIONS

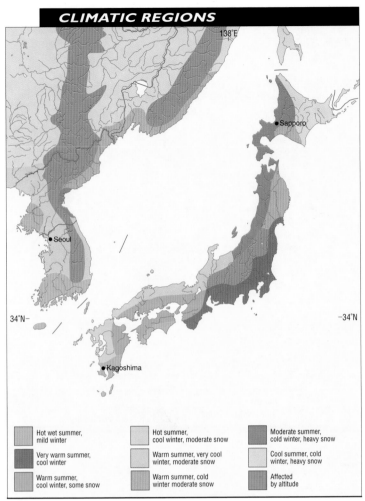

138°E

● Sapporo

● Seoul

34°N—   —34°N

● Kagoshima

	Hot wet summer, mild winter		Hot summer, cool winter, moderate snow		Moderate summer, cold winter, heavy snow
	Very warm summer, cool winter		Warm summer, very cool winter, moderate snow		Cool summer, cold winter, heavy snow
	Warm summer, cool winter, some snow		Warm summer, cold winter moderate snow		Affected by altitude

MINERALS, ENERGY and INDUSTRY

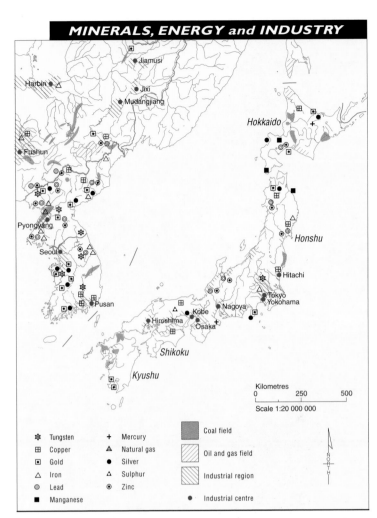

● Jiamusi

Harbin ●   ● Jixi

● Mudangjiang

Hokkaido

● Fushun

Honshu

Pyongyang

● Hitachi

Seoul

Tokyo
Yokohama

● Pusan   Kobe   Nagoya

Hiroshima   Osaka

Shikoku

Kyushu

Kilometres
0   250   500
Scale 1:20 000 000

	Tungsten	+	Mercury		Coal field
⊞	Copper	△	Natural gas		Oil and gas field
⊡	Gold	●	Silver		
△	Iron	△	Sulphur		Industrial region
◎	Lead	⊙	Zinc		
■	Manganese			●	Industrial centre

NORTH

AGRICULTURE, FORESTRY and FISHING

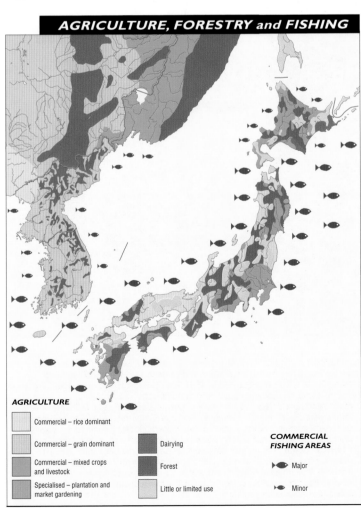

AGRICULTURE

	Commercial – rice dominant				
	Commercial – grain dominant		Dairying		**COMMERCIAL FISHING AREAS**
	Commercial – mixed crops and livestock		Forest		Major
	Specialised – plantation and market gardening		Little or limited use		Minor

POPULATION

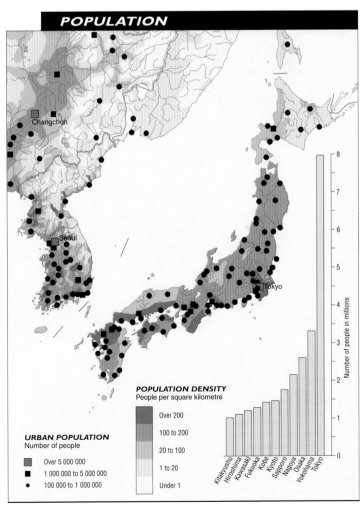

Changchun

Seoul

Tokyo

POPULATION DENSITY
People per square kilometre

	Over 200
	100 to 200
	20 to 100
	1 to 20
	Under 1

URBAN POPULATION
Number of people

	Over 5 000 000
■	1 000 000 to 5 000 000
●	100 000 to 1 000 000

Number of people in millions

8
7
6
5
4
3
2
1
0

Kitakyushu
Hiroshima
Kawasaki
Fukuoka
Kobe
Kyoto
Sapporo
Nagoya
Osaka
Yokohama
Tokyo

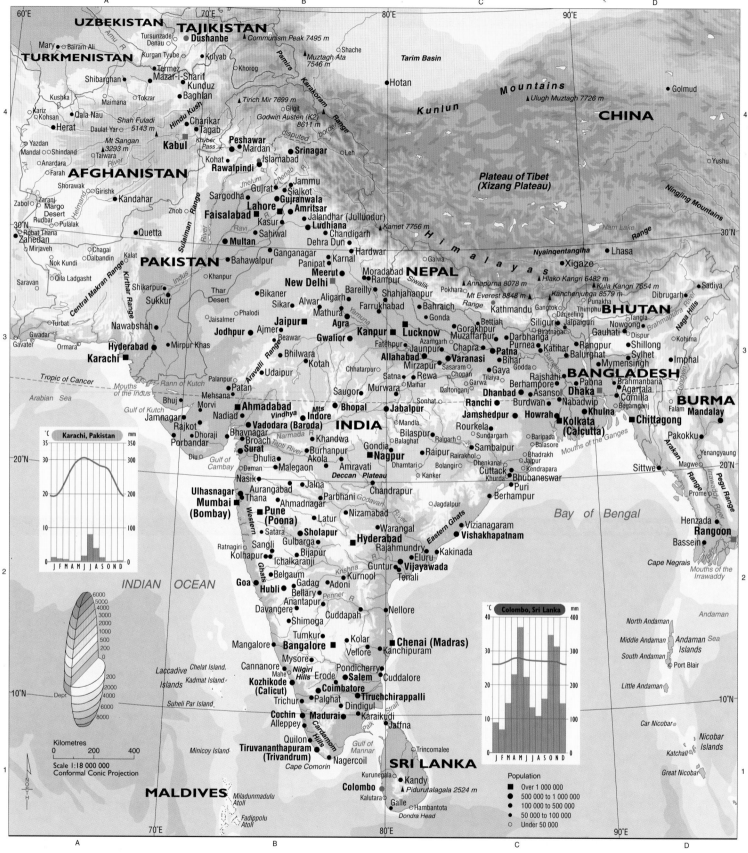

124

FACT FILE

Afghanistan – Land area 652 225 km²; population 21.9 million; capital city Kabul; largest cities Kabul, Kandahar, Herat and Mazar-i-Sharif; main exports sheepskins, cotton, dried fruit and nuts, fresh fruit and natural gas. Clashes with Pakistan and a long period of civil war led to Soviet troops occupying the country from 1979 till 1988. After continued civil war, the Muslim extremist Taliban militia seized control of the country and established an Islamic state.

Bangladesh – Land area 148 393 km²; population 123.1 million; capital city Dhaka; largest cities Dhaka, Chittagong, Khulna and Rajshahi; main exports jute, tea, hides and skins, newsprint, fish and clothing. Bangladesh, formerly known as East Pakistan, became independent in 1971.

Pakistan – Land area 796 095 km²; population 144.5 million; capital city Islamabad; largest cities Karachi, Lahore, Faisalabad, Rawalpindi; main exports raw cotton, cotton cloth, rice, leather and carpets. Indian Muslims wanted independence which was granted in 1947 with the formation of East and West Pakistan – later to become Bangladesh and Pakistan.

India – Land area 3 165 596 km²; population 953 million; capital city New Delhi; largest cities Mumbai (Bombay), Kolkata (Calcutta), Delhi, Chenai (Madras) and Hyderabad; main exports gems and jewellery, clothing, engineering goods, cotton and tea. India was under British rule but gained its independence in 1947.

Sri Lanka – Land area 65 609 km²; population 18.6 million; capital city Colombo; largest cities Colombo, Jaffna and Kandy; main exports tea, rubber and coconut products. Formerly known as Ceylon, it became independent in 1948 and was renamed Sri Lanka in 1972. Civil unrest still exists between the Tamils and the Sinhalese.

CLIMATIC REGIONS

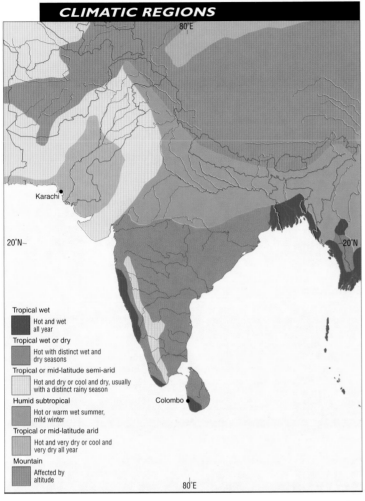

80°E

Karachi

20°N

20°N

Colombo

Tropical wet

Hot and wet
all year

Tropical wet or dry

Hot with distinct wet and
dry seasons

Tropical or mid-latitude semi-arid

Hot and dry or cool and dry, usually
with a distinct rainy season

Humid subtropical

Hot or warm wet summer,
mild winter

Tropical or mid-latitude arid

Hot and very dry or cool and
very dry all year

Mountain

Affected by
altitude

80°E

MINERALS, ENERGY and INDUSTRY

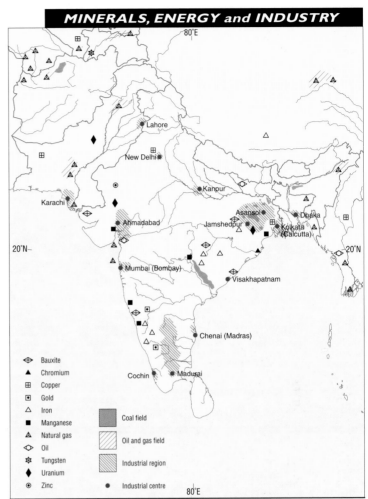

80°E

Lahore

New Delhi

Kanpur

Karachi

Ahmadabad   Asansol

Jamshedpur   Kolkata
(Calcutta)   Dhaka

20°N   20°N

Mumbai (Bombay)

Visakhapatnam

Chenai (Madras)

Cochin   Madurai

⬨	Bauxite		
▲	Chromium		
⊞	Copper		
⊡	Gold		
△	Iron		Coal field
■	Manganese		
⬠	Natural gas		Oil and gas field
⬦	Oil		
✳	Tungsten		Industrial region
◆	Uranium		
⊙	Zinc	●	Industrial centre

80°E

AGRICULTURE, FORESTRY and FISHING

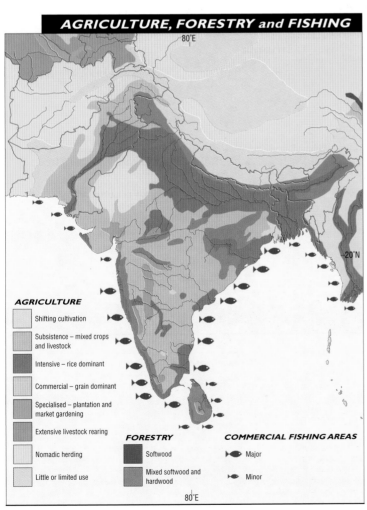

80°E

20°N

AGRICULTURE

Shifting cultivation

Subsistence – mixed crops
and livestock

Intensive – rice dominant

Commercial – grain dominant

Specialised – plantation and
market gardening

Extensive livestock rearing

Nomadic herding

Little or limited use

FORESTRY

Softwood

Mixed softwood and
hardwood

COMMERCIAL FISHING AREAS

Major

Minor

80°E

POPULATION

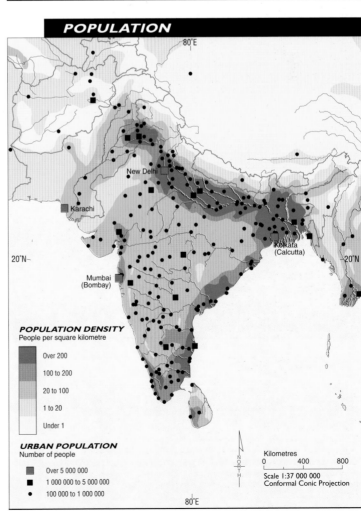

80°E

New Delhi

Karachi

20°N   20°N

Kolkata
(Calcutta)

Mumbai
(Bombay)

POPULATION DENSITY
People per square kilometre

Over 200

100 to 200

20 to 100

1 to 20

Under 1

URBAN POPULATION
Number of people

Over 5 000 000

1 000 000 to 5 000 000

100 000 to 1 000 000

Kilometres
0   400   800

Scale 1:37 000 000
Conformal Conic Projection

80°E

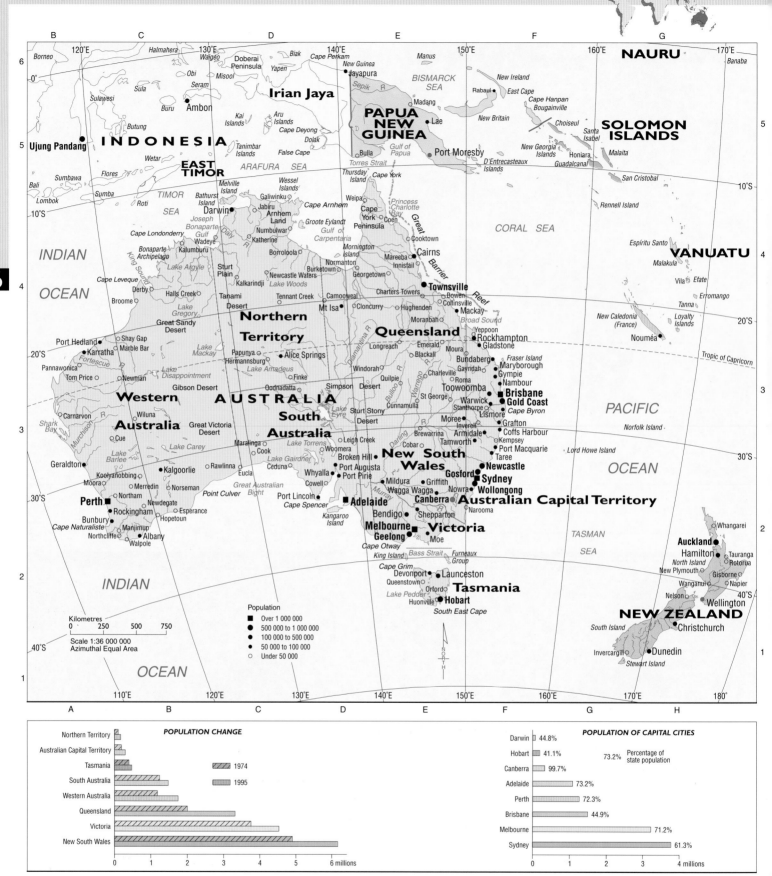

POPULATION CHANGE

1974
1995

Northern Territory
Australian Capital Territory
Tasmania
South Australia
Western Australia
Queensland
Victoria
New South Wales

0   1   2   3   4   5   6 millions

POPULATION OF CAPITAL CITIES

73.2% Percentage of state population

Darwin 44.8%
Hobart 41.1%
Canberra 99.7%
Adelaide 73.2%
Perth 72.3%
Brisbane 44.9%
Melbourne 71.2%
Sydney 61.3%

0   1   2   3   4 millions

FACT FILE

Land area – Largest country Australia (7 682 300 km²); smallest Nauru (21 km²).
Highest point is Mt Wilhelm (4509 m) in Papua New Guinea.
Population – Australia 18.2 million (largest); Nauru 9000 (smallest).
Largest city Sydney in Australia 3.7 million.
Life expectancy – Australia 78 years (longest); Papua New Guinea 56 years (shortest)
Economic development (GDP per capita) – Australia US$16 444 (richest);
Solomon Islands US$800 (poorest).

PERCENTAGE OF AUSTRALIAN POPULATION, 1995

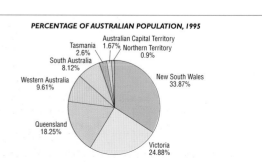

Tasmania 2.6%
Australian Capital Territory 1.67%
Northern Territory 0.9%
South Australia 8.12%
Western Australia 9.61%
New South Wales 33.87%
Queensland 18.25%
Victoria 24.88%

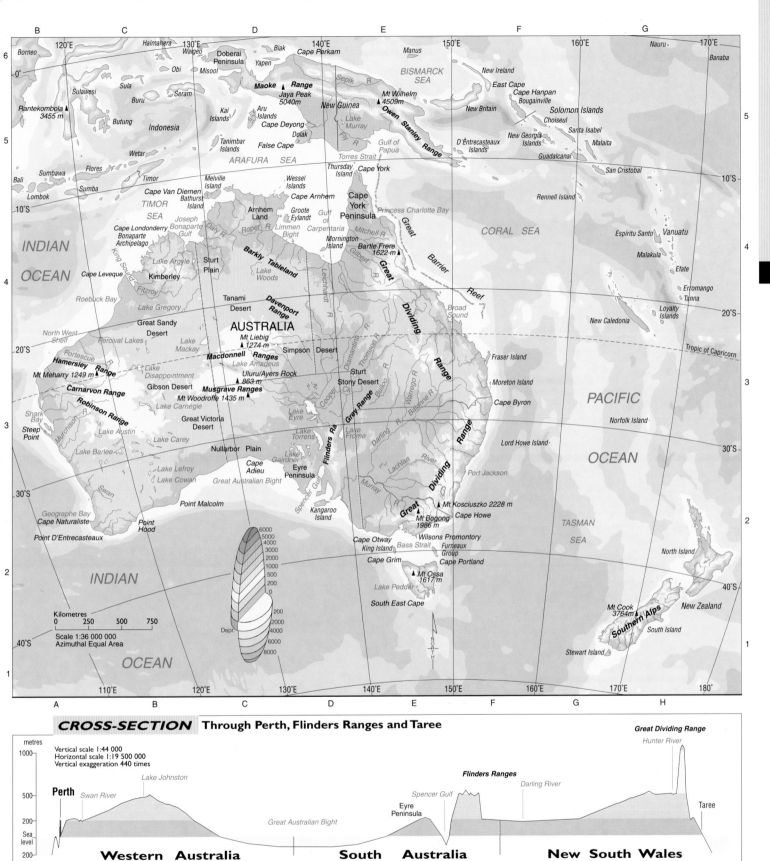

B 120°E C 130°E D 140°E E 150°E F 160°E G 170°E

Borneo
Halmahera
Biak
Cape Perkam
Manus
Nauru
Banaba
Obi
Walgeo
Doberai Peninsula
Yapen
BISMARCK SEA
New Ireland
East Cape
Sulawesi
Sula
Misool
Maoke Range
Jaya Peak 5040m
New Guinea
Sepik R.
Mt Wilhelm ▲4509m
Cape Hanpan
Bougainville
Rantekombola ▲ 3455 m
Buru
Seram
Kai Islands
Aru Islands
Cape Deyong
Lake Murray
Owen Stanley Range
New Britain
Solomon Islands
Choiseul
Indonesia
Butung
Tanimbar Islands
Dolak
Fly R.
Gulf of Papua
D'Entrecasteaux Islands
New Georgia Islands
Santa Isabel
Malaita
Wetar
False Cape
Guadalcanal
Bali
Sumbawa
Flores
Timor
ARAFURA SEA
Torres Strait
Thursday Island
Cape York
San Cristobal
Lombok
Sumba
Melville Island
Wessel Islands
Cape Arnhem
Cape York Peninsula
Princess Charlotte Bay
Rennell Island
10°S
Cape Van Diemen
Bathurst Island
TIMOR SEA
Arnhem Land
Groote Eylandt
Gulf of Carpentaria
Great
CORAL SEA
Espíritu Santo
Vanuatu
INDIAN OCEAN
Cape Londonderry
Joseph Bonaparte Gulf
Daly R.
Roper R.
Limmen Bight
Mornington Island
Mitchell R.
Bartle Frere 1622 m ▲
Barrier
Malakula
Efate
Bonaparte Archipelago
King Sound
Lake Argyle
Barkly Tableland
Gilbert R.
Great
Erromango
Tanna
Cape Leveque
Kimberley
Fitzroy
Sturt Plain
Lake Woods
Leichhardt R.
Dividing
Reef
Broad Sound
New Caledonia
Loyalty Islands
Roebuck Bay
Lake Gregory
Tanami Desert
Davenport Range
Tropic of Capricorn
North West Shelf
Great Sandy Desert
AUSTRALIA
Mt Liebig ▲1274 m
Simpson Desert
Diamantina R.
Range
Thomson R.
Fraser Island
Fortescue
Percival Lakes
Lake Mackay
Macdonnell Ranges
Lake Amadeus
Uluru/Ayers Rock ▲863 m
Sturt Stony Desert
Barcoo R.
Warrego R.
Balonne R.
Moreton Island
Hamersley Range
Mt Meharry 1249 m
Lake Disappointment
Gibson Desert
Mt Woodroffe 1435 m
Musgrave Ranges
Cooper Ck.
Grey Range
Darling R.
Cape Byron
PACIFIC
Carnarvon Range
Lake Carnegie
Great Victoria Desert
Lake Eyre
Cape Byron
Norfolk Island
Robinson Range
Murchison
Lake Austin
Lake Carey
Lake Torrens
Lake Frome
Lachlan River
Lord Howe Island
OCEAN
Shark Bay
Steep Point
Lake Barlee
Nullarbor Plain
Lake Gairdner
Flinders Ra.
Murray
Port Jackson
Lake Lefroy
Lake Cowan
Cape Adieu
Great Australian Bight
Eyre Peninsula
Spencer Gulf
TASMAN SEA
Geographe Bay
Cape Naturaliste
Point Hood
Point Malcolm
Kangaroo Island
Great Dividing Range
Mt Kosciuszko 2228 m ▲
Mt Bogong ▲ 1986 m
Cape Howe
North Island
Point D'Entrecasteaux
Swan R.
Cape Otway
King Island
Bass Strait
Wilsons Promontory
Furneaux Group
Cape Portland
INDIAN
Cape Grim
Mt Ossa ▲ 1617 m
Lake Pedder
South East Cape
Mt Cook 3764m ▲
Southern Alps
South Island
New Zealand
OCEAN
Stewart Island

Kilometres
0 250 500 750
Scale 1:36 000 000
Azimuthal Equal Area

6000 5000 4000 3000 2000 1000 500 200 0
200 2000 4000 6000 8000
Depr.

CROSS-SECTION Through Perth, Flinders Ranges and Taree

metres
1000
500
200
Sea level
200

Vertical scale 1:44 000
Horizontal scale 1:19 500 000
Vertical exaggeration 440 times

Perth
Swan River
Lake Johnston
Great Australian Bight
Eyre Peninsula
Spencer Gulf
Flinders Ranges
Darling River
Great Dividing Range
Hunter River
Taree

Western Australia   **South Australia**   **New South Wales**

Sydney, the business capital and largest city in Australia

Uluru/Ayers Rock, the world's largest monolith, Australia

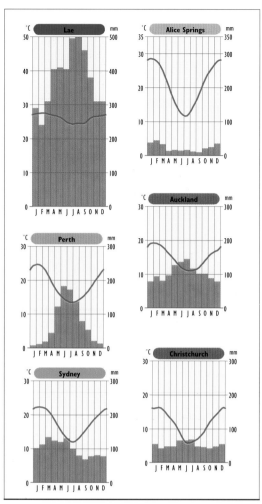

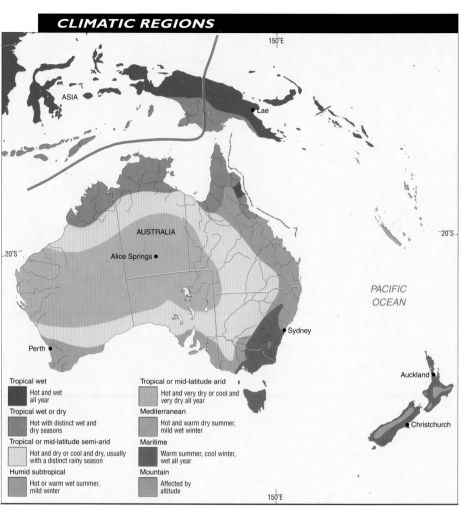

CLIMATIC REGIONS

Tropical wet
Hot and wet all year

Tropical wet or dry
Hot with distinct wet and dry seasons

Tropical or mid-latitude semi-arid
Hot and dry or cool and dry, usually with a distinct rainy season

Humid subtropical
Hot or warm wet summer, mild winter

Tropical or mid-latitude arid
Hot and very dry or cool and very dry all year

Mediterranean
Hot and warm dry summer, mild wet winter

Maritime
Warm summer, cool winter, wet all year

Mountain
Affected by altitude

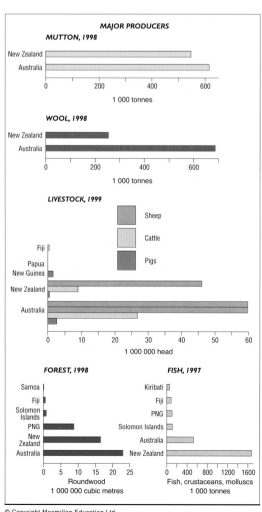

MAJOR PRODUCERS

MUTTON, 1998

WOOL, 1998

LIVESTOCK, 1999
- Sheep
- Cattle
- Pigs

FOREST, 1998
Roundwood
1 000 000 cubic metres

FISH, 1997
Fish, crustaceans, molluscs
1 000 tonnes

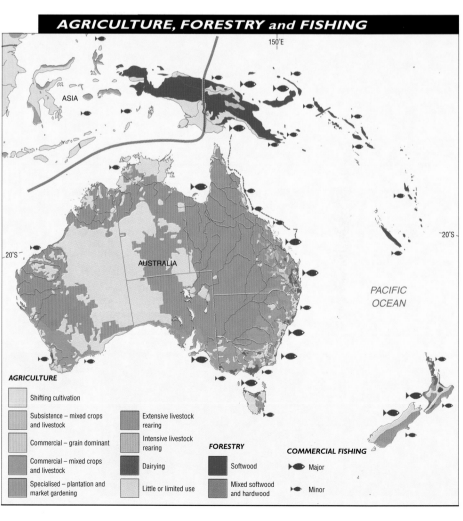

AGRICULTURE, FORESTRY and FISHING

AGRICULTURE

Shifting cultivation

Subsistence – mixed crops and livestock

Commercial – grain dominant

Commercial – mixed crops and livestock

Specialised – plantation and market gardening

Extensive livestock rearing

Intensive livestock rearing

Dairying

Little or limited use

FORESTRY

Softwood

Mixed softwood and hardwood

COMMERCIAL FISHING

Major

Minor

© Copyright Macmillan Education Ltd

MINERALS, ENERGY and INDUSTRY

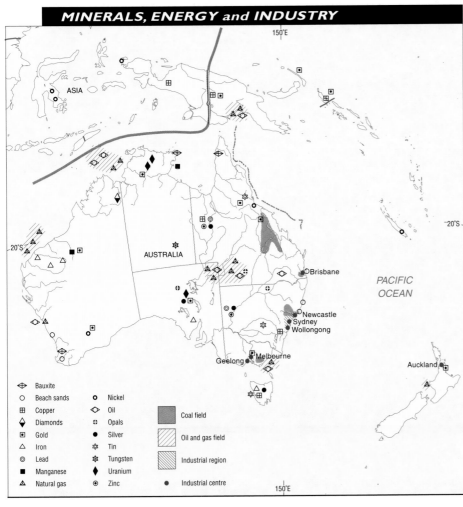

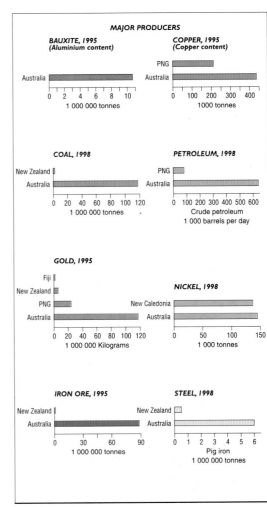

MAJOR PRODUCERS

POPULATION

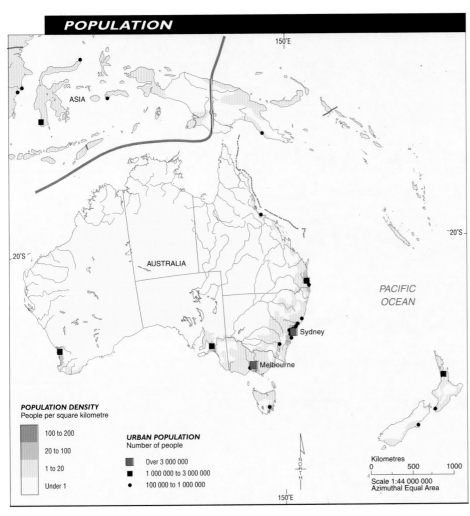

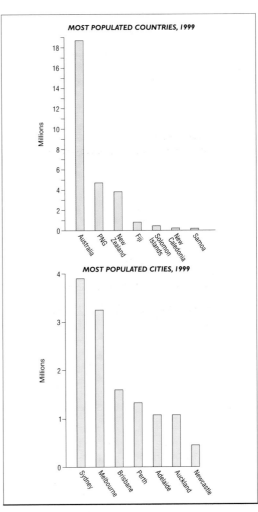

ARCTIC

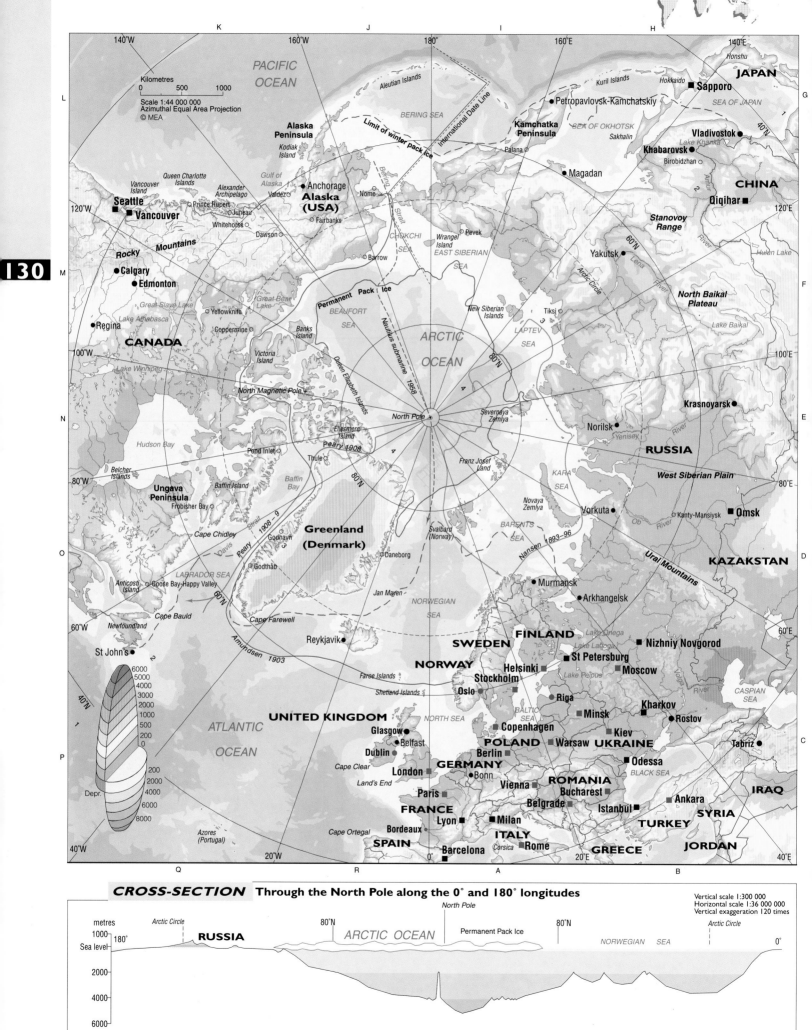

130

PACIFIC OCEAN

Kilometres
0   500   1000
Scale 1:44 000 000
Azimuthal Equal Area Projection
© MEA

140°W   160°W   180°   160°E   140°E

Aleutian Islands
Limit of winter pack ice
International Date Line
BERING SEA
SEA OF OKHOTSK
Kuril Islands   Hokkaido   Sapporo   JAPAN
Honshu
Petropavlovsk-Kamchatskiy
Kamchatka Peninsula
Palana   Sakhalin   SEA OF JAPAN
Vladivostok
Magadan   Khabarovsk   Lake Khanka   40°N
Birobidzhan   120°E

Alaska Peninsula
Kodiak Island
Gulf of Alaska   Anchorage   Alaska (USA)   Nome   Bering Strait
Valdez   Fairbanks
CHUKCHI SEA   Wrangel Island   Pevek
Barrow   EAST SIBERIAN SEA   Tiksi
CHINA
Qiqihar
Stanovoy Range
Yakutsk   60°N   North Baikal Plateau

Vancouver Island
Queen Charlotte Islands   Alexander Archipelago
Prince Rupert   Juneau   Whitehorse   Dawson
Seattle   120°W
Vancouver

Rocky   Mountains
Calgary
Edmonton
Regina   Lake Athabasca
CANADA   100°W

Great Slave Lake   Yellowknife   Great Bear Lake   Coppermine
Banks Island
Victoria Island
BEAUFORT SEA   Permanent   Pack   Ice
Nautilus submarine 1958
North Magnetic Pole
Queen Elizabeth Islands   ARCTIC OCEAN   80°N   LAPTEV SEA
New Siberian Islands   Arctic Circle
Norilsk   Krasnoyarsk
RUSSIA   100°E
Yenisey River   West Siberian Plain   80°E
Severnaya Zemlya
North Pole   Franz Josef Land   KARA SEA   Ob River   Kanty-Mansiysk   Omsk
Vorkuta
Novaya Zemlya   Ural Mountains   KAZAKSTAN   60°E

Hudson Bay   Pond Inlet   Ellesmere Island   Peary 1908
Thule   80°N
Baffin Bay   BARENTS SEA   Nansen 1893-96
Belcher Islands   Baffin Island
Ungava Peninsula   Frobisher Bay
Cape Chidley   Peary 1908-9
Godhavn   Greenland (Denmark)   Svalbard (Norway)   Daneborg
Davis Strait   Godthåb
LABRADOR SEA   Jan Mayen   NORWEGIAN SEA
Anticosti Island   Goose Bay-Happy Valley   60°N   Murmansk   Arkhangelsk
Cape Bauld   Cape Farewell   FINLAND   Lake Onega   60°E
60°W   Newfoundland   Reykjavik   SWEDEN   Lake Ladoga   Nizhniy Novgorod
St John's   NORWAY   Helsinki   St Petersburg
Stockholm   Lake Peipus   Moscow   Volga River
Oslo   Riga   Kharkov   CASPIAN SEA
40°N   Faroe Islands   BALTIC SEA   Minsk   Rostov
Shetland Islands   Denmark   Kiev   Tabriz
ATLANTIC OCEAN   UNITED KINGDOM   NORTH SEA   Copenhagen   Warsaw   UKRAINE
Glasgow   POLAND   Odessa   40°E
Belfast   Berlin   BLACK SEA
Dublin   London   GERMANY   Vienna   ROMANIA
Cape Clear   Bonn   Bucharest   Ankara   IRAQ
Land's End   Paris   Belgrade   Istanbul   SYRIA
FRANCE   Lyon   Milan   TURKEY   JORDAN
Bordeaux   ITALY   Rome   GREECE
Azores (Portugal)   SPAIN   Corsica   40°E
Cape Ortegal   Barcelona   0°   20°E

6000 5000 4000 3000 2000 1000 500 200 0
Depr. 200 2000 4000 6000 8000

CROSS-SECTION Through the North Pole along the 0° and 180° longitudes

Vertical scale 1:300 000
Horizontal scale 1:36 000 000
Vertical exaggeration 120 times

metres
1000   180°   Arctic Circle   80°N   North Pole   80°N   Arctic Circle   0°
Sea level   RUSSIA   ARCTIC OCEAN   Permanent Pack Ice   NORWEGIAN SEA
2000
4000
6000

© Copyright Macmillan Education Ltd

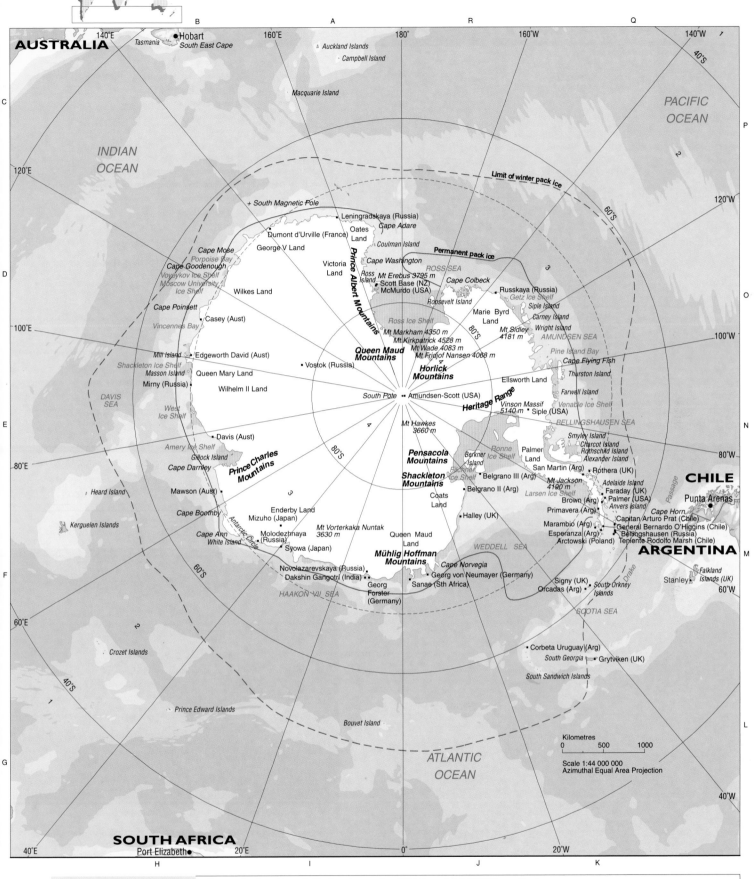

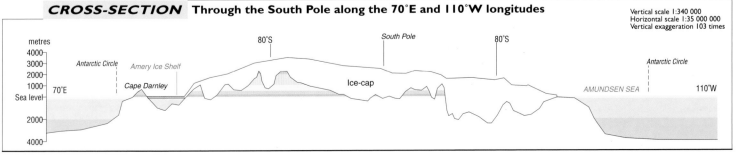

CROSS-SECTION Through the South Pole along the 70°E and 110°W longitudes

Vertical scale 1:340 000
Horizontal scale 1:35 000 000
Vertical exaggeration 103 times

FORESTRY IN CANADA

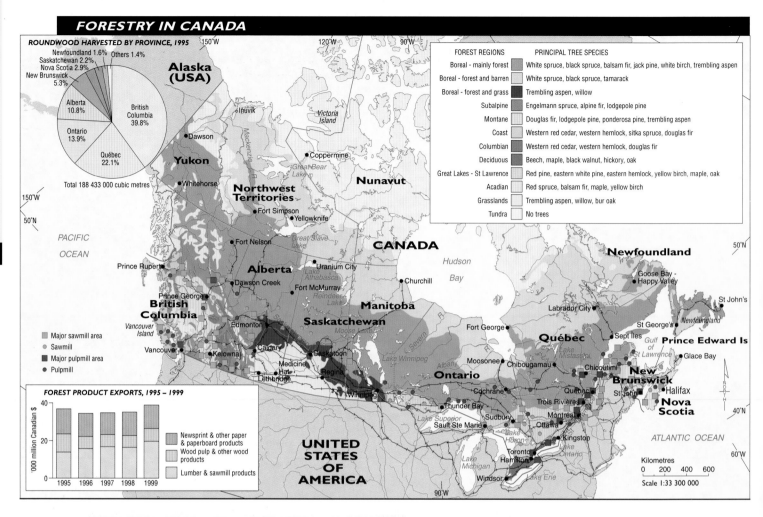

ROUNDWOOD HARVESTED BY PROVINCE, 1995

- Newfoundland 1.6%
- Saskatchewan 2.2%
- Nova Scotia 2.9%
- New Brunswick 5.3%
- Others 1.4%
- Alberta 10.8%
- British Columbia 39.8%
- Ontario 13.9%
- Québec 22.1%

Total 188 433 000 cubic metres

FOREST REGIONS		PRINCIPAL TREE SPECIES
Boreal – mainly forest		White spruce, black spruce, balsam fir, jack pine, white birch, trembling aspen
Boreal – forest and barren		White spruce, black spruce, tamarack
Boreal – forest and grass		Trembling aspen, willow
Subalpine		Engelmann spruce, alpine fir, lodgepole pine
Montane		Douglas fir, lodgepole pine, ponderosa pine, trembling aspen
Coast		Western red cedar, western hemlock, sitka spruce, douglas fir
Columbian		Western red cedar, western hemlock, douglas fir
Deciduous		Beech, maple, black walnut, hickory, oak
Great Lakes – St Lawrence		Red pine, eastern white pine, eastern hemlock, yellow birch, maple, oak
Acadian		Red spruce, balsam fir, maple, yellow birch
Grasslands		Trembling aspen, willow, bur oak
Tundra		No trees

- ■ Major sawmill area
- ● Sawmill
- ■ Major pulpmill area
- ● Pulpmill

FOREST PRODUCT EXPORTS, 1995 – 1999

'000 million Canadian $ (y-axis: 0, 20, 40)

Years: 1995, 1996, 1997, 1998, 1999

- Newsprint & other paper & paperboard products
- Wood pulp & other wood products
- Lumber & sawmill products

Kilometres
0 200 400 600
Scale 1:33 300 000

FISHING IN BRITISH COLUMBIA

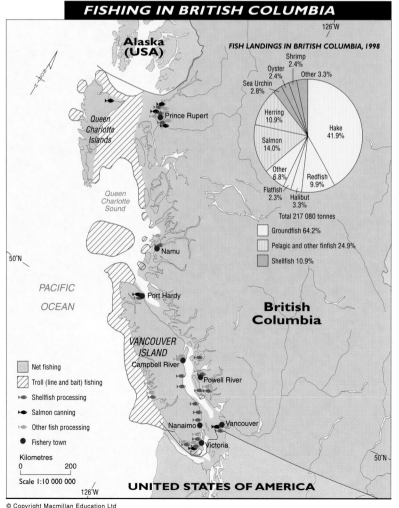

FISH LANDINGS IN BRITISH COLUMBIA, 1998

- Shrimp 2.4%
- Oyster 2.4%
- Other 3.3%
- Sea Urchin 2.8%
- Herring 10.9%
- Hake 41.9%
- Salmon 14.0%
- Other 6.8%
- Redfish 9.9%
- Flatfish 2.3%
- Halibut 3.3%

Total 217 080 tonnes

- Groundfish 64.2%
- Pelagic and other finfish 24.9%
- Shellfish 10.9%

- ▨ Net fishing
- ▧ Troll (line and bait) fishing
- Shellfish processing
- Salmon canning
- Other fish processing
- ● Fishery town

Kilometres
0 200
Scale 1:10 000 000

A pulp and paper mill on Vancouver Island, British Columbia

FISH LANDINGS IN BRITISH COLUMBIA, 1994 – 1998

Weight ('000 tonnes) (left y-axis: 0, 100, 200, 300)
Value (million Canadian $) (right y-axis: 100, 200, 300, 400, 500, 600)
Years: 1994, 1995, 1996, 1997, 1998

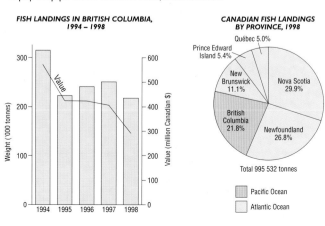

CANADIAN FISH LANDINGS BY PROVINCE, 1998

- Québec 5.0%
- Prince Edward Island 5.4%
- New Brunswick 11.1%
- British Columbia 21.8%
- Nova Scotia 29.9%
- Newfoundland 26.8%

Total 995 532 tonnes

- Pacific Ocean
- Atlantic Ocean

AREA HARVESTED AND PRODUCTION OF MAJOR ARABLE CROPS IN CANADA, 1999

Area harvested ('000 hectares)   Production ('000 tonnes)

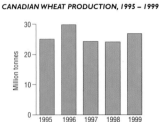
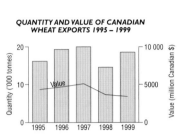

Flaxseed
Soybeans
Oats
Canola
Corn
Barley
Wheat

10 000 7500 5000 2500 0   0 10 000 20 000 30 000

CANADIAN WHEAT PRODUCTION, 1995 – 1999

Million tonnes

30 ─
20 ─
10 ─
0 ─
1995 1996 1997 1998 1999

QUANTITY AND VALUE OF CANADIAN WHEAT EXPORTS 1995 – 1999

Quantity ('000 tonnes)   Value (million Canadian $)

20 ─   ─ 10 000
                Value
10 ─   ─ 5000
0 ─   ─ 0
1995 1996 1997 1998 1999

MAJOR AGRICULTURAL AREAS

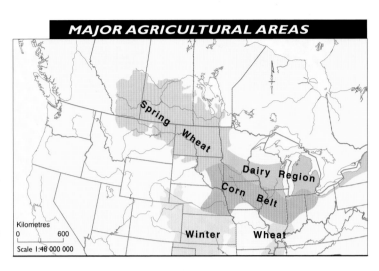

Spring Wheat

Dairy Region

Corn Belt

Winter Wheat

Kilometres
0 ────── 600
Scale 1:48 000 000

133

GREAT PLAINS AND MID WEST REGION

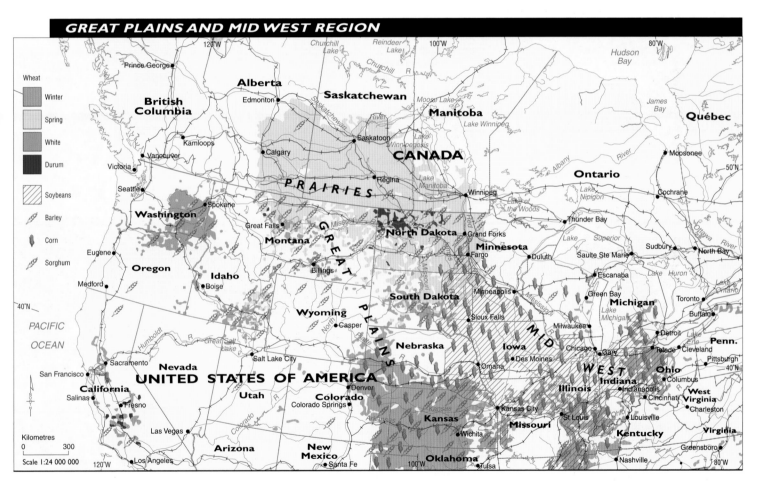

Wheat
- Winter
- Spring
- White
- Durum

Soybeans
Barley
Corn
Sorghum

Kilometres
0 ────── 300
Scale 1:24 000 000

PRODUCTION OF MAJOR ARABLE CROPS IN THE USA, 1999

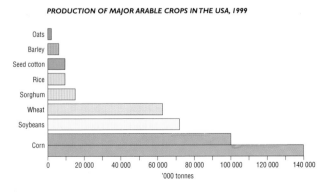

Oats
Barley
Seed cotton
Rice
Sorghum
Wheat
Soybeans
Corn

0 20 000 40 000 60 000 80 000 100 000 120 000 140 000
'000 tonnes

MAJOR WHEAT PRODUCERS, 1999

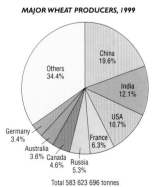

China 19.6%
India 12.1%
USA 10.7%
France 6.3%
Russia 5.3%
Canada 4.6%
Australia 3.6%
Germany 3.4%
Others 34.4%

Total 583 623 696 tonnes

MAJOR WHEAT AND WHEAT FLOUR EXPORTERS, 1998

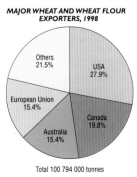

USA 27.9%
Canada 19.8%
Australia 15.4%
European Union 15.4%
Others 21.5%

Total 100 794 000 tonnes

USA Commercial Pastoral Agriculture

FARM RECEIPTS BY ACTIVITY, 1997

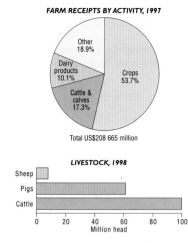

- Other 18.9%
- Crops 53.7%
- Cattle & calves 17.3%
- Dairy products 10.1%

Total US$208 665 million

LIVESTOCK, 1998

- Sheep
- Pigs
- Cattle

Million head (0 20 40 60 80 100)

NUMBER OF BEEF AND MILK COWS BY STATE, 1999

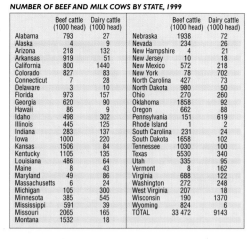

	Beef cattle (1000 head)	Dairy cattle (1000 head)		Beef cattle (1000 head)	Dairy cattle (1000 head)
Alabama	793	27	Nebraska	1938	72
Alaska	4	9	Nevada	234	26
Arizona	218	132	New Hampshire	4	21
Arkansas	919	51	New Jersey	10	18
California	800	1440	New Mexico	572	218
Colorado	827	83	New York	78	702
Connecticut	7	28	North Carolina	427	73
Delaware	3	10	North Dakota	980	50
Florida	973	157	Ohio	270	260
Georgia	620	90	Oklahoma	1858	92
Hawaii	86	9	Oregon	662	88
Idaho	498	302	Pennsylvania	151	619
Illinois	445	125	Rhode Island	1	2
Indiana	283	137	South Carolina	231	24
Iowa	1000	220	South Dakota	1658	102
Kansas	1506	84	Tennessee	1030	100
Kentucky	1105	135	Texas	5530	340
Louisiana	486	64	Utah	335	95
Maine	8	43	Vermont	8	162
Maryland	49	86	Virginia	688	122
Massachusetts	6	24	Washington	272	248
Michigan	105	300	West Virginia	207	18
Minnesota	385	545	Wisconsin	190	1370
Mississippi	591	39	Wyoming	824	6
Missouri	2065	165	TOTAL	33 472	9143
Montana	1532	18			

CATTLE BY TYPE, 1995 – 1999

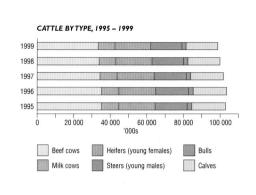

Years: 1999, 1998, 1997, 1996, 1995 ('000s; 0 to 100 000)

Legend: Beef cows; Milk cows; Heifers (young females); Steers (young males); Bulls; Calves

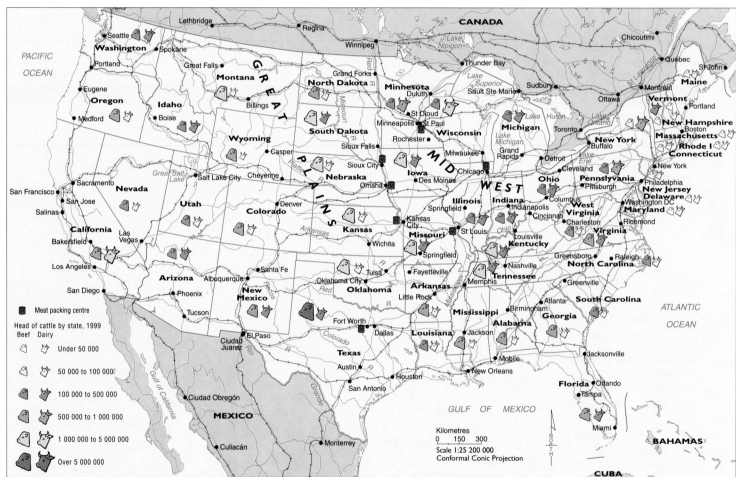

Map of USA – Commercial Pastoral Agriculture

- Meat packing centre
- Head of cattle by state, 1999 (Beef / Dairy):
  - Under 50 000
  - 50 000 to 100 000
  - 100 000 to 500 000
  - 500 000 to 1 000 000
  - 1 000 000 to 5 000 000
  - Over 5 000 000

Kilometres 0 150 300
Scale 1:25 200 000
Conformal Conic Projection

WORLD BEEF PRODUCTION, 1999

- USA 21.6%
- Brazil 11.1%
- China 8.4%
- Argentina 4.7%
- Russia 4.0%
- Australia 3.6%
- France 2.8%
- India 2.5%
- Others 41.3%

Total 55.9 million tonnes

WORLD MILK PRODUCTION, 1999

- USA 15.3%
- India 7.5%
- Russia 6.6%
- Germany 5.9%
- France 5.1%
- Brazil 4.7%
- UK 3.1%
- Ukraine 2.7%
- Others 49.1%

Total 480.7 million tonnes

BEEF AND VEAL PRODUCTION IN USA, 1995–1999

Million tonnes (10–12): 1995, 1996, 1997, 1998, 1999

VOLUME AND VALUE OF BEEF AND VEAL EXPORTS FROM USA, 1995–1999

Volume (tonnes) 800 000–1 000 000; Value (Million US$) 2000–3000: 1995, 1996, 1997, 1998, 1999

CATTLE SLAUGHTERED AND MILK PRODUCTION BY STATE, 1998

	Weight of animals slaughtered ('000 tonnes)	Milk production ('000 tonnes)		Weight of animals slaughtered ('000 tonnes)	Milk production ('000 tonnes)
Alabama	125.4	189.6	Nebraska	4105.9	471.7
Alaska		6.8	Nevada		216.4
Arizona	239.7	1208.4	New Hampshire		148.8
Arkansas	8.3	290.8	New Jersey	12.1	135.6
California	575.0	12 531.7	New Mexico	9.0	1819.4
Colorado	1333.9	761.6	New York	43.9	5237.7
Connecticut		230.9	North Carolina	76.7	571.1
Delaware		69.4	North Dakota		318.4
Florida	22.8	1123.5	Ohio	77.3	2002.6
Georgia	184.2	674.9	Oklahoma	14.9	578.3
Hawaii	8.2	55.8	Oregon	8.6	730.3
Idaho	416.0	2355.5	Pennsylvania	549.8	4872.6
Illinois	560.0	1046.5	Rhode Island		14.5
Indiana	20.7	992.9	South Carolina		177.8
Iowa	510.3	1808.5	South Dakota	148.4	627.8
Kansas	4059.9	582.9	Tennessee		723.0
Kentucky	23.1	823.3	Texas	3506.7	2616.4
Louisiana	9.5	360.2	Utah		698.5
Maine		299.8	Vermont		1179.8
Maryland		604.2	Virginia	8.3	843.2
Massachusetts		197.3	Washington	522.8	2406.3
Michigan	237.7	2454.0	West Virginia	5.8	120.7
Minnesota	408.5	4177.7	Wisconsin	938.6	10 146.1
Mississippi		287.6	Wyoming	3.3	36.6
Missouri	41.3	1072.8	Others	528.0	
Montana	11.2	133.8	TOTAL	19 356.0	71 034.7

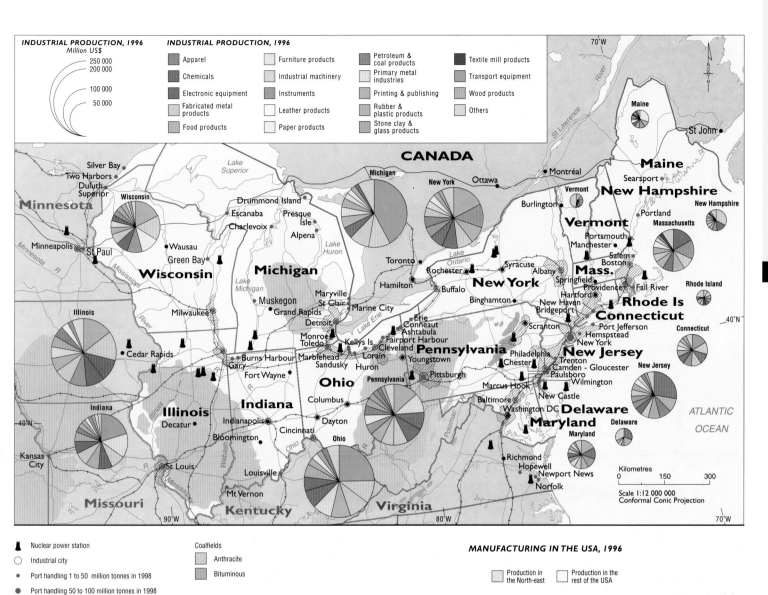

INDUSTRIAL PRODUCTION, 1996
Million US$

- 250 000
- 200 000
- 100 000
- 50 000

INDUSTRIAL PRODUCTION, 1996

- Apparel
- Chemicals
- Electronic equipment
- Fabricated metal products
- Food products
- Furniture products
- Industrial machinery
- Instruments
- Leather products
- Paper products
- Petroleum & coal products
- Primary metal industries
- Printing & publishing
- Rubber & plastic products
- Stone clay & glass products
- Textile mill products
- Transport equipment
- Wood products
- Others

Kilometres 0 150 300
Scale 1:12 000 000
Conformal Conic Projection

Legend

- Nuclear power station
- Industrial city
- Port handling 1 to 50 million tonnes in 1998
- Port handling 50 to 100 million tonnes in 1998
- Port handling over 100 million tonnes in 1998

Coalfields
- Anthracite
- Bituminous
- Industrial area

INDUSTRIAL PRODUCTION BY STATE 1977 AND 1996

	1977 (million US$)	1996 (million US$)		1977 (million US$)	1996 (million US$)
Alabama	21 010 (1.5%)	66 257 (1.8%)	Montana	2670 (0.2%)	4930 (0.1%)
Alaska	1250 (0.1%)	3939 (0.2%)	Nebraska	8713 (0.6%)	25 023 (0.7%)
Arizona	7022 (0.5%)	36 961 (1.0%)	Nevada	942 (0.1%)	6194 (0.2%)
Arkansas	12 276 (0.9%)	44 310 (1.2%)	New Hampshire	4032 (0.3%)	19 348 (0.5%)
California	120 896 (8.9%)	368 329 (9.9%)	New Jersey	51 279 (3.8%)	96 001 (2.6%)
Colorado	10 018 (0.7%)	39 191 (1.1%)	New Mexico	16 364 (0.1%)	2009 (0.4%)
Connecticut	19 842 (1.5%)	44 369 (1.2%)	New York	86 216 (6.3%)	163 697 (4.4%)
Delaware	5209 (0.4%)	13 601 (0.4%)	North Carolina	40 912 (3.0%)	155 911 (4.2%)
Florida	20 981 (1.5%)	76 387 (2.1%)	North Dakota	1313 (0.1%)	4794 (0.1%)
Georgia	32 856 (2.4%)	115 898 (3.1%)	Ohio	95 235 (7.0%)	232 721 (6.3%)
Hawaii	1974 (0.2%)	3146 (0.1%)	Oklahoma	12 565 (0.9%)	35 220 (0.9%)
Idaho	3658 (0.3%)	18 315 (0.5%)	Oregon	14 370 (1.1%)	45 022 (1.2%)
Illinois	93 081 (6.9%)	196 845 (5.3%)	Pennsylvania	79 845 (5.9%)	165 889 (4.5%)
Indiana	52 172 (3.8%)	133 787 (3.6%)	Rhode Island	5365 (0.4%)	9959 (0.3%)
Iowa	23 515 (1.7%)	61 981 (1.7%)	South Carolina	18 882 (1.4%)	66 794 (1.8%)
Kansas	15 987 (1.2%)	46 152 (1.2%)	South Dakota	1794 (0.1%)	10 488 (0.3%)
Kentucky	22 875 (1.7%)	82 531 (2.2%)	Tennessee	28 752 (2.1%)	95 851 (2.6%)
Louisiana	29 493 (2.2%)	75 961 (2.0%)	Texas	92 736 (6.8%)	284 151 (7.6%)
Maine	5145 (0.4%)	14 445 (0.4%)	Utah	5093 (0.4%)	22 010 (0.6%)
Maryland	15 930 (1.2%)	35 700 (1.0%)	Vermont	2189 (0.2%)	8554 (0.2%)
Massachusetts	30 144 (2.2%)	79 254 (2.1%)	Virginia	23 989 (1.8%)	80 795 (2.2%)
Michigan	93 757 (6.9%)	205 744 (5.5%)	Washington	21 747 (1.6%)	71 874 (1.9%)
Minnesota	23 021 (1.7%)	73 273 (2.0%)	West Virginia	8706 (0.6%)	17 679 (0.5%)
Mississippi	12 766 (0.9%)	39 564 (1.1%)	Wisconsin	38 725 (2.9%)	114 464 (3.1%)
Missouri	33 163 (2.4%)	85 222 (2.3%)	Wyoming	1288 (0.1%)	2874 (0.1%)

The figures in brackets are the percentage of total production in the USA

MANUFACTURING IN THE USA, 1996

- Production in the North-east
- Production in the rest of the USA

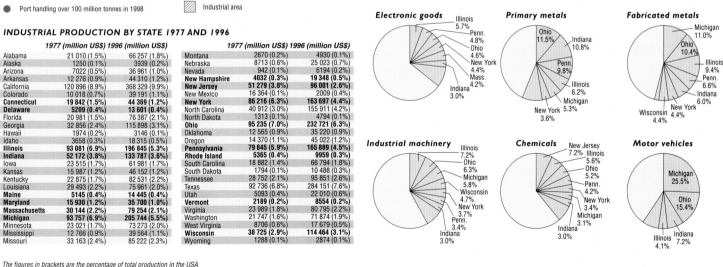

Electronic goods
- Illinois 5.7%
- Penn. 4.8%
- Ohio 4.6%
- New York 4.4%
- Mass. 4.2%
- Indiana 3.0%

Primary metals
- Ohio 11.5%
- Indiana 10.8%
- Penn. 9.8%
- Illinois 6.2%
- Michigan 5.3%
- New York 3.6%

Fabricated metals
- Michigan 11.0%
- Ohio 10.4%
- Illinois 9.4%
- Penn. 6.6%
- Indiana 6.0%
- New York 4.4%
- Wisconsin 4.4%

Industrial machinery
- Illinois 7.2%
- Ohio 6.3%
- Michigan 5.8%
- Wisconsin 4.7%
- New York 3.7%
- Penn. 3.7%
- Indiana 3.0%

Chemicals
- New Jersey 7.2%
- Illinois 5.6%
- Ohio 5.2%
- Penn. 4.2%
- New York 3.4%
- Michigan 3.1%
- Indiana 3.0%

Motor vehicles
- Michigan 25.5%
- Ohio 15.4%
- Indiana 7.2%
- Illinois 4.1%

USA COAL PRODUCTION, 1998

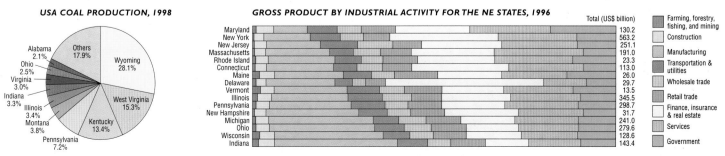

- Wyoming 28.1%
- West Virginia 15.3%
- Kentucky 13.4%
- Pennsylvania 7.2%
- Montana 3.8%
- Illinois 3.4%
- Indiana 3.3%
- Virginia 3.0%
- Ohio 2.5%
- Alabama 2.1%
- Others 17.9%

GROSS PRODUCT BY INDUSTRIAL ACTIVITY FOR THE NE STATES, 1996

Total (US$ billion)

State	Total
Maryland	130.2
New York	563.2
New Jersey	251.1
Massachusetts	191.0
Rhode Island	23.3
Connecticut	113.0
Maine	26.0
Delaware	29.7
Vermont	13.5
Illinois	345.5
Pennsylvania	298.7
New Hampshire	31.7
Michigan	241.0
Ohio	279.6
Wisconsin	128.6
Indiana	143.4

- Farming, forestry, fishing, and mining
- Construction
- Manufacturing
- Transportation & utilities
- Wholesale trade
- Retail trade
- Finance, insurance & real estate
- Services
- Government

135

ADMINISTRATIVE AREAS AND POPULATION DENSITY

New York
Dutchess County
Connecticut
Poughkeepsie
Dutchess
Litchfield
Waterbury
Waterbury
Meriden
Newburgh
Putnam
New Haven
Danbury
Danbury
New Haven-Meriden
Newburgh
Orange
Fairfield
New Haven
Pike
Westchester
Bridgeport
Rockland
Bridgeport
Stamford-Norwalk
Passaic
White Plains
Norwalk
Sussex
Bergen
Stamford
Bergen-Passaic
New York
Warren
Essex
Hudson
Long Island
Newark
Morris
Bronx
Nassau-Suffolk
New Jersey
Jersey City
New York
Suffolk
Newark
Jersey City
Nassau
Union
Bayonne
Hunterdon
Somerset
Richmond
Queens
Middlesex-Somerset-Hunterdon
Middlesex
Kings
Trenton
Mercer
Monmouth
Pennsylvania
Trenton
Dover
Monmouth-Ocean
ATLANTIC OCEAN
Ocean
NORTH

Kilometres 0 30
Scale 1:3 000 000
Conformal Conic projection

Legend:
- State boundary
- **New York** Primary Metropolitan Statistical Area (PMSA)
- Queens County boundary
- New York – Northern New Jersey – Long Island Consolidated Metropolitan Statistical Area (CMSA)
- • Central city (Population over 25 000)

POPULATION DENSITY BY COUNTY, 1999
People per square kilometre
- Over 10 000
- 5 000 to 10 000
- 1 000 to 5 000
- 500 to 1 000
- 100 to 500
- 0 to 100

POPULATION OF NEW YORK CITY, 1950 – 1998

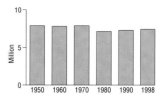

(bar chart, Million, years 1950, 1960, 1970, 1980, 1990, 1998)

POPULATION OF PRIMARY METROPOLITAN STATISTICAL AREAS WITHIN NEW YORK-NORTHERN NEW JERSEY-LONG ISLAND CMSA

Bergen-Passaic	1 344 266
Bridgeport	443 354
Danbury	202 009
Dutchess County	265 317
Jersey City	557 159
Middlesex-Somerset-Hunterdon	1 121 504
Monmouth-Ocean	1 093 253
Nassau-Suffolk	2 673 489
New Haven-Meriden	522 738
New York	8 692 782
Newark	1 952 407
Newburgh	369 392
Stamford-Norwalk	332 941
Trenton	331 629
Waterbury	222 137
Total for CMSA	**20 124 377**

AREA AND POPULATION OF COUNTIES IN THE NEW YORK PMSA, 1999

County	Area (km²)	Population
Bronx	108.9	1 194 099
Kings	182.7	2 268 297
New York	73.5	1 551 844
Putnam	599.7	94 844
Queens	283.3	2 000 642
Richmond	151.8	413 280
Rockland	451.2	284 022
Westchester	1121.2	905 572

LAND USE

Paterson, Bergenfield, Palisades Interstate Park, Mount Vernon, Long Island Sound, Little Falls, Hackensack, Teterboro Airport, Lodi, New Jersey, Bergen, Fort Lee, Bronx, Glen Cove, Cedar Grove, Passaic, Rutherford, Pelham Bay Park, Manorhaven, Port Washington, Montclair, North Arlington, West New York, Central Park, La Guardia Airport, Great Neck, Albertson, Bloomfield, Essex, Orange, Hudson, Hoboken, New York Manhattan, Flushing Meadows-Corona Park, Fresh Meadows, Mineola, Newark, Lincoln Park, Jersey City, Queens, Queens, Hempstead, Milburn, Hillside, Port Newark, New York, Brooklyn, Elmont, Nassau, Union, Newark International Airport, Statue of Liberty, Brooklyn Marine Terminal, Richmond Hill, Valley Stream, Elizabeth, Elizabeth-Port Authority Marine Terminal, Auto Marine Terminal Upper, Red Hook Container Terminal, LONG ISLAND, Lynbrook, Westfield, Linden, Bayonne, Bay, Prospect Park, John F. Kennedy International Airport, Baldwin, Howland and Hook Marine Terminal, Kings, Oceanside, Rahway, Brooklyn, Iselin, Gateway National Recreation Area, Middlesex, Richmond, Carteret, Lower Bay, Long Beach, Woodbridge, STATEN ISLAND, Rockaway Inlet, Fords, ATLANTIC OCEAN, Perth Amboy

Kilometres 0 5 10
Scale 1:500 000

Legend:
- Port area
- Central business district
- Residential/commercial
- Airport area
- Industrial area
- Parkland/forest reserve
- State boundary
- County boundary
- **Union** County name

CARGO HANDLED AT NEW YORK'S PORTS AND AIRPORTS, 1999

(bar chart, Million tonnes)
- Newark Airport
- JFK Airport
- New York & New Jersey Ports (general cargo) 18 181 779 tonnes
- New York & New Jersey Ports (bulk cargo) 40 884 195 tonnes

New York and New Jersey ports handled 1 685 368 containers and 519 214 motor vehicles

NUMBER OF EMPLOYEES BY INDUSTRY AND COUNTY FOR NEW YORK PMSA, 1997

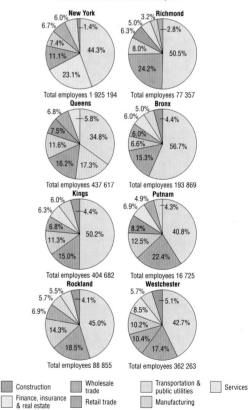

New York — 6.0%, 6.7%, 7.4%, 11.1%, 23.1%, 44.3%, 1.4% — Total employees 1 925 194
Richmond — 3.2%, 5.0%, 6.3%, 8.0%, 24.2%, 50.5%, 2.8% — Total employees 77 357
Queens — 6.8%, 7.5%, 11.6%, 16.2%, 17.3%, 34.8%, 5.8% — Total employees 437 617
Bronx — 5.0%, 6.0%, 6.6%, 15.3%, 56.7%, 4.4% — Total employees 193 869
Kings — 6.0%, 6.3%, 6.8%, 11.3%, 15.0%, 50.2%, 4.4% — Total employees 404 682
Putnam — 4.9%, 6.9%, 8.2%, 12.5%, 22.4%, 40.8%, 4.3% — Total employees 16 725
Rockland — 5.5%, 5.7%, 6.9%, 14.3%, 18.5%, 45.0%, 4.1% — Total employees 88 855
Westchester — 5.7%, 8.5%, 10.2%, 10.4%, 17.4%, 42.7%, 5.1% — Total employees 362 263

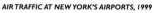

Legend:
- Construction
- Finance, insurance & real estate
- Wholesale trade
- Retail trade
- Transportation & public utilities
- Manufacturing
- Services

AIR TRAFFIC AT NEW YORK'S AIRPORTS, 1999

(chart, Aircraft movements / Total passengers handled — La Guardia, JFK, Newark)
- Aircraft movements
- Total passengers handled

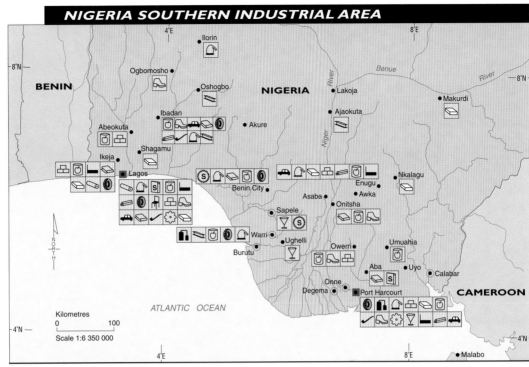

NIGERIA SOUTHERN INDUSTRIAL AREA

Cement
Chemicals and plastics
Construction
Engineering
Food and drink
Furniture
Glassworks
Iron and steel
Metal industry
Oil refinery

Paper
Rubber
Sawmill
Shoes
Soap
Textiles
Tobacco
Vehicle assembly
Wood industry

■ Major port
● Other port

EXPORTS, 1998

Others 2.1%
Other petroleum products 2.1%
Crude oil 95.8%

ECOLOGICAL ZONES AND PETROLEUM RESOURCES IN THE NIGER DELTA

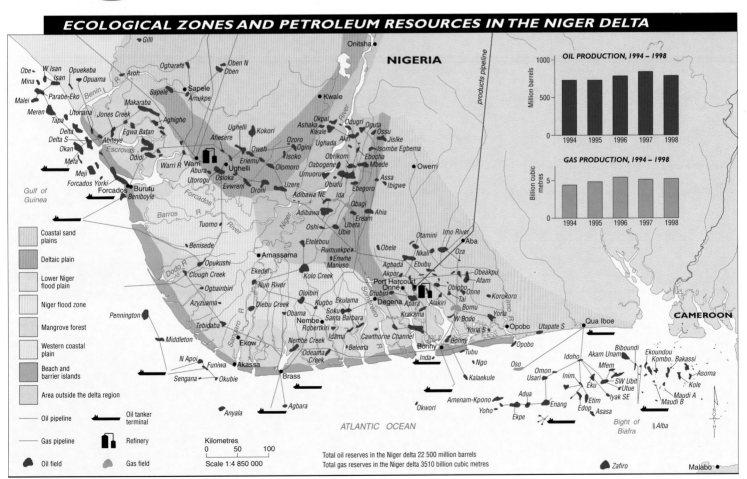

Coastal sand plains
Deltaic plain
Lower Niger flood plain
Niger flood zone
Mangrove forest
Western coastal plain
Beach and barrier islands
Area outside the delta region

— Oil pipeline
— Gas pipeline
▲ Oil field
▬ Oil tanker terminal
Refinery
Gas field

OIL PRODUCTION, 1994 – 1998

GAS PRODUCTION, 1994 – 1998

Total oil reserves in the Niger delta 22 500 million barrels
Total gas reserves in the Niger delta 3510 billion cubic metres

The Nigerian petroleum industry and the environment of the Niger delta.

The Niger delta is a complex combination of ecological zones covering an area about 70 000 km². The delta has a population of about seven million people, has immense reserves of crude oil and has the third largest mangrove forest in the world, covering 6000 km² in a swathe between fifteen and forty-five kilometres wide. The exploration for oil and its exploitation has serious implications for the environment:

* Land has to be cleared for equipment and personnel.
* Roads (on land) or canals (in swamps) have to be constructed for access.
* Large amounts of earth, rock and mud waste are produced during drilling.
* Land has to be cleared for pipelines that carry the crude oil to the terminals for processing.
* For every two barrels of oil produced, one barrel of water has to be separated and this contains salts, heavy metals and residual oil.
* Approximately 1000 cubic feet (85 cubic metres) of gas is produced with every barrel of oil and the bulk of this is flared (burnt off), creating polluting smoke and other noxious emissions.
* Oil spills from equipment failure or mistakes during production can create massive environmental damage. In 1998, 50 200 barrels of oil were spilled.

The government and oil companies work together to try and minimise the impact of the industry, but there is always a conflict between the need to develop such a rich resource and the protection of the local people and their environment.

OIL EXPORTS, 1994 – 1998

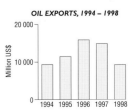

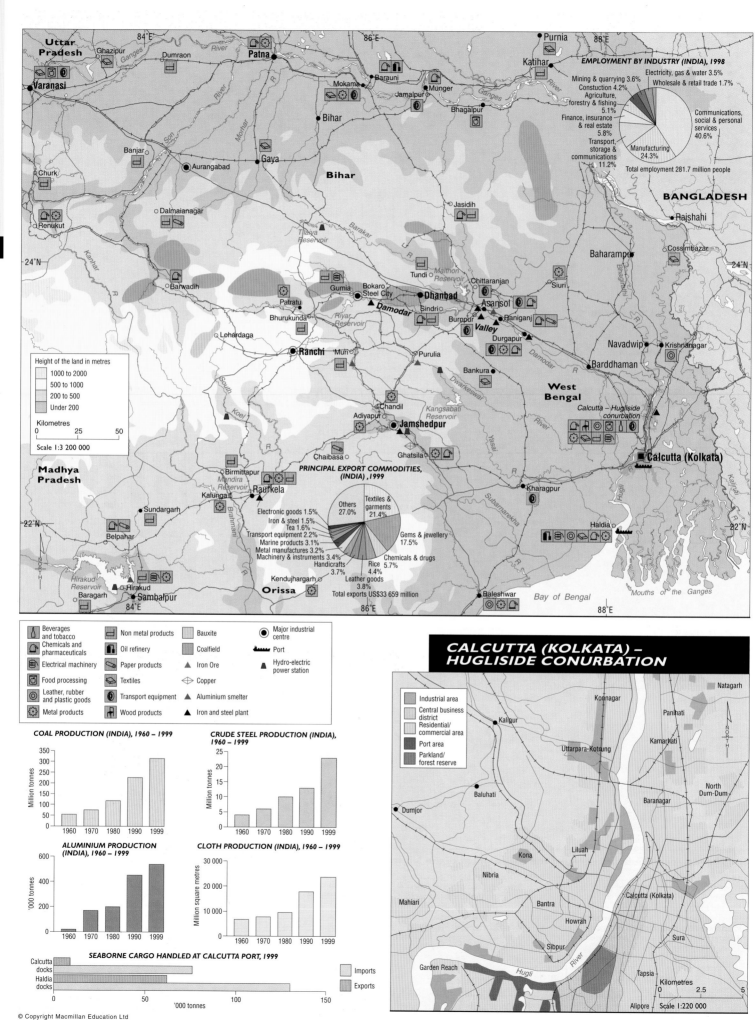

INDIA Bihar/West Bengal Industrial Area

138

EMPLOYMENT BY INDUSTRY (INDIA), 1998

- Mining & quarrying 3.6%
- Construction 4.2%
- Agriculture, forestry & fishing 5.1%
- Finance, insurance & real estate 5.8%
- Transport, storage & communications 11.2%
- Manufacturing 24.3%
- Communications, social & personal services 40.6%
- Electricity, gas & water 3.5%
- Wholesale & retail trade 1.7%

Total employment 281.7 million people

PRINCIPAL EXPORT COMMODITIES, (INDIA), 1999

- Textiles & garments 21.4%
- Gems & jewellery 17.5%
- Chemicals & drugs 5.7%
- Rice 4.4%
- Leather goods 3.8%
- Handicrafts 3.7%
- Machinery & instruments 3.4%
- Metal manufactures 3.2%
- Marine products 3.1%
- Transport equipment 2.2%
- Tea 1.6%
- Iron & steel 1.5%
- Electronic goods 1.5%
- Others 27.0%

Total exports US$33 659 million

Legend

Height of the land in metres
- 1000 to 2000
- 500 to 1000
- 200 to 500
- Under 200

Kilometres
0 25 50
Scale 1:3 200 000

- Beverages and tobacco
- Chemicals and pharmaceuticals
- Electrical machinery
- Food processing
- Leather, rubber and plastic goods
- Metal products
- Non metal products
- Oil refinery
- Paper products
- Textiles
- Transport equipment
- Wood products
- Bauxite
- Coalfield
- Iron Ore
- Copper
- Aluminium smelter
- Iron and steel plant
- Major industrial centre
- Port
- Hydro-electric power station

CALCUTTA (KOLKATA) – HUGLISIDE CONURBATION

- Industrial area
- Central business district
- Residential/commercial area
- Port area
- Parkland/forest reserve

Kilometres
0 2.5 5
Alipore · Scale 1:220 000

COAL PRODUCTION (INDIA), 1960 – 1999
Million tonnes
(350, 300, 250, 200, 150, 100, 50, 0)
1960 1970 1980 1990 1999

CRUDE STEEL PRODUCTION (INDIA), 1960 – 1999
Million tonnes
(25, 20, 15, 10, 5, 0)
1960 1970 1980 1990 1999

ALUMINIUM PRODUCTION (INDIA), 1960 – 1999
'000 tonnes
(600, 400, 200, 0)
1960 1970 1980 1990 1999

CLOTH PRODUCTION (INDIA), 1960 – 1999
Million square metres
(30 000, 20 000, 10 000, 0)
1960 1970 1980 1990 1999

SEABORNE CARGO HANDLED AT CALCUTTA PORT, 1999
Calcutta docks
Haldia docks
0 50 100 150
'000 tonnes
- Imports
- Exports

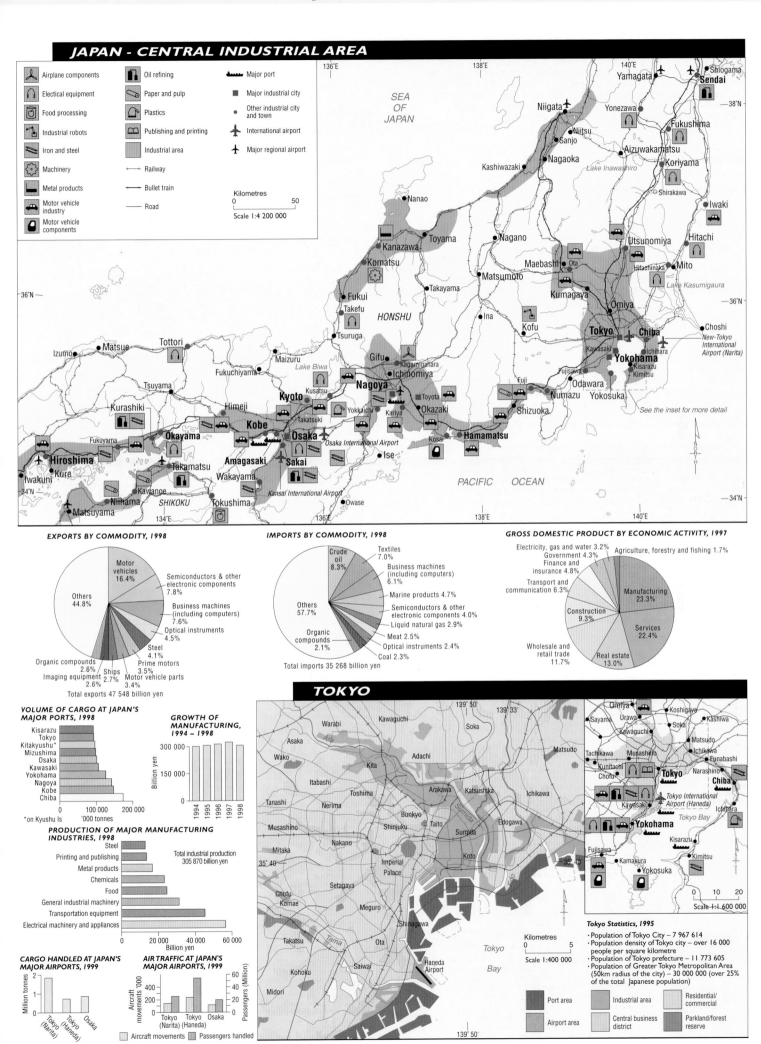

HOW TO USE THE INDEX

The index is a reference to place names and geographic names appearing in the atlas and is arranged in alphabetical order. Each index entry is followed by the most appropriate page number on which the place appears, then its alpha-numeric reference, followed by its geographic coordinates (latitude and longitude).

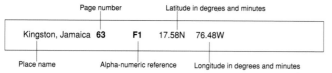

Page number   Latitude in degrees and minutes

Kingston, Jamaica **63**   **F1**   17.58N   76.48W

Place name   Alpha-numeric reference   Longitude in degrees and minutes

The geographic coordinates of latitude and longitude give a more accurate location for each entry (see page 4). Since it is not possible to show every line of latitude and longitude it is necessary to estimate the degrees and minutes to find the exact location of a place.
Extensive features such as states, countries and mountain ranges are indexed to the largest scale map that shows them in their entirety. Where the same place name appears more than once in the index, each is followed by the country name in alphabetical order.

San Juan, Puerto Rico	**69**	**B2**	18.29N	66.08W
San Juan, Trinidad and Tobago	**81**	**C4**	10.35N	61.25W

Names which have two or more words are listed according to the first letter of the first word, for example, Port Harcourt is listed under P. Physical features are indexed under their proper name, for example, Erie, Lake.
Place names in India have undergone recent changes and where possible the new names have been used, for example, Mumbai (formerly Bombay).
Country names are in upper case and are the names that appear on the maps. Full and/or official names of countries are provided on the world statistics pages 44–45.
Index entries relate to political and physical maps only, not thematic maps. (Refer to the Contents on pages 2 and 3 for details of these.)
The entries for physical features such as lakes, rivers, points, gulfs, capes and mountains all have the name first: Superior, Lake; Bengo, Bay of; Albina, Point; Carpentaria, Gulf of; Good Hope, Cape of; Kilimanjaro, Mt.
All abbreviations used in the index are listed below.

Abbreviations
admin.	administrative
ant. base	antarctic base
SADR	Sahrawi Arab Democratic Republic
Pte	Pointe
St	Saint
Ste	Sainte
UK	United Kingdom
USA	United States of America

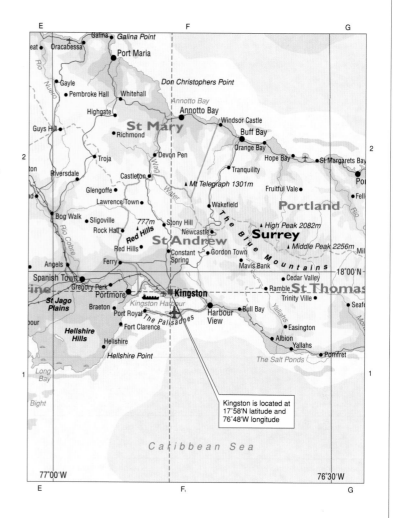

Kingston is located at 17°58'N latitude and 76°48'W longitude

Bray **106 B3** 53.12N 6.06W
BRAZIL, federal republic **98 E6**
Brazilian Highlands **99 F5**
Brazilletto Mountains **63 D1**
Brazos River **96 C2**
Brazzaville **116 B4** 4.14S 15.14E
Breclav **109 G5** 48.45N 16.52E
Breda **106 D3** 51.35N 4.46E
Bremen **106 E3** 53.05N 8.48E
Bremerhaven **106 E3** 53.33N 8.35E
Bremerton **96 A3** 47.34N 122.34W
Brereton **78 C2** 13.02N 59.30W
Brescia **108 F5** 45.33N 10.13E
Brest, Belarus **107 H3** 52.08N 23.40E
Brest, France **108 C5** 48.23N 4.30W
Brewarrina **126 E2** 29.57S 146.52E
Brewers Bay **70 E4**
Brewton **97 E2** 31.07N 87.04W
Brézina **114 D5** 33.03N 1.18E
Bria **115 F2** 6.32N 22.00E
Brick Kiln **71 C2** 17.10N 62.33W
Bridgefield **78 B2** 13.09N 59.35W
Bridgeport **97 F3** 41.12N 73.12W
Bridgetown **78 B2** 13.06N 59.37W
Bridgewater **95 L2** 44.23N 64.32W
Bridlington **106 C3** 54.05N 0.12W
Brievengat **84 E3** 12.12N 68.55W
Brigantine Cays **58 E4**
Brigham City **96 B3** 41.31N 112.01W
Brighton, Jamaica **62 B2** 18.13N 78.17W
Brighton, UK **106 C3** 50.50N 0.10W
Brighton Village **77 A1** 13.07N 61.10W
Brimstone Hill **71 B3** 17.20N 62.49W
Brindisi **109 G4** 40.37N 17.57E
Brisbane **126 F3** 27.28S 153.01E
Bristol **106 C3** 51.27N 2.35W
Bristol Bay **94 B3**
British Isles **103 D3**
British Columbia, province **94 F3**
British Virgin Islands **70 C3**
Brittany, region **108 C5**
Brizon **80 A7** 12.06N 61.45W
Brno **107 G2** 49.12N 16.40E
Broach **124 B3** 21.42N 72.58E
Broad Sound **127 F3**
Brockville **95 K2** 44.35N 75.44W
Brodeur Peninsula **94 J5**
Broken Hill **126 E2** 31.58S 141.27E
Bromefield **78 B4** 13.17N 59.38W
Brookhaven **97 D2** 31.36N 90.28W
Brookings **97 D3** 44.19N 96.47W
Brooks Range **94 C4**
Broome **126 C4** 17.58S 122.14E
Brovary **107 J3** 50.30N 30.45E
Brown, ant. base **131 M3** 64.53S 62.53W
Brownfield **96 C2** 33.11N 102.16W
Brown Hill **71 C1** 17.07N 62.36W
Browns Town **62 D2** 18.23N 77.22W
Brownsville, Tennessee **97 E2** 35.35N 89.15W
Brownsville, Texas **96 D1** 25.54N 97.30W
Brownwood **96 D2** 31.42N 98.59W
Bruce Vale River **78 C3**
Bruck **109 G5** 47.25N 15.17E
Brugge **106 D3** 51.13N 3.14E
BRUNEI, sultanate **118 L4**
Brunsbuttelkoog **106 E3** 53.54N 9.08E
Brunswick, Germany **108 F6** 52.15N 10.30E
Brunswick, USA **97 E2** 31.09N 81.30W
Brussels **106 D3** 50.50N 4.21E
Brute Point **77 E2** 13.04N 61.08W
Bryan, Ohio **97 E3** 41.30N 84.34W
Bryan, Texas **97 D2** 30.41N 96.24W
Bryansk **107 J3** 53.15N 34.09E
Bryukhovetskaya **109 K5** 45.48N 39.00E
Bucaramanga **98 C7** 7.08N 73.10W
Buccament **77 A2** 13.11N 61.15W
Buccament, river **77 A2**
Buchanan **114 B2** 5.57N 10.02W
Bucharest **109 I4** 44.25N 26.07E
Buck Island **70 F2**
Buckleys **72 B4** 17.04N 61.48W
Budapest **107 G2** 47.30N 19.03E
Buenaventura **98 C7** 3.54N 77.02W
Buena Vista **86 B4** 18.16N 88.32W
Buenos Aires **98 E3** 34.40S 58.30W
Buenos Ayres **81 B2** 10.06N 61.41W
Buffalo **97 F3** 42.52N 78.55W
Buff Bay **63 E2** 18.13N 76.39W
Bujumbura **116 C4** 3.22S 29.19E
Bukama **116 C4** 9.13S 25.52E
Bukavu **116 C4** 2.30S 28.49E
Bukoba **116 D4** 1.20S 31.49E
Bulawayo **116 C3** 20.10S 28.43E
BULGARIA, people's republic **109 H4**
Bulkhead Reef **86 B3**
Bulla **126 E5** 9.08S 141.20E
Bull Bay **63 E1** 17.56N 76.40W
Bullenbaai **84 D3** 12.12N 68.55W
Bull Head Mountains **63 D2**
Bulloo River **127 E3**
Bull Savanna **62 C1** 17.53N 77.36W
Bull Shoals Lake **97 D2**
Bumba **116 C5** 2.10N 22.30E
Bunbury **126 B2** 33.20S 115.38E
Bundaberg **126 F3** 24.52S 152.21E
Bungo Channel **122 F3**
Bunia **116 C5** 1.35N 30.13E
Bunkum Bay **73 A4**
Bünyan **109 K3** 38.51N 35.50E
Bura **115 G1** 1.06S 39.58E
Burdur **109 J3** 37.44N 30.17E
Burgas **109 I4** 42.30N 27.29E
Burgersdorp **116 C1** 31.00S 26.20E
Burgos **108 C4** 42.21N 3.41W
Burhaniye **109 I3** 39.29N 26.59E
Burhanpur **124 B3** 21.18N 76.08E
Burica, Point **14 C2** 8.02N 82.52W
Burketown **126 D4** 17.45S 139.33E
BURKINA FASO, republic **114 C3**
Burley **96 B3** 42.31N 113.48W
Burlington, North Carolina **97 F2** 36.05N 79.27W
Burlington, Vermont **97 F3** 44.28N 73.14W
BURMA, socialist republic **118 K6**
Burmudian Landing **86 B3** 17.33N 88.32W
Burns **96 B3** 43.36N 119.03W
Burnt Ground **58 F4** 23.39N 75.20W
Burrell Boom **86 B3** 17.36N 88.28W
Bursa **109 I4** 40.12N 29.04E
Buru, island **127 C5**
BURUNDI, republic **116 C4**
Bush Cay **68 D6**
Businga **116 C5** 3.16N 20.59E
Busira River **115 E2**
Busy Corner **81 C3** 10.18N 61.18W
Buta **116 C5** 2.49N 24.50E
Butare **116 C4** 2.34S 29.43E
Butlers **71 C2** 17.10N 62.33W
Butte **96 B3** 46.00N 112.31W
Butung, island **127 C5**
Buzau **109 I5** 45.09N 26.49E
Buzi River **116 D2**
Bydgoszcz **107 G3** 53.16N 18.00E
Bylands **80 C7** 12.08N 61.39W
Bylot Island **94 K5**
Byron, Cape **127 F3** 28.38S 153.38E
Bytom **109 G6** 50.21N 18.51E

C

Cabaiguan **60 D3** 22.06N 79.39W
Cabaret **66 C2** 18.43N 72.24W
Cabarita, river **62 B2**
Cabimas **54 D3** 10.26N 71.27W
Cabinda **116 B4** 5.34S 12.12E
Caborca **88 A4** 30.42N 112.10W
Cabo Rojo **69 A2** 18.05N 67.05W
Cabot Strait **95 L2**
Cabral **67 D2** 18.15N 71.10W
Cabrera **67 F3** 19.35N 69.50W
Cáceres **108 B3** 39.29N 6.23W
Caconda **116 B3** 13.43S 15.03E
Cades Point **71 C2** 17.11N 62.37W
Cadillac **97 E3** 44.15N 85.23W
Cádiz **108 B3** 36.32N 6.18W
Caen **108 C5** 49.11N 0.22W
Cagliari **108 E3** 39.13N 9.08E
Caguas **69 B2** 18.14N 66.03W
Cahors **108 D4** 44.28N 1.26E
Caibarién **60 D3** 22.30N 79.25W
Caicara **55 E2** 7.38N 66.10W
Caicos Bank **68 C7**
Caicos Islands **54 D5**
Caicos Passage **59 I3**
Caille Island **80 B1**
Cairns **126 E4** 16.55S 145.46E
Cairo, Egypt **115 G5** 30.03N 31.15E
Cairo, USA **97 E2** 30.52N 84.12W
Caja de Muertos Island **69 B1**
Cajamarca **98 C6** 7.09S 78.32W
Cala **108 B3** 37.58N 6.19W
Calabar **114 D2** 4.56N 8.22E
Calabozo **55 E2** 8.58N 67.28W
Calahorra **108 C4** 42.19N 1.58W
Calais **108 D6** 50.57N 1.52E
Calanscio Sand Sea, desert **115 F4**
Calarasi **109 I4** 44.12N 27.22E
Calatayud **108 C4** 41.21N 1.39W
Caldas da Rainha **108 B3** 39.24N 9.08W
Caldwell **96 B3** 43.39N 116.40W
Calgary **94 G3** 51.05N 114.05W
Cali **98 C7** 3.24N 76.30W
California **81 C3** 10.24N 61.28W
California, Gulf of **96 B1**
California, state **96 A2**
Calivigny Island **80 B5**
Callao **98 C5** 12.05S 77.08W
Calliaqua **77 A1** 13.07N 61.11W
Calliste **80 A6** 12.00N 61.46W
Calvinia **116 B1** 31.25S 19.47E
Camagüey **60 E2** 21.25N 77.55W
Camagüey, province **60 E2**
Camagüey, Archipelago de **60 E3**
Cambay, Gulf of **124 B3**
CAMBODIA, republic **118 L5**
Cambrai **106 D3** 50.10N 3.14E
Cambridge **62 C2** 18.19N 77.55W
Cambridge Bay **94 H4** 69.09N 105.00W
Camden Park **77 A2** 13.10N 61.14W
Camden Park Bay **77 A1**
CAMEROON, federal republic **114 E2**
Cameroon, Mount **12 H3** 4.13N 9.10E
Camooweal **126 D4** 19.55S 138.07E
Campbell Island **131 A2**
Campbellton **95 L2** 48.00N 66.41W
Campeche **88 C2** 19.50N 90.30W
Campeche, Bay of **88 C3**
Campeche Banks **14 B5**
Campina Grande **98 G6** 7.15S 35.53W
Campo Grande **98 E4** 20.24S 54.35W
Camuy **69 B2** 18.30N 66.50W
Cana Point **67 G2** 18.06N 68.34W
Canaan **81 C6** 11.10N 60.47W
Canaan Hill **62 D2** 18.24N 77.16W
CANADA, dominion **94 I3**
Canadian River **96 C2**
Canakkale **109 I4** 40.09N 26.25E
Cananea **88 A4** 31.00N 110.20W
Canaries **76 A2** 13.54N 61.04W
Canaries, river **76 A2**
Canary Basin **12 F3**
Canary Islands **114 B4**
Canaveral, Cape **97 E1** 28.28N 80.31W
Canberra **126 E2** 35.17S 149.08E
Cancún **54 A5** 21.09N 86.45W
Candala **115 I3** 11.23N 49.53E
Cane Garden **77 A1** 13.08N 61.13W
Cane Garden Bay **70 E4**
Cane Garden Point **77 A1** 13.08N 61.13W
Canelles, river **76 B1**
Cane Wood **78 B2** 13.08N 59.35W
Cangrejos Point **81 B3** 10.25N 61.30W
Canicatti **108 F3** 37.22N 13.51E
Canje, river **85 C3**
Cankiri **109 J4** 40.35N 33.37E
Cannanore **124 B2** 11.53N 75.23E
Cannarreos, Archipelago de los **60 C2**
Cannes **108 E4** 43.33N 7.00E
Canon City **96 C2** 38.27N 105.16W
Canouan, island **77 C2**
Cantabrian Mountains **108 B4**
Canterbury **106 D3** 51.17N 1.05E
Canton **97 E3** 40.48N 81.23W
Canyon **96 C2** 34.58N 101.56W
Canyon City **96 B3** 44.24N 118.58W
Caonillas, Lake **69 B2**
Cap Point **76 B3** 14.06N 60.57W
Caparo **81 C3** 10.28N 61.20W
Cape Basin **12 H1**
Cape Breton Island **95 L2**
Cape Coast **114 C2** 5.06N 1.15W
Cape Girardeau **97 E2** 37.19N 89.31W
Capesterre **74 D3** 15.55N 61.10W
Capesterre, river **74 A4**
Capesterre-Belle-Eau **74 A4** 16.02N 61.32W
Cape Town **116 B1** 33.56S 18.28E
CAPE VERDE, independent state **111 A6**
Cape York Peninsula **127 E4**
Cap-Haïtien **66 C3** 19.47N 72.17W
Caphareus, Cape **109 H3** 38.10N 24.35E
Capitan Arturo Prat, ant. base **131 M3** 62.30S 59.41W
Capoeiras Falls **99 E6** 6.34S 58.25W
Capucin, Cape **75 A4** 15.37N 61.28W
Caquetá River **99 C7**
Caracas **55 E3** 10.35N 66.56W
Caracol **66 C3** 19.40N 72.00W
Caransebes **107 H2** 45.23N 22.13E
Carapo **81 C4** 10.36N 61.18W
Carapuse Bay **81 D6**
Caratasca Lagoon **14 C4**
Caravaca **108 C3** 38.06N 1.51W
Carbet, river **74 A2**
Carbonara, Cape **108 E3** 39.07N 9.33E
Cardamom Hills **124 B1**
Cárdenas **60 C3** 23.02N 81.12W
Cardiff **106 C3** 51.30N 3.13W
Carei **107 H2** 47.40N 22.28E
Carenage **81 B4** 10.41N 61.36W
Carey, Lake **127 C3**
Cariaco Trench **15 F3**
Caribbean Sea **14 D4**
Caribou **97 G3** 46.52N 68.01W
Carib Reserve **75 B3**
Carlisle **106 C3** 54.54N 2.55W
Carlisle Bay **78 B2**
Carlow **106 B3** 52.50N 6.55W
Carlsbad, California **96 B2** 33.09N 117.20W
Carlsbad, New Mexico **96 C2** 32.25N 104.14W
Carmarthen **106 C3** 51.52N 4.19W
Carmelita **86 B4** 18.02N 88.34W
Carmen Island **96 B1**
Carnarvon, Australia **126 B3** 24.53S 113.40E
Carnarvon, South Africa **116 C1** 30.59S 22.08E
Carnarvon Range **127 B3**
Carnegie, Lake **127 C3**
Carney Island **131 O3**
Car Nicobar, island **124 D1**
Carolina **69 C2** 18.23N 65.57W
Caroni **81 C4** 10.36N 61.23W
Caroni, river **81 C4**
Caroní River **89 F1**
Caroni Swamp **81 C4**
Carpathian Mountains **107 H2**
Carpentaria, Gulf of **127 D4**
Carriacou, island **80 C4**
Carrière **80 C8** 12.10N 61.38W
Carsamba **109 K4** 41.13N 36.43E
Carson City **94 G1** 39.10N 119.46W
Cartagena, Colombia **54 C3** 10.24N 75.33W
Cartagena, Spain **108 C3** 37.36N 0.59W
Cartago **54 B2** 9.50N 83.52W
Cartwright **95 M3** 53.40N 57.00W
Carúpano **55 F3** 10.39N 63.14W
Casablanca **114 C5** 33.39N 7.35W
Casa Grande **96 B2** 32.50N 111.45W
Cascade **62 B2** 18.23N 78.06W
Cascade Range **96 A3**
Case-Pilote **74 A1** 14.38N 61.08W
Caserta **108 F4** 41.04N 14.20E
Casey, ant. base **131 D3** 66.17S 110.32E
Caspe **108 D4** 41.14N 0.03W
Casper **96 C3** 42.50N 106.20W
Caspian Depression **119 F8**
Caspian Sea **119 F8**
Castañuelas **66 D3** 19.43N 71.29W
Castara **81 D7** 11.15N 60.40W
Castel **74 A4** 16.16N 61.38W
Castello de la Plana **108 D4** 39.59N 0.03W
Castelo Branco **108 B3** 39.50N 7.30W
Castelvetrano **108 F3** 37.41N 12.47E
Castillo **67 F3** 19.12N 70.01W
Castle Bruce **75 B3** 15.26N 61.15W
Castle Harbour **68 B2**
Castle Island **59 G3**
Castleton **63 E2** 18.11N 76.52W
Castres **108 D4** 43.36N 2.14E
Castries **76 B3** 14.01N 60.59W
Castries, district **76 B2**
Castries Waterworks Forest Reserve **76 B2**
Castrovillari **109 G3** 39.48N 16.12E
Castuera **108 B3** 38.44N 5.33W
Cat Island **58 F5**
Catadupa **62 C2** 18.17N 77.53W
Catalina, Isla **67 F2**
Catania **108 G3** 37.31N 15.06E
Cataño **69 B2** 18.26N 66.07W
Catanzaro **109 G3** 38.54N 16.36E
Cat Cays **58 B6**
Catoche, Cape **88 D3** 21.38N 87.08W
Cattlewash **78 C3** 13.13N 59.32W
Caucasus Mountains **119 F8**
Caura River **89 F1**
Cavalla Hill **73 A4** 16.46N 62.11W
Cave Hill **78 B4** 13.17N 59.35W
Caves Branch **86 B3** 17.10N 88.43W
Cave Valley **62 D2** 18.13N 77.21W
Caxias **98 F6** 4.53S 43.20W
Caxias do Sul **98 E4** 29.14S 51.10W
Cay **109 J3** 38.35N 31.01E
Cayenne **98 E7** 4.55N 52.18W
Caye Plate, cape **74 D3** 16.00N 61.14W
Caye Verte, island **84 E8**
Cayey **69 B2** 18.07N 66.10W
Cayey, Sierra de, mountains **69 B2**
Cayman Brac, island **65 C2**
Cayman Islands **65**
Cayman Ridge **14 C4**
Cayman Trench **14 C4**
Cayo, district **86 B2**
Cayo Icacos, island **69 C2**
Cayon **71 B3** 17.20N 62.43W
Cay Sal **58 A4**
Cay Sal Bank **14 C5**
Cazombo **116 C3** 11.54S 22.56E
Cecina **108 F4** 43.18N 10.31E
Cedar City **96 B2** 37.40N 113.04W
Cedar Crossing **86 B3** 17.42N 89.02W
Cedar Falls **97 D3** 42.34N 92.26W
Cedar Grove **72 B4** 17.09N 61.48W
Cedar Rapids **97 D3** 41.59N 91.39W
Cedar Tree Point **72 A2** 17.41N 61.52W
Cedar Valley **63 E1** 17.59N 76.35W
Cedros Bay **81 A2**
Cedros Island **96 B1**
Ceduna **126 D2** 32.08S 133.41E
Cegled **107 G2** 47.10N 19.47E
Ceiba **69 C2** 18.17N 65.39W
Cekhira **114 D5** 34.16N 10.03E
Celeste **80 C8** 12.12N 61.38W
Celje **107 G2** 46.15N 15.16E
Celle **106 E3** 52.37N 10.05E
Central Lagoon **86 C3**
Central Range **81 C3**
CENTRAL AFRICAN REPUBLIC **115 E2**
Central Aguirre **69 B1** 17.57N 66.14W
Central, Cordillera, mountains, Colombia **14 D1**
Central, Cordillera, mountains, Dominican Republic **67 D3**
Central, Cordillera, mountains, Puerto Rico **69 B2**
Centralia **94 F2** 46.43N 122.58W
Central Makran Range **124 A3**
Central Siberian Plateau **119 K10**
Centre, department **66 C3**
Centre Hills **73 A4**
Cephalonia, island **109 H3**
Cerigo, island **109 H3**
Cernavoda **109 I4** 44.20N 28.03E
Cerro de Pasco **98 C5** 10.43S 76.15W
Cerro de Punta, mountain **69 B2** 18.12N 66.36W
Cerrón, mountain **14 E3** 10.21N 70.40W
Cesis **107 I4** 57.18N 25.18E
Ceske Budejovice **106 F2** 49.00N 14.30E
Cesky Krumlov **108 F5** 48.49N 14.20E
Cesme **109 I3** 38.19N 26.20E
Cetinje **109 G4** 42.23N 18.55E
Ceuta **114 C5** 35.53N 5.19W
Cevicos **67 F3** 19.00N 69.59W
Ceyhan **109 K3** 37.02N 35.48E
Ceyhan River **109 K3**
Chacachacare, island **81 A4**
Chacorão Falls **99 E6** 6.20S 58.16W
Chad, Lake **114 E3**
CHAD, republic **115 E3**
Chagai **124 A3** 29.20N 64.44E
Chagos Archipelago **47 J2**
Chaguanas **81 C4** 10.31N 61.25W
Chaguanas, regional corporation **81 C4**
Chaguaramas **81 B4** 10.41N 61.39W
Chake Chake **116 D4** 5.12S 39.44E
Chalk Sound **68 B4**
Chalky Mountain **78 C3** 13.14N 59.33W
Challengers **71 B2** 17.18N 62.47W
Châlons-sur-Marne **108 D5** 48.58N 4.22E
Chalon-sur-Saône **108 C5** 46.47N 4.51E
Cham **106 F2** 49.13N 12.41E
Chambéry **108 E5** 45.34N 5.55E
Chamo, Lake **115 G2**
Champ Flore **74 A2** 14.44N 61.08W
Champlain, Lake **97 F3**
Champotón **88 C2** 19.20N 90.43W
Chancery Lane **78 C1** 13.03N 59.30W
Chances Peak **73 A3** 16.43N 62.10W
Chan Chen **86 B4** 18.28N 88.25W
Chandigarh **124 B4** 30.43N 76.47E
Chandler **96 B2** 33.19N 111.49W
Chandrapur **124 B2** 19.58N 79.21E
Changbai Mountains **122 D8**
Changchun **122 B8** 43.50N 125.20E
Chang Jiang, river **119 M7**
Changjin **122 C7** 40.21N 127.20E
Changyon **122 B6** 38.16N 125.04E
Channel Islands **108 C5**
Chantal **66 B2** 18.08N 73.52W
Chantimelle **80 C8** 12.12N 61.39W
Chaouèn **108 B3** 35.10N 5.16W
Chapala, Lake **88 B2**
Chapare, river **81 C4**
Chapelton **62 D2** 18.04N 77.16W
Chapra **124 C3** 25.46N 84.44E
Charcot Island **131 M3**
Chardonnières **66 A2** 18.15N 74.10W
Chari River **114 E3**
Charikar **124 A4** 35.02N 69.13E
Charity **85 B4** 7.15N 58.30W
Charleroi **106 D3** 50.25N 4.27E
Charles, Cape **91 L4** 37.08N 75.59W
Charles Rowe Bridge **78 C2** 13.07N 59.34W
Charleston, South Carolina **97 F2** 32.48N 79.58W
Charleston, St Vincent **77 D2** 12.42N 61.20W
Charleston, West Virginia **97 E2** 38.23N 81.40W
Charlestown **71 C1** 17.08N 62.37W
Charleville **126 E3** 26.24S 146.15E
Charlotte **97 E2** 35.12N 80.50W
Charlotte, parish **77 B2**
Charlotte Amalie, US Virgin Islands **70 B2** 18.22N 64.56W
Charlottesville **97 F2** 38.02N 78.29W
Charlottetown **95 L2** 46.14N 63.09W
Charlotteville **81 D7** 11.15N 60.30W
Charnocks **78 D1** 13.05N 59.30W
Charters Towers **126 E4** 20.05S 146.16E
Chartres **108 D5** 48.27N 1.30E
Charuma **81 D3** 10.23N 61.10W
Chateaubelair **77 A2** 13.17N 61.14W
Chateaubelair Island **77 A2**
Châteaubriant **108 C5** 47.43N 1.22W
Châteaudun **108 D5** 48.04N 1.20E
Château-Gaillard **74 B4** 16.18N 61.22W
Château Murat **74 C3** 15.55N 61.15W
Châteauroux **108 D5** 46.49N 1.41E
Châteaux, Pointe du **74 B4** 16.14N 61.10W
Châtellerault **106 D2** 46.49N 0.33E
Chatham, Canada **97 G3** 47.02N 65.30W
Chatham, Jamaica **62 C2** 18.28N 77.46W
Chatham Islands **47 N1**
Chato, Mount **99 C2** 42.35S 72.04W
Chattahoochee River **97 E2**
Chattanooga **97 E2** 35.02N 85.18W
Chaumont **108 D5** 48.07N 5.08E
Chaves **108 B4** 41.44N 7.28W
Cheb **106 F3** 50.08N 12.20E
Chechon **122 D5** 37.05N 128.09E
Cheeyou **81 D4** 10.33N 61.08W
Cheju **122 C3** 33.31N 126.29E

Danakil Depression **115 G3**
Daneborg **130 R3** 74.22N 20.07W
Danger Point **116 B1** 34.37S 19.17E
Dangila **115 G3** 11.18N 36.56E
Dangriga **86 B2** 16.59N 88.15W
Danli **54 A3** 14.00N 86.20W
Danube River **103 E2**
Danville **97 F2** 36.34N 79.25W
Daqing **122 B10** 46.37N 124.59E
d'Arago, Pointe **84 D8** 18.05N 63.05W
Daraj **114 E5** 30.10N 10.29E
Darbhanga **124 C3** 26.10N 85.54E
Dardanelles, passage **109 I3**
Dar es Salaam **116 D4** 6.51S 39.18E
Darién, Gulf of **14 D2**
Darjeeling **124 C3** 27.02N 88.20E
Darling River **127 E2**
Darliston **62 C2** 18.14N 77.58W
Darmstadt **106 E2** 49.52N 8.39E
Darnah **115 F5** 32.46N 22.39E
Darnley, Cape **131 F3** 67.16S 69.53E
Dartmouth **95 L2** 44.40N 63.35W
Darwin **126 D4** 12.27S 130.50E
Darwin, Mount **99 C1** 54.45S 69.20W
Dash Valley **78 C2** 13.06N 59.34W
Date **122 J8** 42.20N 140.53E
Daugavpils **107 I4** 55.52N 26.31E
Daulat Yar **124 A4** 34.33N 65.46E
Dauphin, district **76 B3**
Davangere **124 B2** 14.30N 75.52E
Davenport **97 D3** 41.32N 90.36W
Davenport Range **127 D3**
David **54 B2** 8.26N 82.26W
David Point **80 B8** 12.14N 61.39W
Davis, ant. base **131 F3** 68.35S 77.58E
Davis Cove **62 B2** 18.24N 78.14W
Davis Sea **131 E2**
Davis Strait **95 M4**
Davy Bight **68 B5**
Davy Hill **73 A4** 16.46N 62.11W
Dawa River **115 G2**
Dawson **94 E4** 64.04N 139.24W
Dawson Creek **94 F3** 55.46N 120.14W
Dayr az Zawr **115 G5** 35.20N 40.09E
Daytona Beach **97 E1** 29.11N 81.01W
De Aar **116 C1** 30.40S 24.01E
Deadman's Cay **58 F4** 23.13N 75.08W
Dead Sea **109 K2**
Deans Valley, river **62 B2**
Death Valley **96 B2**
Débé **81 C2** 10.13N 61.27W
Deblin **107 H3** 51.34N 21.50E
Debra Tabor **115 G3** 11.50N 38.26E
Debrecen **107 H2** 47.30N 21.37E
Debre Markos **115 G3** 10.19N 37.41E
Debundseha **114 D2** 4.15N 9.09E
Decatur **97 E3** 39.51N 88.57W
Deccan Plateau **124 B3**
Deep Creek **58 E5** 24.45N 76.16W
Deer Cay **86 B4**
Deering **94 B4** 66.04N 162.50W
Dehra Dun **124 B4** 30.19N 78.03E
Dej **109 H5** 47.08N 23.55E
Dekemhare **115 G3** 15.06N 39.00E
Delaford **81 D7** 11.15N 60.30W
Delagoa Bay **116 D2**
De Land **97 E1** 29.02N 81.18W
Delano **96 B2** 35.45N 119.16W
Delano Peak **96 B2** 38.23N 112.22W
Delaware Bay **97 F2**
Delaware, state **97 F2**
Delhi **97 F3** 42.17N 74.57W
Délices **75 B2** 15.17N 61.16W
Delicias **88 B3** 28.10N 105.30W
Del Rio **96 C1** 29.23N 100.56W
Dembidolo **115 G2** 8.34N 34.50E
Demerara, river **85 B3**
Demerara/Mahaica, admin. region **85 B5**
Deming **96 C2** 32.17N 107.46W
Demirci **109 I3** 39.03N 28.40E
Demnate **108 B2** 31.44N 6.59W
Demopolis **88 D4** 32.31N 87.50W
Denau **124 A4** 38.20N 67.54E
Dendi, mountain **115 G2** 8.50N 37.43E
Denham, Mount **62 C2** 18.13N 77.32W
Den Helder **106 D3** 52.58N 4.46E
Denizli **109 I3** 37.46N 29.05E
DENMARK, kingdom **106 E4**
Denmark Strait **95 O4**
Dennery **76 B2** 13.54N 60.53W
Dennery, district **76 B2**
Dennery, river **76 B2**
Dennery Waterworks Forest Reserve **76 B2**
Denton **96 D2** 33.14N 97.18W
D'Entrecasteaux Islands **127 F5**
D'Entrecasteaux, Point **127 B2** 34.50S 116.00E
Denver **96 C2** 39.45N 105.00W
Derby, Australia **126 C4** 17.19S 123.38E
Derby, UK **106 C3** 52.55N 1.30W
Dernberg, Cape **116 B2** 27.45S 15.33E
Dernière Riviere **76 B2** 13.57N 60.55W
Derrick **77 D1** 12.58N 61.17W
Desalination Plant **72 B4** 17.07N 61.45W
Desbarra **76 B2** 13.59N 60.54W
Dese **115 G3** 11.05N 39.40E
Desecheo Island **70 A9**
Deshaies **74 A4** 16.18N 61.46W
Desmariniéres **74 B1** 14.30N 60.58W
Des Moines **97 D3** 41.35N 93.35W
Desna River **107 J3**
Desruisseaux **76 B1** 13.47N 60.56W
Dessalines **66 C3** 19.15N 72.30W
Dessau **106 F3** 51.51N 12.15E
Dete **116 C3** 18.38S 26.50E
Detroit **97 E3** 42.23N 83.05W
Deva **109 H5** 45.53N 22.55E
Devil's Island **15 I2**
Devils Lake **96 D3** 48.08N 98.50W
Devil's Point **58 F5** 24.08N 75.30W
Devon Island **94 J5**
Devon Pen **63 E2** 18.11N 76.48W
Devonport **126 E1** 41.09S 146.16E
Devrek **109 J4** 41.14N 31.57E
Dewey **69 C2** 18.19N 65.18W
Dexter **97 D2** 36.48N 89.58W
Deyong, Cape **127 D5** 6.56S 138.33E
Dhaka **124 D3** 23.42N 90.22E
Dhamtari **124 C3** 20.43N 81.36E
Dhanbad **124 C3** 23.47N 86.32E
Dhenkanal **124 C3** 20.40N 85.39E
Dhoraji **124 B3** 21.42N 70.32E
Dhulia **124 B3** 20.54N 74.47E
Diable, du Pte, cape **74 B2** 14.46N 60.52W
Diamant, mountain **84 E7** 18.03N 63.04W
Diamant, Pte du **74 A1** 14.26N 61.02W
Diamantina River **127 E3**
Diamond Island **80 B1**
Diamond Corner **78 B4** 13.16N 59.36W
Dibrugarh **124 D3** 27.29N 94.56E
Dickinson **96 C3** 46.52N 102.49W
Dickinson Bay **72 A4**
Diego Martin, regional corporation **81 B4**
Diego Martin Village **81 B4** 10.43N 61.34W
Dieppe **108 D5** 49.55N 1.05E
Dieppe Bay **71 B3** 17.24N 62.50W
Diffa **114 E3** 13.28N 12.35E
Digne **108 E4** 44.05N 6.14E
Digoin **106 D2** 46.29N 3.54E
Dijon **108 D5** 47.20N 5.02E
Dikwa **114 E3** 12.01N 13.55E
Dillingham **94 C3** 59.03N 158.30W
Dinan **108 C5** 48.27N 2.02W
Dinar **109 I3** 38.05N 30.09E
Dinaric Alps **103 F2**
Dindigul **124 B2** 10.23N 78.00E
Dire Dawa **115 H2** 9.35N 41.50E
Disappointment, Lake **127 C3**
Discovery Bay **62 D2**
Discovery Bay **62 D2** 18.27N 77.24W
Disko Bay **95 M4**
Disko Island **95 M5**
Dispur **124 D3** 26.03N 91.52E
Distriti Nacional, province **67 F2**
Diu **124 B3** 20.41N 71.03E
Divnoye **109 L5** 45.55N 43.21E
Divrigi **109 K3** 39.23N 38.06E
Diyarbakir **109 K3** 37.55N 40.14E
Djambala **116 B4** 2.32S 14.43E
Djanet **114 D4** 24.34N 9.30E
Djelfa **114 D5** 34.43N 3.14E
Djerid, Lake **114 D5**
Djibouti **115 H3** 11.36N 43.09E
DJIBOUTI, republic **115 H3**
Djougou **114 D2** 9.40N 1.47E
Dmitrov **107 K4** 56.21N 37.34E
Dnepr River **103 H3**
Dneprodzerzhinsk **107 J2** 48.30N 34.37E
Dnepropetrovsk **109 K5** 48.29N 35.00E
Dnestr River **103 G2**
Dnieper River **107 J3**
Dniester River **107 I2**
Doberai Peninsula **127 D5**
Dobrich **109 I4** 43.34N 27.51E
Dodge City **96 C2** 37.45N 100.02W
Dodoma **116 D4** 6.10S 35.40E
Dog Island, Anguilla **70 C9**
Dog Island, US Virgin Islands **70 B2**
Dogo, island **122 F5**
Doha **118 G6** 25.15N 51.36E
Dolak, island **127 D5**
Dole **106 E2** 47.05N 5.30E
Dolo **115 H2** 4.11N 42.03E
Dolphin Head **116 B2** 25.43S 14.50E
Dolphin Head, mountain **62 B2** 18.22N 78.09W
Domazlice **106 F2** 49.26N 12.57E
Dombay **109 K4** 43.18N 41.39E
Dominica Passage **70 D7**
DOMINICA, republic **75**
DOMINICAN REPUBLIC **67 D2**
Don River **109 K6**
Don Christophers Point **63 E2** 18.20N 76.19W
Dondon **66 C3** 19.30N 72.10W
Dondra Head **124 C1** 5.55N 80.35E
Donetsk **109 K5** 48.00N 37.50E
Donets River **107 K2**
Dongola **115 G3** 19.10N 30.27E
Donna Cay **68 D4**
Dorado **69 B2** 18.28N 66.16W
Dordogne River **108 D4**
Dori **114 C3** 14.03N 0.02W
Dorohoi **109 I5** 47.57N 26.31E
Dortmund **106 E3** 51.32N 7.27E
Dothan **97 E2** 31.12N 85.25W
Douala **114 D2** 4.04N 9.43E
Douarnenez **108 C5** 48.05N 4.20W
Douglas, UK **106 C3** 54.09N 4.29W
Douglas, USA **89 D4** 31.30N 82.54W
Douro River **108 B4**
Douville **74 B4** 16.16N 61.22W
Dover, Barbados **78 C1** 13.03N 59.33W
Dover, UK **106 D3** 51.08N 1.19E
Dover, Strait of **108 D6**
Downtown **68 B4** 21.47N 72.15W
Dozen, island **122 F5**
Dragon Bay **63 F2**
Dragon's Mouth, passage **81 B4**
Drakensberg Mountains **111 F1**
Drake Passage **131 L2**
Drama **109 H4** 41.10N 24.11E
Drammen **106 F4** 59.45N 10.15E
Dresden **106 F3** 51.03N 13.45E
Drogheda **106 B3** 53.43N 6.21W
Drogobych **107 H2** 49.20N 23.30E
Drowned Cays **86 B3**
Drum Point **68 D8** 21.44N 71.28W
Drumheller **94 G3** 51.30N 112.46W
Drummondville **97 F3** 45.52N 72.30W
Dryden **94 I2** 49.48N 92.48W
Dry Ghaut, river **73 B3**
Dry Harbour Mountains **62 D2**
Duarte, Pico, mountain **67 E3** 19.02N 70.59W
Duarte, province **67 E3**
Duba **115 G4** 37.19N 35.46E
Dubawnt Lake **94 H4**
Dubawnt River **94 H4**
Dublanc **75 A3** 15.30N 61.28W
Dublanc, river **75 A3**
Dublin, Ireland **106 B3** 53.20N 6.15W
Dublin, USA **97 E2** 32.31N 82.54W
Dubna **107 K3** 54.09N 36.59E
Dubno **107 I3** 50.28N 25.40E
Dubrovnik **109 G4** 42.40N 18.07E
Dubuque **97 D3** 42.31N 90.41W
Duchesne **96 B3** 40.10N 110.24W
Duckenfield **63 F1** 17.54N 76.15W
Ducos **74 B1** 14.34N 60.58W
Dudley **106 C3** 52.30N 2.05W
Dugi Island **108 F4**
Duisburg **106 E3** 51.26N 6.45E
Duluth **97 D3** 46.45N 92.10W
Dumaine **74 A2** 14.42N 61.00W
Dumas **96 C2** 35.51N 101.57W
Dumfries, Grenada **80 C1** 12.28N 61.27W
Dumfries, UK **106 C4** 55.04N 3.37W
Dumont d'Urville, ant. base **131 B3** 68.40S 140.01E
Dumyât **109 J2** 31.26N 31.48E
Dunaujvaros **109 G5** 47.00N 18.55E
Duncan, Trinidad and Tobago **81 C3** 10.15N 61.28W
Duncan, USA **96 D2** 34.30N 97.57W
Duncans **62 C2** 18.28N 77.33W
Duncan Town **58 F3** 22.12N 75.42W
Dundalk **106 B3** 54.01N 6.25W
Dundas **94 L5** 76.35N 68.30W
Dundee, South Africa **116 D2** 28.10S 30.15E
Dundee, UK **106 C4** 56.28N 3.00W
Dunedin **126 H1** 45.53S 170.31E
Dunkirk **106 D3** 51.02N 2.23E
Dun Laoghaire **106 B3** 53.17N 6.08W
Dunmore Hill **81 C3** 10.16N 61.20W
Dunmore Town **58 E6** 25.31N 76.40W
Duquesne **80 B8** 12.12N 61.40W
Durango, Mexico **88 B3** 24.01N 104.40W
Durango, USA **96 C2** 37.15N 107.55W
Durban **116 D2** 29.53S 31.00E
Durham, UK **106 C3** 54.47N 1.34W
Durham, USA **97 F2** 36.00N 78.54W
Durmitor, mountain **109 G4** 43.08N 19.04E
Durrës **109 G4** 41.18N 19.28E
Dushanbe **124 A4** 38.38N 68.51E
Düsseldorf **106 E3** 51.13N 6.47E
Duvergé **66 D2** 18.22N 71.31W
Duvno **109 G4** 43.42N 17.13E
Düzce **109 J4** 40.51N 31.09E
Duzer **74 A5** 16.20N 61.43W
Dyer's **73 A3** 16.44N 62.11W
Dzerzhinsk **107 L4** 56.15N 43.30E
Dzhankoi **109 J5** 45.40N 34.20E

E

Eagle Pass **96 C1** 28.44N 100.31W
Easington **63 E1** 17.54N 76.34W
East Berbice/Corentyne, admin. region **85 C2**
East Caicos, island **68 D8**
East Cape **127 F5** 4.15S 153.00E
East Cay **68 E7**
East China Sea **122 C3**
East End, Anguilla **73 C2** 18.14N 62.59W
East End, Cayman Islands **65 A1** 19.18N 81.07W
East End Point **59 C1** 26.31N 77.54W
East End, US Virgin Islands **70 C2** 18.27N 64.40W
Easter Island **12 D2**
Eastern Ghats, mountains **124 C2**
Eastern Pointe **84 E8** 18.07N 63.01W
Eastern Sierra Madre, mountains **88 B3**
East Falkland, island **99 E1**
East Hampton **95 K2** 40.58N 72.11W
East Korea Bay **122 C6**
East London **116 C1** 33.00S 27.54E
Eastmain **95 K3** 52.10N 78.30W
Eastmain River **95 K3**
East Pacific Ridge **12 D2**
East Point, British Virgin Islands **70 D3** 18.33N 64.17W
East Point, Cayman Islands **65 C2** 19.41N 79.59W
East Point, Curaçao **84 F3** 12.02N 68.45W
East Point, US Virgin Islands **70 F2** 17.45N 64.37W
East Siberian Sea **119 R11**
Eau Claire **97 D3** 44.50N 91.30W
Ebenezer **72 A4** 17.05N 61.51W
Eberswalde **106 F3** 52.50N 13.50E
Ebolowa **114 E2** 2.56N 11.11E
Ebro River **108 C4**
Ecclesville **81 D3** 10.19N 61.08W
Ech Cheliff **114 D5** 36.11N 1.21E
Ech Chergui, Lake **108 C2**
ECUADOR, republic **98 B6**
Edd **115 H3** 13.57N 41.38E
Ed Damer **115 G3** 17.37N 33.59E
Ed Dueim **115 G3** 14.00N 32.20E
Edéa **114 D2** 3.47N 10.13E
Edessa **109 H4** 40.48N 22.03E
Edey **78 C2** 13.05N 59.32W
Edgeworth David **131 D3** 65.50S 102.00E
Edinburgh **106 C4** 55.57N 3.13W
Edirne **109 I4** 41.40N 26.34E
Edmond **96 D2** 35.40N 97.30W
Edmond Forest Reserve **76 A2**
Edmonton **94 G3** 53.34N 113.25W
Edmundston **97 G3** 47.22N 68.20W
Edremit **109 I3** 39.34N 27.01E
Edson **94 G3** 53.36N 116.28W
Edward, Lake **116 C4**
Efate, island **127 G4**
Eger **107 H2** 47.53N 20.28E
Egersund **106 E4** 58.27N 6.01E
Egridir **109 J3** 37.52N 30.51E
EGYPT, Arab republic **115 F4**
Eidsvoll **106 F5** 60.19N 11.14E
Eight Mile Rock **59 B1** 26.33N 78.46W
Eil **115 H2** 8.00N 49.49E
Eindhoven **106 D3** 51.26N 5.30E
Eisenach **106 F3** 50.59N 10.19E
Eisenhüttenstadt **109 F6** 52.09N 14.39E
El Aaiún **114 B4** 27.10N 13.11W
El Alamein **115 F5** 30.48N 28.58E
El Aricha **108 C2** 34.12N 1.18W
El Arîsh **109 J2** 31.08N 33.48E
Elat **109 J1** 29.33N 34.57E
El Atrun Oasis **115 F3** 18.12N 26.40E
Elazig **109 K3** 38.41N 39.14E
Elba, island **108 E4**
El Banco **54 D2** 9.04N 73.59W
Elbasan **109 G4** 41.07N 20.05E
El Bayadh **108 D2** 33.40N 1.00E
Elbe River **106 E3**
Elbert, Mount **96 C2** 39.05N 106.27W
Elbistan **109 K3** 38.14N 37.11E
Elblag **107 G3** 54.10N 19.25E
Elbrus, Mount **109 L4** 43.21N 42.29E
El Cajon **96 B2** 32.48N 116.58W
El Callao **55 F2** 7.18N 61.50W
El Carrizal **66 D3** 19.20N 71.37W
El Cercado **66 D2** 18.43N 71.31W
Elche **108 C3** 38.16N 0.41W
Elderslie **62 C2** 18.13N 77.47W
El Djem **114 E5** 35.15N 10.15E
El Dorado **97 D2** 37.51N 96.52W
Elektrostal **107 K4** 55.46N 38.30E
Eleuthera, island **54 C6**
Eleuthera Island **58 E6**
El Faiyûm **115 G4** 29.19N 30.50E
El Ferrol **108 B4** 43.29N 8.14W
Elgin **106 C4** 57.39N 3.20W
El Gir **115 F3** 19.50N 28.18E
El Gîza **115 G5** 30.01N 31.12E
El Golea **114 D5** 30.35N 2.51E
Elgon, Mount **115 G2** 1.07N 34.35E
El Hamma **114 D5** 33.50N 9.45E
el Hodna, Lake **108 E3**
Elías Pina, province **66 D3**
Elista **109 L5** 46.18N 44.14E
Elizabeth **97 F3** 40.40N 74.13W
Elizabeth City **97 F2** 36.18N 76.16W
El Jobo **67 D2** 18.21N 71.12W
Elk **107 H3** 53.51N 22.20E
El Khârga **115 G4** 25.27N 30.32E
Elko **96 B3** 40.50N 115.46W
Ellerton **78 C2** 13.07N 59.32W
Ellesmere Island **94 K6**
Elliot Lake **97 E3** 46.24N 82.41W
Ellsworth Land **131 N3**
Elmali **109 J3** 36.43N 29.56E
El Mansûra **109 J2** 31.03N 31.23E
El Minya **115 G4** 28.06N 30.45E
El Obeid **115 F3** 13.11N 30.13E
El Oued **114 D5** 33.30N 6.45E
El Paso **96 C2** 31.45N 106.30W
El Portillo **67 F3** 19.19N 69.33W
El Real **54 C2** 8.10N 77.35W
EL SALVADOR, republic **88 C2**
El Seibo **67 F2** 18.45N 69.00W
El Seibo, province **67 F2**
El Shab **115 F4** 22.34N 29.52E
El Tigre **55 F2** 8.44N 64.18W
El Tucuche, mountain **81 C4** 10.44N 61.25W
El Tûr **109 J1** 28.14N 33.36E
Eluru **124 C2** 16.45N 81.10E
El Valle **67 F2** 18.58N 69.22W
Elverum **106 F5** 60.54N 11.33E
El Wak **115 H2** 2.48N 40.55E
Ely **96 B2** 39.15N 114.53W
El Yunque, mountain **69 C2** 18.19N 65.48W
Emanuel **72 B4** 17.04N 61.49W
Emden **106 E3** 53.23N 7.13E
Emerald **126 E3** 23.30S 148.10E
Emi Koussi, mountain **115 E3** 19.52N 18.31E
Emine, Cape **109 I4** 42.40N 27.56E
Emirdag **109 J3** 39.01N 31.09E
Emmastad **84 E3** 12.10N 68.57W
Emmen **106 E3** 52.47N 6.55E
Emporia **97 D2** 38.24N 96.10W
Enderby Land **131 G3**
Enfida **108 F3** 36.03N 10.27E
Engaño, Cape **67 G2** 18.35N 68.20W
England, state **106 D3**
Englewood **96 C2** 39.39N 105.00W
English Channel **106 D3**
English Harbour **72 B3**
English Point **68 E3** 21.27N 71.09W
English Harbour Town **72 B4** 17.00N 61.45W
Enid **96 D2** 36.24N 97.54W
En Nahud **115 F3** 12.41N 28.28E
En Nebk **109 K2** 34.02N 36.43E
Ennedi Plateau **115 F3**
Ennis **106 B3** 52.50N 8.59W
Enniskillen **106 B3** 54.21N 7.38W
Enriquillo **67 D1** 17.54N 71.14W
Enriquillo, Lake **66 D2**
Enschede **106 E3** 52.13N 6.55E
Ensenada **88 A4** 31.53N 116.35W
Ensenado **69 B1** 17.58N 66.55W
Entebbe **115 G2** 0.05N 32.29E
Enterprise, Barbados **78 C1** 13.03N 59.32W
Enterprise, Trinidad and Tobago **81 C4** 10.31N 61.23W
Enugu **114 D2** 6.20N 7.29E
Épernay **106 D2** 49.02N 3.58E
Épinal **108 E5** 48.10N 6.28E
Epira **85 C3** 5.05N 57.20W
EQUATORIAL GUINEA, republic **114 D2**
Erbaa **109 K4** 40.42N 36.37E
Erciyas, Mount **109 K3** 38.32N 35.27E
Erdemli **109 J3** 36.35N 34.19E
Erebus, Mount **131 A3** 77.40S 167.20E
Eregli **109 J4** 41.17N 31.26E
Erfurt **106 F3** 50.58N 11.02E
Ergani **109 K3** 38.17N 39.44E
Erg Chech, desert **114 C4**
Erg Iguidi, desert **114 C4**
Erie **97 E3** 42.07N 80.05W
Erie, Lake **97 E3**
Erigavo **115 H3** 10.40N 47.20E
Erimo, Cape **122 K7** 41.55N 143.13E
Erin Bay **81 B2**
ERITREA, republic **115 G3**
Erlangen **106 F2** 49.36N 11.02E
Erode **124 B2** 11.21N 77.43E
Errol **95 K2** 44.47N 71.10W
Erromango, island **127 G4**
Er Roseires **115 G3** 11.52N 34.23E
Erymanthus, mountain **109 H3** 37.50N 21.55E
Erzincan **109 K3** 39.44N 39.30E
Esan, Cape **122 J7** 41.49N 141.12E
Esashi **122 K9** 44.58N 142.38E
Esbjerg **106 E4** 55.28N 8.28E
Escambray, Sierra del, mountains **60 D2**
Escanaba **97 E3** 45.47N 87.04W
Escocesa Bay **67 F3**
Escondido **96 B2** 33.07N 117.07W
Escuinapa **88 B3** 22.49N 105.44W
Escuintla **88 C2** 14.18N 90.47W
Esfahan **118 G7** 32.41N 51.41E
Eskisehir **109 J3** 39.46N 30.30E
Esla River **108 B4**
Espagnol Point **77 B3** 13.21N 61.07W
Espaillat, province **67 E3**
Espanola **96 C2** 35.59N 106.05W
Esperalvillo **67 E2** 18.49N 70.01W
Esperance **126 C2** 33.52S 121.54E
Esperanza, ant. base **131 L3** 63.24S 56.59W
Esperanza, Cuba **60 C3** 22.20N 80.10W

Madurai **124 B1** 9.55N 78.07E
Maebashi **122 I5** 36.24N 139.04E
Maestra, Sierra, mountains **60 E2**
Mafia Island **116 E4**
Magadan **130 H2** 59.38N 150.50E
Magangue **54 D2** 9.14N 74.46W
Magdalena, Mexico **88 A4** 30.38N 110.59W
Magdalena, USA **96 C2** 34.06N 107.14W
Magdalena River **89 E1**
Magdeburg **106 F3** 52.08N 11.37E
Magellan, Strait of **99 C1**
Maggotty **62 C2** 18.09N 77.46W
Maghâgha **109 J1** 28.39N 30.50E
Maghnia **108 C2** 34.50N 1.45W
Magwe **124 D3** 20.08N 94.55E
Mahaica/Berbice, admin. region **85 B5**
Mahaicony **85 C4** 6.30N 57.45W
Mahajanga **116 F2** 15.40S 46.20E
Mahalapye **116 C2** 23.05S 26.51E
Mahalla **109 J2** 30.59N 31.10E
Maharès **114 E5** 34.35N 10.30E
Mahaut, Dominica **75 B2** 15.21N 61.24W
Mahaut, Guadeloupe **74 A4** 16.10N 61.46W
Mahdia, Algeria **108 D3** 35.26N 1.40E
Mahdia, Guyana **85 B3** 5.10N 59.10W
Mahe **124 B2** 11.41N 75.31E
Mahogany Tree **73 B2** 18.13N 63.03W
Mahón **108 D3** 39.54N 4.15E
Maiduguri **114 E3** 11.53N 13.16E
Maihar **124 C3** 24.14N 80.50E
Maikop **109 L4** 44.37N 40.48E
Maimana **124 A4** 35.54N 64.43E
Mai-Ndombe, Lake **116 B4**
Maine, state **97 G3**
Main Ridge, mountains **81 D7**
Maintirano **116 F2** 18.01S 44.03E
Mainz **106 E2** 50.00N 8.16E
Maipo, mountain **99 D3** 34.10S 69.52W
Maipuri Landing **85 B3** 4.30N 58.30W
Maiquetía **55 E3** 10.38N 66.59W
Maisí, Cape **61 F2** 20.10N 74.05W
Maïssade **66 C3** 19.10N 72.08W
Maizuru **122 G4** 35.30N 135.20E
Majorca, island **108 D3**
Major's Bay **71 C2**
Majuro **47 M3** 7.05N 171.23E
Makeni **114 B2** 8.57N 12.02W
Makeyevka **109 K5** 48.01N 38.00E
Makgadikgadi Pan, lake **116 C2**
Makkah **115 H4** 21.26N 39.49E
Mako **109 H5** 46.11N 20.30E
Makokou **116 B5** 0.38N 12.47E
Makoua **114 E1** 0.01S 15.40E
Maktar **108 E3** 35.50N 9.12E
Makurdi **114 D2** 7.44N 8.35E
Malabo **114 D2** 3.45N 8.48E
Mal Aborder, island **84 F7**
Málaga **108 C3** 36.43N 4.25W
Malaimbandy **116 F1** 20.20S 45.35E
Malaita, island **127 G5**
Malakal **115 G2** 9.31N 31.40E
Malakula, island **127 G4**
Malange **116 B4** 9.36S 16.21E
Malatya **109 K3** 38.22N 38.18E
Malawi, Lake **116 D3**
MALAWI, republic **116 D3**
Malay Peninsula **119 L4**
MALAYSIA, federal republic **118 L4**
Malcolm, Point **127 C2** 33.48S 123.45E
Malcolm Roads, bay **68 A4**
MALDIVES, republic **124 B1**
Male **118 I4** 4.00N 73.28E
Malea, Cape **109 H3** 36.27N 23.12E
Malegaon **124 B3** 20.32N 74.38E
MALI, republic **114 C3**
Malin **109 I6** 50.48N 29.08E
Malindi **115 H1** 3.14S 40.08E
Malmesbury **116 B1** 33.28S 18.43E
Malmö **106 F4** 55.35N 13.00E
Maloyaroslavets **107 K4** 55.00N 36.28E
Malpelo Island **14 C1**
MALTA, independent state **108 F3**
Malvern **62 C1** 17.58N 77.41W
Mambéré River **114 E2**
Mamma Cannes **80 C6** 12.04N 61.39W
Mamon **81 D3** 10.28N 61.10W
Mamoré River **99 D5**
Mamou **114 B3** 10.24N 12.05W
Man **114 C2** 7.31N 7.37W
Managua **54 A3** 12.06N 86.18W
Managua, Lake **14 B3**
Manakara **116 F1** 22.09S 48.00E
Mananjary **116 F1** 21.13S 48.20E
Manar, Mount **115 H3** 14.01N 44.23E
Manassas **108 B3** 38.45N 8.00W
Manati **69 B2** 18.27N 66.30W
Manaus **98 E6** 3.06S 60.00W
Manavgat **109 J3** 36.47N 31.28E
Manchester, UK **106 C3** 53.30N 2.15W
Manchester, USA **97 F3** 42.59N 71.28W
Manchester, parish **62 C2**
Manchineel Bay **80 C1**
Manchioneal **63 F2** 18.06N 76.17W
Manchuria, region **119 N8**
Mandab, Strait of **115 H3**
Mandal, Afghanistan **124 A4** 33.14N 61.50E
Mandal, Norway **106 E4** 58.02N 7.30E
Mandalay **124 D3** 21.57N 96.04E
Mandan **96 C3** 46.49N 100.54W
Mandeville **62 C2** 18.03N 77.31W
Mandla **124 C3** 22.35N 80.28E
Manfalût **115 G4** 27.23N 30.58E
Manfredonia **109 G4** 41.37N 15.55E
Mangalia **109 I4** 43.48N 28.36E
Mangalore **124 B2** 12.54N 74.51E
Mangoky River **116 F1**
Mangrove Cay, Bahamas **58 C5**
Mangrove Cay, Turks and Caicos Islands **68 D4**
Manhattan **97 D2** 39.11N 96.35W
Maniche **66 B2** 18.20N 73.48W
Manila **118 N5** 14.36N 120.59E
Manisa **109 I3** 38.36N 27.29E
Manistee **97 E3** 44.14N 86.20W
Manitoba, Lake **94 I3**
Manitoba, province **94 I3**
Manizales **98 C7** 5.03N 75.32W
Manja **116 F1** 21.24S 44.20E
Manjimup **126 B2** 34.15S 116.09E
Mankono **114 C2** 8.01N 6.09W
Mannar, Gulf of **124 B1**
Man of War Bay **81 D7**
Manono **116 C4** 7.18S 27.24E
Man Point **77 E2** 13.07N 61.09W
Mansa **116 C3** 11.10S 28.52E
Mansel Island **94 J4**
Mansfield, Louisiana **88 C4** 32.02N 93.41W
Mansfield, Ohio **97 E3** 40.46N 82.31W
Mantes-la-Jolie **108 D5** 48.59N 1.43E
Manus, island **127 E5**
Manzanilla Point **81 D4** 10.31N 61.01W
Manzanillo, Cuba **60 E2** 20.21N 77.10W
Manzanillo, Mexico **88 B2** 19.00N 104.20W
Manzanillo, Point **14 D2** 9.37N 79.36W
Manzini **116 D2** 26.30S 31.22E
Mao **67 D3** 19.30N 71.10W
Maoke Range **127 D5**
Mapp Hill **78 C2** 13.06N 59.34W
Maputo **116 D2** 25.58S 32.35E
Maquela do Zombo **116 B4** 6.06S 15.12E
Mara **85 C3** 6.00N 57.30W
Maracaibo **54 D3** 10.44N 71.37W
Maracaibo, Lake **14 E3**
Maracas Bay **81 C5**
Maracas, river **81 C4**
Maracay **55 E3** 10.20N 67.28W
Maradah **115 E4** 29.15N 19.14E
Maradi **114 D3** 13.29N 7.10E
Marahuaca **15 F1** 3.37N 65.25W
Marajó Island **99 F6**
Maralal **115 G2** 1.05N 36.42E
Maralinga **126 D2** 30.10S 131.35E
Marambio, ant. base **131 L3** 64.13S 56.38W
Maran **80 B8** 12.10N 61.43W
Marañón River **99 C6**
Maras **109 K3** 37.34N 36.54E
Maraval **81 B4** 10.42N 61.31W
Maraval, river **81 B4**
Marble Bar **126 C3** 21.10S 119.45E
Marchena **108 B3** 37.20N 5.24W
March Town **62 B2** 18.21N 78.16W
Mardan **124 B4** 34.14N 72.05E
Mar del Plata **98 E3** 38.00S 57.32W
Mardin **115 H5** 37.19N 40.43E
Mareeba **126 E4** 17.00S 145.26E
Marek **115 H2** 3.46N 47.15E
Marganets **109 J5** 47.35N 34.37E
Margarita, island **55 F3**
Margate **116 D1** 30.51S 30.22E
Margherita, mountain **116 C5** 0.23N 29.54E
Margo Desert **124 A4**
Marguerita Bay **73 A4**
Marhoum **114 D5** 34.26N 0.05W
Maria Island **76 B1**
Mariana Trench **13 L3**
Marianao **60 B3** 23.00N 82.20W
Marianske Lazne **106 F2** 49.59N 12.40E
Marías Islands **88 B3**
Mariato, Point **14 C2** 7.12N 80.52W
María Trinidad Sánchez, province **67 E3**
Maribor **109 G5** 46.34N 15.38E
Maricao **69 B2** 18.11N 66.58W
Marie Byrd Land **131 P3**
Marie Galante, island **70 D7**
Mariel **60 B3** 22.55N 82.45W
Mariental **116 B2** 24.36S 17.59E
Marigot, Dominica **75 B3** 15.32N 61.17W
Marigot, Grenada **80 A7** 12.07N 61.44W
Marigot, Guadeloupe **74 A4** 16.04N 61.46W
Marigot, Haiti **66 C2** 18.13N 72.18W
Marigot, Martinique **74 A2** 14.48N 61.02W
Marigot, St Martin **84 D7** 18.04N 63.05W
Marigot Bay **76 A2** 13.58N 61.01W
Marijampole **107 H3** 54.31N 23.20E
Marin, province **74 B1**
Marinette **97 E3** 45.06N 87.38W
Marion **97 E2** 37.42N 88.58W
Marion, Lake **97 E2**
Maripa **85 B4** 6.30N 58.15W
Maris, The, islands **58 D7**
Marisule **76 B3** 14.02N 60.58W
Mariupol **109 K5** 47.05N 37.34E
Markham, Mount **131 A4** 82.45S 160.25E
Marmande **108 C4** 44.30N 0.10E
Marmara, island **109 I4**
Marmara, Sea of **109 I4**
Marmaris **109 I3** 36.52N 28.17E
Marmora, mountain **108 E4** 39.59N 9.20E
Maroa **55 E1** 2.43N 67.33W
Maromokotro, mountain **116 F2** 14.01S 49.00E
Marondera **116 D3** 18.15S 31.33E
Maroni, river **15 I2**
Maroon Town **62 C2** 18.21N 77.48W
Maroua **114 E3** 10.35N 14.20E
Marovoay **116 F2** 16.05S 46.40E
Marquesas Islands **12 C2**
Marquette **97 E3** 46.33N 87.23W
Marquis, Cape **76 B3** 14.02N 60.52W
Marquis Island **80 C7**
Marquis, river **76 B3**
Marrakech **114 C5** 31.49N 8.00W
Marrupa **116 D3** 13.10S 37.30E
Marsabit **115 G2** 2.20N 37.59E
Marsala **108 F3** 37.48N 12.27E
Mars Bay **58 D4** 23.49N 77.33W
Marseille **108 E4** 43.18N 5.22E
Marshall, Liberia **114 B2** 6.10N 10.23W
Marshall, USA **97 D3** 44.26N 95.46W
MARSHALL ISLANDS, independent state **47 M3**
Marsh Harbour **58 D7** 26.31N 77.05W
Marte **114 E3** 12.23N 13.46E
Martha Brae, river **62 C2**
Martin **109 G5** 49.05N 18.55E
Martinique, island **74**
Martinique Passage **70 D7**
Marudi Mountains **85 B2**
Mary **124 A4** 37.42N 61.54E
Maryborough **126 F3** 25.32S 152.42E
Maryland, state **97 F2**
Masan **122 D4** 35.10N 128.35E
Maseru **116 C2** 29.19S 27.29E
Mason City **97 D3** 43.10N 93.10W
Mason Hall **81 D6** 11.10N 60.40W
Massachusetts, state **97 F3**
Massacre **75 B2** 15.20N 61.24W
Massenya **114 E3** 11.21N 16.09E
Massiah Street **78 D2** 13.09N 59.29W
Massif Central, mountains **108 D4**
Massif de la Hotte, mountains **66 A2**
Massif de la Selle, mountains **66 C2**
Massif du Nord, mountains **66 C3**
Masson Island **131 E3**
Mastic Point **58 D6** 25.05N 77.59W
Masuda **122 E4** 34.42N 131.51E
Masvingo **116 D3** 20.10S 30.49E
Matadi **116 B4** 5.50S 13.32E
Matagalpa **54 A3** 12.52N 85.58W
Matam **114 B3** 15.40N 13.18W
Matamoros, central Mexico **88 B3** 25.33N 103.15W
Matamoros, eastern Mexico **88 C3** 25.50N 97.31W
Matandu, river **116 D4**
Matane **95 L2** 48.50N 67.31W
Matanzas **60 C3** 23.04N 81.35W
Matanzas, province **60 C3**
Matatiele **116 C1** 30.20S 28.49E
Matehuala **88 B3** 23.40N 100.40W
Matelot **81 D5** 10.49N 61.12W
Matersons Point **68 E3** 21.27N 71.08W
Mateur **108 E3** 37.03N 9.40E
Mathura **124 B3** 27.30N 77.42E
Mato Grosso, Plateau of **99 E5**
Matouba **74 A4** 16.02N 61.40W
Matruh **109 I2** 31.21N 27.15E
Matsue **122 F4** 35.29N 133.04E
Matsumae **122 I7** 41.28N 140.06E
Matsumoto **122 I5** 36.18N 137.58E
Matsuyama **122 F3** 33.50N 132.47E
Matterhorn, mountain **108 E5** 45.59N 7.39E
Matthews Ridge **85 A4** 7.30N 60.03W
Matthew Town **59 H1** 20.55N 73.42W
Matura **81 D4** 10.40N 61.04W
Matura Bay **81 D4**
Matura, river **81 D4**
Maturín **55 F2** 9.45N 63.10W
Maui, island **96 B1**
Maun **116 C2** 20.00S 23.25E
Maunabo **69 C2** 18.00N 65.55W
Mauna Kea, mountain **96 B1** 19.50N 155.25W
MAURITANIA, Islamic republic **114 B3**
MAURITIUS, independent state **47 I2**
Mavinga **116 C3** 15.44S 20.21E
Mavis Bank **63 E2** 18.01N 76.40W
Mawson, ant. base **131 F3** 67.36S 62.52E
Maxwell Coast **78 C1** 13.03N 59.33W
Maya Mountains **14 B4**
Mayaguana Island **59 H3**
Mayaguana Passage **59 H3**
Mayagüez **69 A2** 18.13N 67.09W
Mayagüez Bay **69 A2**
Mayagüez, district **69 B2**
Mayari **61 F2** 20.40N 75.35W
Mayaro Bay **81 E2**
Mayaro, regional corporation **81 D2**
May Day Mountains **62 C1**
Mayo **81 C3** 10.21N 61.23W
May Pen **63 D1** 17.58N 77.14W
Mayreau, island **77 C1**
Mayumba **116 B4** 3.23S 10.38E
Mazabuka **116 C3** 15.50S 27.47E
Mazar-i-Sharif **124 A4** 36.43N 67.05E
Mazaruni, river **85 B4**
Mazatlán **88 B3** 23.11N 106.25W
Mbabane **116 D2** 26.20S 31.08E
Mbaiki **115 E2** 3.53N 18.01E
Mbala **116 D4** 8.49S 31.20E
Mbale **115 G2** 1.04N 34.12E
Mbandaka **116 B5** 0.03N 18.28E
Mbanza-Ngungu **116 B4** 5.17S 14.51E
Mbarara **115 G1** 0.36S 30.40E
Mbeya **116 D4** 8.54S 33.29E
Mbour **114 B3** 14.22N 16.54W
Mbuji-Mayi **116 C4** 6.10S 23.39E
Mead, Lake **96 B2**
Mechelen **106 D3** 51.02N 4.29E
Mecheria **114 C5** 33.31N 0.20W
Medan **118 K4** 3.35N 98.39E
Medea **108 D3** 36.15N 2.48E
Medellín **98 C7** 6.15N 75.36W
Medford **96 A3** 42.19N 122.52W
Media Luna **60 E2** 20.05N 77.25W
Medias **109 H5** 46.10N 24.21E
Medicine Hat **94 G3** 50.03N 110.41W
Medina **97 F3** 43.14N 78.23W
Medina Bank **86 B2** 16.28N 88.45W
Medina del Campo **108 C4** 41.18N 4.55W
Mediterranean Sea **108 E3**
Medvezhegorsk **107 J5** 62.56N 34.28E
Medvezhya, Mount **122 I10** 47.26N 137.56E
Meerut **124 B3** 29.00N 77.42E
Mega **115 G2** 4.00N 38.19E
Meharry, Mount **127 B3** 22.59S 118.35E
Mehsana **124 B3** 23.36N 72.24E
Mejaz el Bab **108 E3** 36.39N 9.40E
Mekele **115 G3** 13.32N 39.33E
Meknès **114 C5** 33.53N 5.37W
Mekong River **119 L5**
Melbourne, Australia **126 E2** 37.49S 144.58E
Melbourne, USA **97 E1** 28.04N 80.38W
Melilla **114 C5** 35.20N 3.00W
Melitopol **109 K5** 46.51N 35.22E
Melrhir, Lake **108 E2**
Melun **106 D2** 48.32N 2.40E
Melverton **78 C2** 13.07N 59.31W
Melville **94 H3** 50.57N 102.49W
Melville Island, Australia **127 D4**
Melville Island, Canada **94 G5**
Melville Peninsula **94 J4**
Melville Hall, river **75 B3**
Melvin Hill **78 C3** 13.12N 59.33W
Memmingen **106 F2** 47.59N 10.11E
Memphis **97 E2** 35.10N 90.00W
Mendocino, Cape **96 A3** 40.26N 124.24W
Mendoza **98 D3** 32.48S 68.52W
Menemen **109 I3** 38.34N 27.03E
Menihec, Lake **95 L3**
Menominee **97 E3** 45.07N 87.37W
Menongue **116 B3** 14.40S 17.41E
Merano **106 F2** 46.41N 11.10E
Merca **115 H2** 1.42N 44.47E
Merced **96 A2** 37.17N 120.30W
Mérida, Mexico **54 A5** 20.59N 89.39W
Mérida, Spain **108 B3** 38.55N 6.20W
Mérida, Venezuela **54 D2** 8.37N 71.08W
Mérida Mountains **89 E1**
Mérida, Cordillera de, mountains **14 E2**
Meridian **97 E2** 32.21N 88.48W
Méro **75 A2** 15.25N 61.26W
Merowe **115 G3** 18.30N 31.49E
Merredin **126 B2** 31.29S 118.16E
Merritt **94 F3** 50.09N 120.49W
Mersin **109 J3** 36.47N 34.37E
Merume Mountains **85 A3**
Mesolongion **109 H3** 38.21N 21.26E
Mesopotamia **77 A2** 13.10N 61.10W
Messina, Italy **108 G3** 38.13N 15.33E
Messina, South Africa **116 D2** 22.23S 30.00E
Meta River **14 E1**
Metz **108 E5** 49.07N 6.11E
Mexia **97 D2** 31.41N 96.30W
Mexicali **88 A4** 32.36N 115.30W
MEXICO, federal republic **88 B3**
Mexico, Gulf of **88 C3**
Mexico City **88 C2** 19.25N 99.10W
Mezen **102 I4** 65.50N 44.20E
Mezotur **107 H2** 47.00N 20.37E
Miami **97 E1** 25.45N 80.15W
Miami Beach **97 E1** 25.47N 80.07W
Miches **67 F2** 18.58N 69.03W
Michigan, Lake **97 E3**
Michigan, state **97 E3**
Michurinsk **107 L3** 52.54N 40.30E
Micoud **76 B1** 13.49N 60.53W
Micoud, district **76 B1**
MICRONESIA, FEDERATED STATES OF **47 L3**
Mid-Atlantic Ridge **12 G2**
Middle Andaman, island **124 D2**
Middle Bank **86 B2** 16.50N 88.20W
Middle Caicos, island **68 B8**
Middle Island **71 B2** 17.20N 62.50W
Middle Peak **63 E2** 18.03N 76.34W
Middle Quarters **62 C2** 18.06N 77.49W
Middle Region **84 E7** 18.02N 63.02W
Middlesbrough **106 C3** 54.35N 1.14W
Middlesex **62 B2** 18.23N 78.11W
Middlesex, county **63 D2**
Mid-Indian Ridge **13 J2**
Midland, Michigan **97 E3** 43.38N 84.14W
Midland, Texas **96 C2** 32.00N 102.09W
Mielec **109 H6** 50.18N 21.25E
Mieres **108 B4** 43.15N 5.46W
Mikhailovka **109 L6** 50.05N 43.15E
Mikindani **116 D3** 10.16S 40.05E
Mikkeli **107 I5** 61.44N 27.15E
Mikonos, island **109 I3**
Mikuni Range **122 I5**
Miladunmadulu Atoll **124 B1**
Milan **108 E5** 45.28N 9.12E
Milas **109 I3** 37.19N 27.48E
Milbank **97 D3** 45.15N 96.32W
Mildura **126 E2** 34.11S 142.10E
Mile and a Quarter **78 B4** 13.15N 59.37W
Mile Gully **62 C2** 18.08N 77.33W
Milepa **116 D3** 11.45S 36.17E
Miles City **96 C3** 46.24N 105.48W
Milford Haven **106 B3** 51.44N 5.02W
Milk River, Canada,U.S.A. **96 B3**
Milk, river, Jamaica **62 D1**
Millau **108 D4** 44.06N 3.05E
Millbank **63 F2** 18.03N 76.24W
Mille Lacs, lake **97 D3**
Millet **76 B2** 13.54N 61.00W
Milligan Cay **77 B1**
Millinocket **95 L2** 45.42N 68.43W
Mill Island **131 E3**
Mill Reef **72 B2** 17.03N 61.41W
Mill River Canal **62 D1**
Milos, island **109 H3**
Milton Keynes **108 C6** 52.02N 0.42W
Milwaukee **97 E3** 43.03N 87.56W
Milwaukee Deep **15 F4**
Mimizan **108 C4** 44.12N 1.14W
Minas de Matahambre **60 A3** 22.35N 83.50W
Mindanao, island **119 N4**
Minden **106 E3** 52.18N 8.54E
Mingan **95 L3** 50.19N 64.02W
Minho River **108 B4**
Minicoy Island **124 B1**
Ministre Point **76 B1** 13.42N 60.56W
Minna **114 D2** 9.39N 6.32E
Minneapolis **97 D3** 45.00N 93.15W
Minnesota River **97 D3**
Minnesota, state **97 D3**
Minorca, island **108 D4**
Minot **96 C3** 48.16N 101.19W
Minsk **107 I3** 53.51N 27.30E
Minto, Lake **95 K3**
Miquelon, island **95 M2**
Mira **108 B4** 40.26N 8.44W
Miragoâne **66 B2** 18.25N 73.00W
Miranda de Ebro **108 C4** 42.41N 2.57W
Mirebalais **66 C2** 18.50N 72.00W
Mirgorod **107 J2** 49.58N 33.37E
Mirim, Lake **99 E3**
Mirjaveh **124 A3** 29.01N 61.30E
Mirny, ant. base **131 E3** 66.33S 93.01E
Mirpur Khas **124 A3** 25.33N 69.05E
Miryang **122 D4** 35.31N 128.45E
Mirzapur **124 C3** 25.09N 82.34E
Misâha Oasis **115 F4** 22.13N 27.59E
Misawa **122 J7** 40.42N 141.26E
Misery, Mount **78 B3** 13.11N 59.35W
Miskolc **107 H2** 48.07N 20.47E
Misool, island **127 D5**
Misratah **114 E5** 32.24N 15.04E
Mississippi River **97 D3**
Mississippi, state **97 D2**
Missoula **96 B3** 46.52N 114.00W
Missouri River **96 B3**
Missouri, state **97 D2**
Mistassini **97 F3** 48.54N 72.13W
Mistassini, Lake **95 K3**
Mita, Point **88 B3** 20.46N 105.33W
Mitchell **96 D3** 43.40N 98.01W
Mitchell, Mount **97 E2** 35.47N 82.16W
Mitchell River **127 E4**
Mito **122 J5** 36.22N 140.29E
Mitsio, island **116 F2**
Mitsiwa **115 G3** 15.37N 39.28E
Mitú **89 E1** 1.08N 70.03W
Miyake Island **122 I4**
Miyako **122 K6** 39.38N 141.59E
Miyakonojo **122 E2** 31.43N 131.02E
Miyazaki **122 E2** 31.56N 131.27E

Nikki **114 D2** 9.55N 3.18E
Nikolayev **107 J2** 46.57N 32.00E
Nikolsk **102 I3** 59.33N 45.30E
Nikopol **109 J5** 47.34N 34.25E
Niksar **109 K4** 40.35N 36.59E
Nikšić **109 G4** 42.48N 18.56E
Nile Delta **115 G5**
Nile River **115 G3**
Niles **97 E3** 41.51N 86.15W
Nilgiri Hills **124 B2**
Nîmes **108 D4** 43.50N 4.21E
Nine Mile **62 D2** 18.17N 77.17W
Ninety East Ridge **13 J2**
Ningjing Mountains **124 D4**
Ninohe **122 J7** 40.12N 141.20E
Niobrara River **96 C3**
Nioro du Sahel **114 C3** 15.12N 9.35W
Niort **108 C5** 46.19N 0.27W
Nipigon **94 J2** 49.02N 88.26W
Nipigon, Lake **94 J2**
Nipissing, Lake **95 J2**
Niquero **60 E2** 20.00N 77.30W
Nis **109 H4** 43.20N 21.54E
Nitra **107 G2** 48.20N 18.05E
NIUE, independent state **47 N2**
Nizamabad **124 B2** 18.40N 78.05E
Nizhniy Novgorod **118 F9** 56.20N 44.00E
Nizmennyy, Cape **122 G8** 43.32N 135.12E
Njombe **116 D4** 9.20S 34.47E
Nkongsamba **114 E2** 4.59N 9.53E
Nobeoka **122 E3** 32.36N 131.40E
Nogales, Mexico **88 A4** 31.20N 111.00W
Nogales, USA **96 B2** 31.20N 110.56W
Noginsk **107 K4** 55.52N 38.29E
Noirmoutier Island **108 C5**
Nojima, Cape **122 J4** 34.54N 139.54E
Nokia **107 H5** 61.29N 23.31E
Nok Kundi **124 A3** 28.49N 62.50E
Nokomis **94 H3** 51.30N 105.00W
Noma, Cape **122 E2** 31.27N 130.06E
Nome **94 B4** 64.30N 165.30W
Nonsuch Bay **72 B4**
Nord, department **66 C3**
Nord-Est, department **66 D3**
Nord-Quest, department **66 B3**
Norfolk, Nebraska **94 I2** 42.01N 97.25W
Norfolk, Virginia **97 F2** 36.54N 76.18W
Norfolk Island **127 G3**
Norilsk **130 E3** 69.21N 88.02E
Norman **96 D2** 35.14N 97.27W
Norman Island **70 C2**
Normandy, region **108 C5**
Norman's Cay **58 E5**
Normanton **126 E4** 17.40S 141.04E
Norman Wells **94 F4** 65.18N 126.42W
Norrköping **107 G4** 58.35N 16.10E
Norrtalje **107 G4** 59.46N 18.43E
Norseman **126 C2** 32.12S 121.47E
Norte, Cape **15 I1** 1.43N 49.55W
Norte, Point **99 D2** 42.05S 63.46W
North, Cape, Canada **95 M2** 47.03N 60.24W
North Cape, Norway **103 G5** 71.11N 25.40E
North Island **127 H1**
North Point, Barbados **78 B5** 13.20N 59.37W
North Point, Curaçao **84 D4** 12.35N 69.10W
North Sea **106 D4**
North Sound, Antigua and Barbuda **72 B4**
North Sound, Cayman Islands **65 A1**
Northam **126 B2** 31.39S 116.40E
North America, continent **12 D4**
North American Basin **12 E4**
Northampton **106 C3** 52.14N 0.54W
North Andaman, island **124 D2**
North Atlantic Ocean **12 F4**
North Baikal Plateau **130 F2**
North Bay **95 K2** 46.20N 79.28W
North Bimini, island **58 B6**
North Caicos, island **68 B8**
North Carolina, state **97 F2**
Northcliffe **126 B2** 34.38S 116.07E
North Creek **68 E3**
North Dakota, state **96 C3**
North Dvina River **103 I4**
North East Point, Cayman Islands **65 C2** 19.46N 79.49W
North East Point, Turks and Caicos Islands **68 E4** 21.31N 71.08W
Northeast Providence Channel **58 D6**
Northern Lagoon **86 B3**
Northern Range **81 C4**
Northern Territory **126 D3**
Northern Cay **86 C3**
Northern Ireland, state **106 B3**
Northern Marianas, islands **119 P5**
North Frigate Bay **71 B2**
North Hill **73 B2** 18.12N 63.05W
NORTH KOREA, democratic people's republic **122 D7**
North Magnetic Pole **130 M3** 77.18N 101.48W
North Negril Point **62 B2** 18.23N 78.21W
North Pacific Ocean **46 C4**
North Platte **96 C3** 41.09N 100.45W
North Platte River **96 C3**
North Pole **130 N4** 90.00N
North Saskatchewan River **94 G3**
North Side, Anguilla **73 B2** 18.14N 63.03W
North Side, Cayman Islands **65 A1** 19.21N 81.10W
North Sound Settlement **70 D3** 18.30N 64.24W
North Union **77 B2** 13.13N 61.08W
North Wells **68 E3** 21.29N 71.09W
North West Bluff **73 A4** 16.47N 62.11W
North West Point, St Vincent **77 D2** 13.03N 61.15W
North West Point, Turks and Caicos Islands **68 B5** 21.52N 72.20W
Northwest Providence Channel **58 C7**
North West Shelf **127 B4**
Northwest Territories, province **94 H5**
Norton Sound **94 B4**
Norvegia, Cape **131 J3** 71.28S 12.25W
NORWAY, kingdom **106 E5**
Norway House **94 I3** 53.59N 97.50W
Norwegian Basin **12 G5**
Norwegian Sea **12 G5**
Norwich **106 D3** 52.38N 1.18E
Noshiro **122 I7** 40.13N 140.00E
Notodden **106 E4** 59.35N 9.18E
Notre Dame Bay **95 M3**
Notre Dame Mountains **97 G3**
Nottingham **106 C3** 52.58N 1.10W
Nouâdhibou **114 B4** 20.54N 17.01W
Nouakchott **114 B3** 18.09N 15.58W
Nouméa **126 G3** 22.16S 166.26E
Nova Mambone **116 D2** 21.00S 35.00E
Novara **108 E5** 45.27N 8.37E
Nova Scotia, province **95 L2**
Novaya Kakhovka **109 J5** 46.45N 33.20E
Novaya Zemlya, islands **119 G11**
Novelda **108 C3** 38.24N 0.45W
Nove Zamky **107 G2** 48.00N 18.10E
Novgorod **107 J4** 58.30N 31.20E
Novi Pazar, Bulgaria **109 I4** 43.20N 27.12E
Novi Pazar, Yugoslavia **109 H4** 43.09N 20.29E
Novi Sad **109 G5** 45.15N 19.51E
Novocherkassk **109 L5** 47.25N 40.05E
Novograd-Volynskiy **107 I3** 50.34N 27.32E
Novogrudok **107 I3** 53.35N 25.50E
Novolazarevskaya, ant. base **131 I3** 70.46S 11.50E
Novomoskovsk, Russia **107 K3** 54.05N 38.13E
Novomoskovsk, Ukraine **107 K2** 48.38N 35.15E
Novopokrovskaya **109 L5** 45.56N 40.42E
Novopolotsk **107 I4** 55.32N 28.39E
Novorossisk **109 K4** 44.44N 37.46E
Novoshakhtinsk **109 L5** 47.46N 39.55E
Novosibirsk **118 J9** 55.04N 83.05E
Novozybkov **107 J3** 52.31N 31.58E
Nowgong **124 D3** 26.20N 92.41E
Nowra **126 F2** 34.53S 150.36E
Nowy Targ **109 H5** 49.28N 20.00E
Nubian Desert **115 G4**
Nueces River **96 C1**
Nueltin Lake **94 I4**
Nueva Gerona **60 B2** 21.55N 82.45W
Nueva Rosita **88 B3** 27.58N 101.11W
Nuevitas **60 E2** 21.30N 77.15W
Nuevo Casas Grandes **88 B4** 30.22N 107.53W
Nuevo Laredo **88 B3** 27.30N 99.30W
Nuku'alofa **47 N2** 21.08S 175.12W
Nullarbor Plain **127 C2**
Numazu **122 I4** 35.08N 138.50E
Numbulwar **126 D4** 14.17S 135.44E
Nunavut **94 I4**
Nunivak Island **94 B3**
Nuoro **108 E4** 40.20N 9.21E
Nuremberg **106 F2** 49.27N 11.05E
Nurmes **107 I5** 63.31N 29.10E
Nurse Cay **58 F3**
Nuuk .... see Godthåb
Nyahururu **115 G2** 0.04N 36.22E
Nyainqentanglha Range **124 C3**
Nyala **115 F3** 12.01N 24.50E
Nyandoma **107 L5** 61.43N 40.11E
Nyanza **116 C4** 4.19S 29.35E
Nyiregyhaza **107 H2** 47.57N 21.43E
Nyiru, Mount **115 G2** 2.11N 36.49E
Nykøbing **106 F3** 54.47N 11.53E
Nyköping **107 G4** 58.45N 17.03E
Nylstroom **116 C2** 24.42S 28.20E
Nyong River **114 E2**
Nysa **109 G6** 50.30N 17.20E
Nzérékoré **114 C2** 7.49N 8.48W
N'zeto **116 B4** 7.13S 12.54E

O

Oahe Reservoir **96 C3**
Oahu, island **96 B1**
Oak Harbor **96 A3** 48.17N 122.40W
Oakland **96 A2** 37.50N 122.15W
Oaks **63 D2** 18.05N 77.13W
Oates Land **131 A3**
Oaxaca de Juarez **88 C2** 17.05N 96.41W
Ob, Gulf of **119 I11**
Ob River **119 H10**
Oban **102 D3** 56.25N 5.29W
Obbia **115 H2** 5.20N 48.30E
Obi, island **127 C5**
Obihiro **122 K8** 42.56N 143.10E
Oblachnaya, Mount **122 G8** 43.46N 134.10E
Obninsk **107 K4** 55.05N 36.37E
Obo **115 F2** 5.18N 26.28E
Obock **115 H3** 11.59N 43.16E
O'Briens **77 B2** 13.17N 61.07W
Obuasi **114 C2** 6.12N 1.40W
Ocala **97 E1** 29.11N 82.09W
Ocaña **54 D2** 8.16N 73.21W
Occidental, Cordillera, mountains **14 D1**
Ocean Bight **59 H2**
Ocean Point **68 B3** 21.45N 72.17W
Ocean Cay **58 B6**
Oceanside **96 B2** 33.12N 117.23W
Ochamchire **109 L4** 42.44N 41.30E
Ocho Rios **63 D2** 18.24N 77.07W
Ocho Rios Bay **63 D2**
Ocoa, Bay of **67 E2**
Odate **122 J7** 40.18N 140.32E
Odawara **122 I4** 35.15N 139.08E
Ödemis **109 I3** 38.11N 27.58E
Odendaalsrus **116 C2** 27.52S 26.42E
Odense **106 F4** 55.24N 10.25E
Oder River **106 F3**
Odessa, USA **96 C2** 31.50N 102.23W
Odessa, Ukraine **107 J2** 46.30N 30.46E
Odienné **114 C2** 9.36N 7.32W
Odorhei **109 I5** 46.18N 25.19E
Oga **122 I6** 39.56N 139.47E
Ogaden Desert **115 H2**
Ogbomosho **114 D2** 8.05N 4.11E
Ogden **96 B3** 41.14N 111.59W
Ogoja **114 D2** 6.40N 8.45E
Ogooué River **114 D1**
Ohio River **97 E2**
Ohio, state **97 E3**
Ohrid **109 H4** 41.06N 20.49E
Ohrid Lake **109 G4**
Oistins **78 C1** 13.03N 59.32W
Oistins Bay **78 C1**
Oita **122 E3** 33.15N 131.36E
Ojerada **108 C2** 34.20N 2.03W
Ojinaga **88 B3** 29.35N 104.26W
Oka River **107 J3**
Okavango Delta **116 C3**
Okavango River **111 F3**
Okaya **122 I5** 36.03N 138.00E
Okayama **122 F4** 34.40N 133.54E
Okazaki **122 H4** 34.58N 137.10E
Okeechobee, Lake **97 E1**
Okene **114 D2** 7.31N 6.14E
Okhotsk, Sea of **119 P9**
Oki Archipelago **122 F5**
Oklahoma, state **96 D2**
Oklahoma City **96 D2** 35.28N 97.33W
Oktyabriskiy **107 I3** 52.33N 28.47E
Öland, island **107 G4**
Olbia **108 E4** 40.56N 9.30E
Old Bahama Channel **14 D5**
Oldenburg **106 E3** 53.08N 8.13E
Old Fort Point **73 A3** 16.42N 62.10W
Old Harbour **63 D1** 17.56N 77.07W
Old Harbour Bay **63 D1** 17.54N 77.05W
Old Man Bay **65 A1** 19.21N 81.09W
Old Norwood **73 A4** 16.46N 62.11W
Old Road, Antigua and Barbuda **72 B4** 17.01N 61.50W
Old Road, St Kitts and Nevis **71 B2** 17.19N 62.48W
Old Road Bay, Montserrat **73 A3**
Old Road Bay, St Kitts and Nevis **71 B2**
Old Road Bluff, Antigua and Barbuda **72 A4** 17.00N 61.50W
Old Road Bluff, Montserrat **73 A3** 16.44N 62.12W
Old Town **97 G3** 44.55N 68.41W
Old Woman's Point **62 C1** 17.51N 77.31W
Olean **97 F3** 42.05N 78.26W
Oléron Island **108 C5**
Oleśnica **107 G3** 51.12N 17.21E
Olevsk **109 I6** 51.12N 27.35E
Olga **122 G8** 43.46N 135.14E
Olinda **98 G6** 8.00S 34.51W
Olivenza **108 B3** 38.41N 7.06W
Olomouc **107 G2** 49.48N 17.15E
Olsztyn **107 H3** 53.48N 20.29E
Olten **108 E5** 47.22N 7.55E
Oltu **109 L4** 40.34N 41.59E
Olympia **96 A3** 47.03N 122.53W
Olympus, Mount **109 H4** 40.05N 22.21E
Oma, Cape **122 J7** 41.31N 140.55E
Omaha **97 D3** 41.15N 96.00W
OMAN, Gulf of **119 H6**
Oman, sultanate **118 G5**
Omdurman **115 G3** 15.37N 32.29E
Omiya **122 I4** 35.54N 139.39E
Omo River **115 G2**
Omsk **130 D2** 55.00N 73.22E
Omuta **122 E3** 33.02N 130.26E
Ondangua **116 B3** 17.52S 15.59E
Ondjiva **116 B3** 17.03S 15.41E
Onega, Lake **107 K5**
Ongjin **122 B6** 37.56N 125.21E
Onitsha **114 D2** 6.10N 6.47E
Onslow Bay **97 F2**
Ontario, Belize **86 B3** 17.15N 88.55W
Ontario, USA **96 B3** 44.02N 116.58W
Ontario, Lake **97 F3**
Ontario, province **94 J3**
Oodnadatta **126 D3** 27.33S 135.27E
Opava **109 G5** 49.58N 17.55E
Opole **107 G3** 50.40N 17.56E
Oporto **108 B4** 41.09N 8.37W
Opp **97 E2** 31.16N 86.18W
Opuwo **116 B3** 18.03S 13.54E
Oracabessa **63 E2** 18.24N 76.56W
Oradea **109 H5** 47.03N 21.55E
Oran **114 C5** 35.45N 0.38W
Orange Bay **62 B2**
Orange Bay **63 E2** 18.14N 76.37W
Orange, Cape **15 I1** 4.25N 51.32W
Orange Cay **58 B5**
Orange, France **108 D4** 44.08N 4.48E
Orange Hill, Barbados **78 B3** 13.12N 59.36W
Orange Hill, Jamaica **62 C2** 18.17N 77.58W
Orange Hill, St Vincent **77 B2** 13.19N 61.07W
Orange, Jamaica **62 C2** 18.27N 77.50W
Orange River **116 B2**
Orange, USA **97 D2** 30.05N 93.43W
Orange Walk **86 B4** 18.06N 88.34W
Orange Walk, district **86 A3**
Oranjestad, Aruba **84 B2** 12.32N 70.02W
Oranjestad, St Eustatius **84 C5** 17.30N 62.58W
Orastie **109 H5** 45.50N 23.11E
Orbetello **108 F4** 42.27N 11.07E
Orcadas, ant. base **131 L3** 60.45S 44.43W
Orchila, island **55 E3**
Ordu **109 K4** 41.00N 37.52E
Orealla **85 C3** 5.20N 57.20W
Örebro **106 G4** 59.18N 15.05E
Oregon, state **96 A3**
Oregon City **96 A3** 45.21N 122.36W
Orekhovo-Zuyevo **107 K4** 55.49N 38.59E
Orel **107 K3** 52.58N 36.04E
Orem **96 B3** 40.20N 111.42W
Orense **108 B4** 42.20N 7.52W
Orford **126 E1** 42.32S 147.50E
Orgeyev **107 I2** 47.24N 28.50E
Oriental, Cordillera, mountains **14 D1**
Orinduik **85 B3** 4.45N 60.00W
Orinoco River **15 F2**
Oristano **108 E3** 39.54N 8.36E
Orizaba **88 C2** 18.51N 97.08W
Orkney Islands **106 C4**
Orlando **97 E1** 28.33N 81.21W
Orléans **108 D5** 47.54N 1.54E
Ormara **124 A3** 25.12N 64.39E
Orocovis **69 B2** 18.14N 66.24W
Orocué **89 E1** 4.51N 71.21W
Oronoque **85 C2** 2.40N 57.20W
Oropuche **81 D4** 10.36N 61.06W
Oropuche, river **81 D4**
Orsha **107 J3** 54.30N 30.23E
Ørsta **106 E5** 62.12N 6.00E
Ortegal, Cape **108 B4** 43.46N 7.54W
Orthez **108 C4** 43.29N 0.46W
Ortoire, river **81 D2**
Orvieto **108 F4** 42.43N 12.06E
Oryakhovo **109 H4** 43.40N 23.57E
Osaka **122 G4** 34.40N 135.30E
Oshawa **95 K2** 43.53N 78.51W
Oshkosh **97 E3** 44.01N 88.32W
Oshogbo **114 D2** 7.50N 4.35E
Osijek **109 G5** 45.33N 18.41E
Osipovichi **107 I3** 53.19N 28.36E
Oskarshamn **107 G4** 57.16N 16.25E
Oslo **106 F4** 59.56N 10.45E
Osmancik **109 K4** 40.58N 34.50E
Osnabrück **108 E6** 52.17N 8.03E
Ossa, Mount, Australia **127 E1** 41.52S 146.02E
Ossa, Mount, Portugal **108 B3** 38.45N 7.36W
Ostashkov **107 J4** 57.09N 33.10E
Ostend **106 D3** 51.13N 2.55E
Östersund **106 F5** 63.10N 14.40E
Ostrava **109 G5** 49.50N 18.15E
Ostróda **107 G3** 53.42N 19.59E
Ostrogozhsk **107 K3** 50.52N 39.03E
Ostroleka **107 H3** 53.05N 21.32E
Ostrov **107 I4** 57.22N 28.22E
Ostrowiec **107 H3** 50.58N 21.22E
Ostrów Mazowiecka **107 H3** 52.50N 21.51E
Osumi Strait **122 E2**
Otaru **122 J8** 43.14N 140.59E
Otjiwarongo **116 B2** 20.29S 16.36E
Otranto **109 G4** 40.08N 18.30E
Otranto, Strait of **109 G4**
Ottawa **95 K2** 45.25N 75.43W
Ottawa River **95 K2**
Ottumwa **97 D3** 41.02N 92.26W
Oturkpo **114 D2** 7.16N 8.16E
Otway, Cape **127 E2** 38.52S 143.31E
Ouachita River **97 D2**
Ouadda **115 F2** 8.09N 22.20E
Ouagadougou **114 C3** 12.20N 1.40W
Ouahigouya **114 C3** 13.31N 2.20W
Ouanda Djailé **115 F2** 8.55N 22.53E
Ouare, river **81 D4**
Ouargla **114 D5** 32.00N 5.16E
Oudtshoorn **116 C1** 33.35S 22.12E
Ouenza **114 D5** 35.55N 8.08E
Ouésso **116 B5** 1.38N 16.03E
Ouezzane **108 B2** 34.52N 5.35W
Oujda **114 C5** 34.41N 1.45W
Ouled Djellal **114 D5** 34.25N 5.02E
Oulu **102 G4** 65.00N 25.26E
Ounianga Kebir **115 F3** 19.05N 20.29E
Outer Hebrides, islands **106 B4**
Outjo **116 B2** 20.08S 16.08E
Ovar **108 B4** 40.52N 8.38W
Overland Park **97 D2** 38.57N 94.47W
Overland Village **77 B2** 13.20N 61.07W
Over-the-Top Camp **86 B3** 17.06N 88.37W
Oviedo, Dominican Republic **66 D1** 17.45N 71.20W
Oviedo, Spain **108 B4** 43.21N 5.50W
Owase **122 H4** 34.03N 136.12E
Owensboro **97 E2** 37.45N 87.05W
Owia **77 B3** 13.22N 61.08W
Owia Bay **77 B3**
Oxford, Jamaica **62 C2** 18.12N 77.38W
Oxford, UK **106 C3** 51.46N 1.15W
Oxnard **96 B2** 34.11N 119.10W
Oyapock, river **15 I1**
Oyo **114 D2** 7.50N 3.55E
Ozark **97 E2** 31.27N 85.40W
Ozurgeti **109 L4** 41.55N 42.02E

P

Paarl **116 B1** 33.45S 18.58E
Pabna **124 C3** 24.00N 89.15E
Pachino **108 G3** 36.43N 15.06E
Pachuca **88 C3** 20.10N 98.44W
Pacific Ocean **13 M3**
Pacific Antarctic Ridge **12 C1**
Padang **118 K3** 1.00S 100.21E
Paderborn **106 E3** 51.43N 8.44E
Padre Las Casas **67 E2** 18.40N 70.50W
Padua **108 F5** 45.24N 11.53E
Pag, island **108 F4**
Pagua Bay **75 B3**
Pagua, river **75 B3**
Painted Desert **91 H4**
Pakani **85 B3** 4.15N 58.25W
Pakaraima Mountains **85 A3**
PAKISTAN, Islamic republic **124 A3**
Pakokku **124 D3** 21.20N 95.05E
Pakwach **115 G2** 2.17N 31.28E
Palamós **108 D4** 41.51N 3.07E
Palana **130 I2** 59.05N 159.59E
Palanpur **124 B3** 24.12N 72.29E
Palapye **116 C2** 22.37S 27.06E
Palatka **97 E1** 29.38N 81.40W
PALAU, independent state **47 L3**
Palawan, island **119 M5**
Palembang **118 L3** 2.59S 104.45E
Palencia **108 C4** 42.01N 4.32W
Palenque **88 C2** 9.34N 79.22W
Palenque Point **67 E2** 18.13N 70.09W
Palermo **108 F3** 38.08N 13.23E
Palghat **124 B2** 10.46N 76.42E
Palikir **47 M3** 6.57N 158.10E
Palisadoes, The, islands **63 E1**
Palk Strait **124 B1**
Palma **108 D3** 39.35N 2.39E
Palmas, Cape **114 C2** 4.25N 7.50W
Palma Soriano **61 F2** 20.10N 75.55W
Palmeirinhas Point **116 B4** 9.09S 12.58E
Palmer **94 D4** 61.35N 149.10W
Palmer, ant. base **131 M3** 64.46S 64.03W
Palmer Land **131 M3**
Palmers **78 D3** 13.09N 59.28W
Palmetto Point, Antigua and Barbuda **72 A1** 17.34N 61.51W
Palmetto Point, St Kitts and Nevis **71 B2** 17.17N 62.46W
Palm Grove **68 E3** 21.27N 71.09W
Palmi **109 G3** 38.21N 15.51E
Palmira **89 E1** 3.33N 76.17W
Palm Island **77 C1**
Palmiste Bay **80 B7**
Palm Springs **96 B2** 33.49N 116.34W
Palmyra **109 K2** 34.33N 38.17E
Palo Seco **81 B2** 10.05N 61.35W
Pamiers **108 D4** 43.07N 1.36E
Pamirs, mountains **124 B4**
Pamlico Sound **97 F2**
Pampa **96 C2** 35.32N 100.58W
Pampas, plains **99 D3**
Pamplona **108 C4** 42.49N 1.39W
Panama Canal **89 D1**
Panama City, Panama **89 E1** 8.57N 79.30W
Panama City, USA **97 E1** 30.10N 85.41W
Panamá, Gulf of **89 E1**
PANAMA, republic **54 B2**
Panay, island **119 N5**
Pancevo **109 H4** 44.52N 20.40E
Panevezys **107 H4** 55.44N 24.24E
Pangani River **115 G1**
Panipat **124 B3** 29.24N 76.58E
Pannawonica **126 B3** 21.39S 116.19E
Pantelleria, island **108 F3**

Puerto Cabezas **54 B3** 14.02N 83.24W
Puerto Carreño **55 E2** 6.08N 67.27W
Puerto Inírida **55 E1** 4.03N 67.45W
Puerto Juárez **88 D3** 21.10N 86.50W
Puerto Limón **89 D2** 10.00N 83.01W
Puertollano **108 C3** 38.41N 4.07W
Puerto Montt **98 C2** 41.28S 73.00W
Puerto Padre **60 E2** 21.10N 76.35W
Puerto Páez **55 E2** 6.14N 67.26W
Puerto Plata **67 E3** 19.48N 70.41W
Puerto Plata, province **67 E3**
Puerto Rico, island **69**
Puerto Rico Trench **15 G4**
Puerto Yabucoa, bay **69 C2**
Pukchong **122 D7** 40.15N 128.17E
Puksubaek, Mount **122 C7** 40.40N 127.15E
Pula **108 F4** 44.52N 13.52E
Pulalak **124 A4** 30.15N 62.54E
Pular, mountain **99 D4** 24.12S 68.05W
Pullman **96 B3** 46.44N 117.10W
Pump Bay **71 A3**
Punakha **124 D3** 27.38N 89.50E
Pune **124 B2** 18.34N 73.58E
Punta Arenas **98 C1** 53.10S 70.56W
Punta Cana **67 G2** 18.31N 68.21W
Punta Gorda **86 B2** 16.07N 88.50W
Punta La Cruz **55 F3** 10.15N 64.30W
Puntarenas **54 A2** 10.00N 84.50W
Punto Fijo **54 D3** 11.42N 70.13W
Puri **124 C2** 19.49N 85.54E
Purnia **124 C3** 25.47N 87.28E
Purus River **99 D6**
Pusan **122 D4** 35.05N 129.02E
Pushkin **107 J4** 59.43N 30.22E
Pweto **116 C4** 8.28S 28.52E
Pyatigorsk **109 L4** 44.04N 43.06E
Pyongyang **122 B6** 39.00N 125.47E
Pyramid Lake **96 A3**
Pyrenees, mountains **108 C4**
Pyrgos **109 H3** 37.40N 21.27E

Q

Qaanaaq **94 L5** 77.30N 69.29W
Qala Nau **124 A4** 34.58N 63.04E
QATAR, sheikdom **118 F6**
Qattâra Depression **115 F5**
Qena **115 G4** 26.08N 32.42E
Qila Ladgasht **124 A3** 27.55N 62.59E
Qingdao **118 M7** 36.04N 120.22E
Qiqihar **118 N8** 47.23N 124.00E
Qishn **115 I3** 15.25N 51.40E
Qitaihe **122 E9** 45.47N 130.50E
Qu'Appelle River **96 C4**
Quartier de Grand' Case **84 E8** 18.06N 63.04W
Quartier d'Orléans **84 E7** 18.04N 63.01W
Quatre, Isla a, island **77 D3**
Québec **95 K2** 46.50N 71.15W
Québec, province **95 K3**
Quebradillas **69 B2** 18.29N 66.56W
Queen Charlotte Islands **94 E3**
Queen Charlotte Sound **94 E3**
Queen Elizabeth Islands **94 G5**
Queen Mary Land **131 E3**
Queen Maud Land **131 I3**
Queen Maud Mountains **131 B4**
Queensland, state **126 E3**
Queenstown, Australia **126 E1** 42.05S 145.33E
Queenstown, South Africa **116 C1** 31.54S 26.53E
Quelimane **116 D3** 17.53S 36.51E
Querétaro **88 B3** 20.38N 100.23W
Quetta **124 A4** 30.15N 67.00E
Quezaltenango **88 C2** 14.50N 91.30W
Quibdó **89 E1** 5.40N 76.40W
Quick Step **62 C2** 18.15N 77.42W
Quilesse Forest Reserve **76 B2**
Quilon **124 B1** 8.53N 76.38E
Quilpie **126 E3** 26.37S 144.16E
Quimper **108 C5** 48.00N 4.06W
Quincy **97 D2** 39.55N 91.22W
Quipungo **116 B3** 14.50S 14.32E
Quisqueya **67 F2** 18.33N 69.24W
Quitapa **116 B3** 10.10S 18.16E
Quito **98 C6** 0.14S 78.30W
Qurnet es Sauda, mountain **109 K2** 34.18N 36.07E
Quseir **115 G4** 26.04N 34.15E

R

Raahe **107 H5** 64.42N 24.30E
Rabacca Dry River **77 B2**
Rabat **114 C5** 34.02N 6.51W
Rabaul **126 F5** 4.13S 152.11E
Rabbit Island **72 B2**
Rabigh **115 G4** 22.48N 39.01E
Rabyanah Sand Sea **115 F4**
Raccoon Cay **58 F3**
Race, Cape **95 M2** 46.38N 53.10W
Race Course **62 D1** 17.50N 77.17W
Racine **97 E3** 42.42N 87.50W
Radhwa, Mount **115 G4** 24.36N 38.18E
Radom **107 H3** 51.26N 21.10E
Radomyshl **107 I3** 50.30N 29.13E
Rafah **109 J2** 31.18N 34.15E
Raga **115 F2** 8.26N 25.46E
Ragged Island Range, islands **58 F3**
Ragged Point **78 D2** 13.09N 59.25W
Ragusa **108 F3** 36.56N 14.44E
Raigarh **124 C3** 21.53N 83.28E
Rainier, Mount **96 A3** 46.52N 121.45W
Rainy Lake **94 I2**
Raipur **124 C3** 21.16N 81.42E
Rairakhol **124 C3** 21.03N 84.23E
Rajahmundry **124 C2** 17.01N 81.52E
Rajkot **124 B3** 22.18N 70.53E
Rajo, Cape **69 A1** 17.56N 67.11W
Rajshahi **124 C3** 24.24N 88.40E
Rakvere **107 I4** 59.22N 26.28E
Raleigh **97 F2** 35.46N 78.39W
Raleigh Bay **97 F2**
Ram, Mount **109 K1** 29.36N 35.24E
Rama **54 B3** 12.00N 84.00W
Rambaud **84 E8** 18.05N 63.04W
Ramble, St Thomas, Jamaica **63 E1** 17.58N 76.37W
Ramble, Hanover, Jamaica **62 B2** 18.19N 77.59W
Ramón Santana **67 F2** 18.33N 69.10W
Rampanalgas **81 E4** 10.44N 60.59W
Rampur **124 B3** 28.48N 79.03E
Ramville ou Chancel, Ilet, island **74 B2**
Ranchi **124 C3** 23.22N 85.20E
Rancho Dolores **86 B3** 17.35N 88.37W
Ranchuelo **60 C3** 22.15N 80.10W
Randers **106 F4** 56.28N 10.03E
Rangoon **118 K5** 16.47N 96.10E
Rangpur **124 C3** 25.45N 89.21E
Rankin Inlet **94 I4** 62.52N 92.00W
Rantekombola, mountain **127 B5** 3.23S 120.02E
Rapallo **108 E4** 44.21N 9.13E
Rapid City **96 C3** 44.06N 103.14W
Ras Dashen, mountain **115 G3** 13.15N 38.27E
Râs Ghârib **109 J1** 28.21N 33.06E
Rasskazovo **107 L3** 53.39N 41.54E
Rat Island **76 B3**
Ratnagiri **124 B2** 17.00N 73.20E
Ratno **109 H6** 51.40N 24.32E
Raton **96 C2** 36.54N 104.27W
Rauma **107 H5** 61.09N 21.30E
Raurkela **124 C3** 22.16N 85.01E
Ravenna **108 F4** 44.25N 12.12E
Ravensburg **106 E2** 47.47N 9.37E
Ravi River **124 B4**
Rawalpindi **124 B4** 33.40N 73.08E
Rawlinna **126 C2** 31.01S 125.20E
Rawlins **96 C3** 41.46N 107.16W
Re Island **108 C5**
Reading, Jamaica **62 C2** 18.26N 77.57W
Reading, UK **108 C6** 51.28N 0.59W
Reading, USA **97 F3** 40.20N 75.55W
Rebun, island **122 J9**
Rechitsa **107 J3** 52.21N 30.24E
Recife **98 G6** 8.06S 34.53W
Red Bays **58 C6** 25.07N 78.07W
Red Bluff **96 A3** 40.10N 122.14W
Red Cliff **71 C1** 17.06N 62.32W
Red Deer **94 G3** 52.15N 113.48W
Redding **96 A3** 40.35N 122.24W
Redhead **81 E5** 10.47N 60.57W
Red Hills **63 E2**
Red Hills **63 E2** 18.02N 76.50W
Red Lake **97 D3**
Redonda, island **70 C8**
Redoute **74 A1** 14.36N 61.02W
Red River, Minnesota **97 D3**
Red River, Texas **96 C2**
Red Sea **115 G4**
Reform **81 C3** 10.18N 61.25W
Regensburg **106 F2** 49.01N 12.07E
Reggane **114 D4** 26.42N 0.13E
Reggio di Calabria **109 G3** 38.06N 15.39E
Regina **94 H3** 50.30N 104.38W
Rehoboth **116 B2** 23.18S 17.03E
Reims **108 D5** 49.15N 4.02E
Reindeer Lake **94 H3**
Reinosa **108 C4** 43.01N 4.09W
Relizane **108 D3** 35.44N 0.35E
Rendezvous, Barbados **78 C1** 13.04N 59.34W
Rendezvous, Montserrat **73 A4** 16.47N 62.11W
Rendezvous Bay, Anguilla **73 B2**
Rendezvous Bay, Montserrat **73 A4**
Rendezvous Bluff **73 A4** 16.46N 62.11W
Rendsburg **106 E3** 54.19N 9.39E
Rennell Island **127 F4**
Rennes **108 C5** 48.06N 1.40W
Reno **96 B2** 39.32N 119.49W
Republican River **96 C2**
Requena **108 C3** 39.29N 1.08W
Requin Point **80 C6** 12.02N 61.38W
Resita **109 H5** 45.16N 21.55E
Resolute Bay **94 I5** 74.40N 95.00W
Resolution Island **95 L4**
Rest **62 D1** 17.53N 77.21W
Restauración **66 D3** 19.18N 71.41W
Rethymnon **109 H3** 35.23N 24.28E
Retreat **63 D2** 18.22N 77.01W
Réunion, island **47 I2**
Reutlingen **106 E2** 48.30N 9.13E
Revelstoke **94 F3** 51.02N 118.12W
Revenge Lagoon **86 B3**
Rewa **124 C3** 24.32N 81.18E
Rexburg **96 B3** 43.50N 111.48W
Rey Island **14 D2**
Reykjavik **102 B4** 64.09N 21.58W
Reynosa **88 C3** 26.05N 98.18W
Rezekne **107 I4** 56.30N 27.22E
Rhafsai **108 C2** 34.40N 4.55W
Rhinelander **97 E3** 45.39N 89.23W
Rhine River **106 E3**
Rhode Island **80 A1**
Rhode Island, state **97 F3**
Rhodes **109 I3** 36.26N 28.14E
Rhodes, island **109 I3**
Rhône River **108 D4**
Ribadeo **108 B4** 43.32N 7.04W
Ribat Qila **124 A3** 29.48N 61.00E
Ribe **106 E4** 55.20N 8.47E
Ribeirão Prêto **98 F4** 21.09S 47.48W
Ribera **108 F3** 37.31N 13.16E
Rices **78 D2** 13.05N 59.27W
Richardson Peak **86 B2** 16.37N 88.46W
Richfield **96 B2** 38.45N 112.05W
Richland **96 B3** 46.17N 119.19W
Richland Park **77 A2** 13.11N 61.10W
Richmond Hills **68 C4** 21.47N 72.13W
Richmond, Jamaica **63 E2** 18.14N 76.54W
Richmond Peak **77 A2** 13.17N 61.11W
Richmond, river **77 A2**
Richmond, St Vincent **77 E1** 12.59N 61.14W
Richmond, USA **97 F2** 37.43N 77.27W
Ridgecrest **96 B2** 35.38N 117.36W
Riding Point **59 B1** 26.47N 78.08W
Rietfontein **116 C2** 26.43S 20.03E
Riga **107 H4** 56.53N 24.08E
Riihimäki **107 H5** 60.45N 24.45E
Rijeka **108 F5** 45.20N 14.27E
Rimini **108 F4** 44.03N 12.34E
Rimnicu Sarat **107 I2** 45.24N 27.06E
Rimnicu Vilcea **109 H5** 45.06N 24.21E
Rimouski **95 L2** 48.26N 68.32W
Rincon, Bonaire **84 C2** 12.05N 68.30W
Rincón, Puerto Rico **69 A2** 17.56N 66.20W
Rincon Bay **69 B1**
Rincón Lagoon **67 D2**
Ringkøbing **106 E4** 56.06N 8.15E
Rio Branco **98 D6** 9.59S 67.49W
Rio Bravo, river **86 A3**
Rio Bueno **62 D2** 18.28N 77.27W
Rio Claro **81 D3** 10.18N 61.11W
Rio Claro, regional corporation **81 D3**
Rio Cobre, river **63 E2**
Río de Janeiro **98 F4** 22.53S 43.17W
Rio Grande **69 C2** 18.23N 65.50W
Rio Grande, river, Belize **86 B2**
Rio Grande, river, Jamaica **63 F2**
Rio Grande, river, USA **96 C2**
Rio Grande de Añasco, river **69 A2**
Rio Grande de Manati, river **69 B2**
Ríohacha **54 D3** 11.34N 72.58W
Rio Hondo, river **86 B4**
Rio Minho, river **63 D2**
Rio Nuero, river **63 D2**
Rio Piedras **69 B2** 18.24N 66.02W
Rio San Juan **67 E3** 19.38N 70.04W
Ripoll **108 D4** 42.12N 2.12E
Rishiri, island **122 J9**
Riva **106 F2** 45.53N 10.50E
Rivas **54 A3** 11.25N 85.45W
River Bay **78 B4**
Riversdale, Belize **86 B2** 16.44N 88.18W
Riversdale, Jamaica **63 E2** 18.09N 76.57W
Rivière-du-Loup **97 G3** 47.49N 69.32W
Rivière-Pilote **74 B1** 14.28N 60.54W
Rivière-Salée **74 B1** 14.30N 60.58W
Riyadh **118 F6** 24.39N 46.46E
Rize **109 L4** 41.03N 40.31E
Road Bay, Anguilla **73 B2**
Road Bay, British Virgin Islands **70 E4**
Road Town **70 E4** 18.26N 64.37W
Roanne **108 D5** 46.02N 4.05E
Roanoke **97 F2** 37.15N 79.58W
Roaring Creek **86 B3**
Roaring Creek **86 B3** 17.17N 88.47W
Roatán, island **54 A4**
Roberts, Mount **81 D5** 10.46N 61.09W
Robinson Range **127 B3**
Robinsons **78 D2** 13.07N 59.26W
Robson, Mount **94 G3** 53.08N 119.18W
Roca, Cape **108 B3** 38.42N 9.30W
Rochefort **106 C2** 45.57N 0.58W
Roche's Bluff **73 B3** 16.43N 62.09W
Rochester, Minnesota **97 D3** 44.01N 92.27W
Rochester, New York **97 F3** 43.12N 77.37W
Rockford **97 E3** 42.16N 89.06W
Rock Hall, St Lucy, Barbados **78 B4** 13.18N 59.36W
Rock Hall, St Thomas, Barbados
78 B3 13.11N 59.36W
Rock Hall, Jamaica **63 E2** 18.04N 76.53W
Rockhampton **126 F3** 23.22S 150.32E
Rock Hill **97 E2** 34.55N 81.01W
Rockingham **126 B2** 32.17S 115.43E
Rockley **78 B1** 13.04N 59.36W
Rockly Bay **81 C6**
Rock River **63 D2** 18.04N 77.13W
Rock Sound **58 E5** 24.54N 76.08W
Rock Springs **96 C3** 41.35N 109.13W
Rockstone **85 B3** 6.00N 58.30W
Rocky Mountains **91 H6**
Rocky Point, Belize **86 B4** 18.25N 88.10W
Rocky Point, Jamaica **63 D1** 17.49N 77.08W
Rodney Bay **76 B3**
Roebuck Bay **127 C4**
Rogachev **107 J3** 53.04N 30.00E
Roger **75 B2** 15.20N 61.23W
Rokugo, Cape **122 H5** 37.30N 137.21E
Rolla **97 D2** 37.56N 91.55W
Rolleville **58 F4** 23.40N 75.58W
Roma **126 E3** 26.35S 148.47E
Roman **109 I5** 46.56N 26.56E
Romanche Deep **111 B4**
ROMANIA, socialist republic **109 H5**
Romano Cay **60 D3**
Romans-sur-Isere **108 E5** 45.03N 5.03E
Rome, Italy **108 F4** 41.53N 12.30E
Rome, USA **97 E2** 34.01N 85.02W
Romilly **108 D5** 48.31N 3.44E
Romny **107 J3** 50.45N 33.30E
Romorantin **108 D5** 47.22N 1.44E
Ronda **108 B3** 36.45N 5.10W
Ronde, Pointe **75 A3** 15.32N 61.29W
Rønne **106 F4** 55.07N 14.43E
Ronne Ice Shelf **131 M3**
Roosevelt Island **131 R3**
Roper River **127 D4**
Roraima, Mount **85 A3** 5.14N 60.44W
Rosa, Lake **59 H2**
Rosalie **75 B2** 15.22N 61.15W
Rosalie Bay **75 B2**
Rosalie Point **75 B2** 15.22N 61.15W
Rosalind Bank **14 C4**
Rosario **98 D3** 33.00S 60.40W
Rosario, Sierra del, mountains **60 B3**
Roseau **75 B2** 15.18N 61.23W
Roseau, river, Dominica **75 B2**
Roseau, river, St Lucia **76 A2**
Roseau Dam **76 B2** 13.54N 60.59W
Roseaux **66 B2** 18.35N 74.01W
Roseburg **96 A3** 43.13N 123.21W
Rose Hall, Guyana **85 C4** 6.10N 57.20W
Rose Hall, Jamaica **62 C2** 18.31N 77.48W
Rosehall, St Vincent **77 A2** 13.16N 61.14W
Rose Hill, Barbados **78 B4** 13.16N 59.37W
Rose Hill, Grenada **80 C8** 12.12N 61.37W
Rose Island **58 D6**
Rose, Pte de la, cape **74 B1** 14.38N 60.52W
Rosetta **109 J2** 31.25N 30.25E
Rosignal **85 C4** 6.15N 57.30W
Rosita **86 B3** 17.55N 88.56W
Roslavl **107 J3** 53.55N 32.53E
Ross Ice Shelf **131 A4**
Ross Island **131 A3**
Ross Sea **131 R3**
Rossano **109 G3** 39.35N 16.38E
Rossosh **107 K3** 50.12N 39.35E
Rostock **106 F3** 54.06N 12.09E
Rostov, north-western Russia **107 K4** 57.11N 39.23E
Rostov, south-western Russia **109 K5** 47.15N 39.45E
Roswell **96 C2** 33.24N 104.33W
Rothera, ant. base **131 M3** 68.07S 68.16W
Rothschild Island **131 M3**
Roti, island **126 C4**
Rotorua **126 H2** 38.09S 176.15E
Rotterdam **106 D3** 51.55N 4.29E
Rouche Island **76 B2**
Rouen, Barbados **78 B2** 13.06N 59.35W
Rouen, France **108 D5** 49.26N 1.05E
Round Hill **62 D1** 17.51N 77.23W
Round Rock **96 D2** 30.32N 97.42W
Routhiers **74 A4** 16.02N 61.36W
Rouyn **95 K2** 48.15N 79.00W
Rovaniemi **102 G4** 66.29N 25.40E
Rovereto **106 F2** 45.53N 11.03E
Rovno **107 I3** 50.39N 26.10E
Roxborough **81 D6** 11.15N 60.35W
Royal Island **58 E6**
Royan **108 C5** 45.38N 1.02W
R.Sallee **80 C8** 12.11N 61.37W
Rubi River **116 C5**
Rudbar **124 A4** 30.10N 62.39E
Rufiji River **116 D4**
Ruiz, mountain **14 D1** 4.53N 75.22W
Rukwa, Lake **116 D4**
Rum Point **65 A1** 19.23N 81.17W
Rum Cay, island **58 G4**
Rumoi **122 J8** 43.57N 141.40E
Runaway Bay **62 D2** 18.27N 77.21W
Rundu **116 B3** 17.52S 19.45E
Rungwa **116 D4** 6.58S 33.31E
Rupert River **95 K3**
Rupununi, river **85 B2**
Ruse **109 I4** 43.50N 25.59E
Rushville **81 D2** 10.03N 61.03W
RUSSIA, republic **118 J9**
Russkaya, ant. base **131 P3** 74.46S 136.51W
Rustenburg **116 C2** 25.40S 27.15E
Rutba **115 G5** 33.02N 40.07E
Ruth Howard **80 A6** 12.01N 61.45W
Rutland, river **77 A2**
Ruvuma River **111 G3**
Ruzomberok **107 G2** 49.04N 19.15E
RWANDA, republic **116 C4**
Ryazan **107 K3** 54.37N 39.43E
Rybinsk **107 K4** 58.01N 38.52E
Rybinsk Reservoir **107 K4**
Rybnitsa **109 I5** 47.42N 29.00E
Ryukyu Islands **119 N6**
Rzeszów **107 H3** 50.04N 22.00E
Rzhev **107 J4** 56.15N 34.18E

S

Saarbrücken **106 E2** 49.15N 6.58E
Saaremaa, island **107 H4**
Saba, island **70 C8**
Sabadell **108 D4** 41.33N 2.07E
Sabana, Archipelago de **60 D3**
Sabana de la Mar **67 F3** 19.00N 69.20W
Sabana Grande de Boyá **67 F2** 18.50N 69.45W
Sabanalarga **54 C3** 10.25N 74.50W
Sabaneta **67 D3** 19.30N 71.20W
Sabha **114 E4** 27.02N 14.26E
Sabinal Cay **60 E2**
Sabinas Hidalgo **88 B3** 26.33N 100.10W
Sabine River **97 D2**
Sable, Cape, Canada **95 L2** 43.27N 65.33W
Sable, Cape, USA **91 K3** 25.12N 81.10W
Sachs Harbour **94 F5** 72.00N 124.30W
Sacramento **96 A2** 38.33N 121.30W
Sacramento River **96 A2**
Saddlers **71 B3** 17.24N 62.47W
Sadhoowa **81 C2** 10.08N 61.26W
Sadiya **124 D3** 27.49N 95.38E
Sado, island **122 I6**
Safi **114 C5** 32.20N 9.17W
Safonovo **107 J4** 55.08N 33.16E
Saga **122 E3** 33.16N 130.18E
Sagami Bay **122 I4**
Saginaw **97 E3** 43.25N 83.54W
Saginaw Bay **97 E3**
Sagua de Tánamo **61 F2** 20.35N 75.15W
Sagua la Grande **60 C3** 22.48N 80.06W
Sagunto **108 C3** 39.40N 0.17W
Sahara Desert **114 D4**
Saharan Atlas, mountains **114 C5**
Sahiwal **124 B4** 30.14N 73.10E
Saïda **108 D2** 34.50N 0.10E
Saigo **122 F5** 36.12N 133.19E
St Albans **95 K2** 44.49N 73.07W
St Andrew, Mount **77 A2** 13.11N 61.12W
St Andrew, parish, Barbados **78 B3**
St Andrew, parish, Dominica **75 B3**
St Andrew, parish, Grenada **80 C7**
St Andrew, parish, Jamaica **63 E2**
St Andrew, parish, St Vincent **77 A2**
St Ann, parish **62 D2**
St Anne Sandy Point, parish **71 B1**
St Ann's Bay **63 D2** 18.26N 77.12W
St Anthony, province **73 A3**
St Augustine **97 E1** 29.54N 81.19W
Saint Barthélemy Channel **84 C7**
St Barthélemy, island **84 C7**
St Brieuc **108 C5** 48.31N 2.45W
St Catherine, Mount **80 B7** 12.09N 61.40W
St Catherine, parish **63 D1**
St Christoffelburg, Mount **84 D4** 12.30N 69.10W
St Claude **74 A4** 16.00N 61.40W
St Cloud **97 D3** 45.34N 94.10W
St Croix, island, US Virgin Islands **70 B8**
St David, parish, Dominica **75 B2**
St David, parish, Grenada **80 B6**
St David, parish, St Vincent **77 A2**
St Davids **78 C2** 13.05N 59.33W
St David's Island **68 C2**
St David's Point **80 B6** 12.01N 61.40W
St Dizier **106 E2** 48.38N 4.58E
Ste-Anne, Guadeloupe **74 B4** 16.12N 61.22W
Ste-Anne, Martinique **74 B1** 14.26N 60.52W
St Elizabeth, parish **62 C2**
Ste-Luce **74 B1** 14.28N 60.54W
Ste-Marguerite **74 B5** 16.22N 61.24W
Ste-Marie, Guadeloupe **74 A4** 16.06N 61.32W
Ste-Marie, Martinique **74 B2** 14.46N 61.00W
Sainte-Marie, Cape **116 F1** 25.34S 45.10E
Ste-Rose **74 A5** 16.20N 61.42W
Saintes **108 C5** 45.44N 0.38W
Saintes, Îles des, islands **70 D7**
St Etienne **108 D5** 45.26N 4.23E
St Eustatius, island **70 C8**
St Evstratios, island **109 H3**
St-François **74 B4** 16.14N 61.16W
St George, Australia **126 E3** 28.03S 148.35E
St George, Bermuda **68 B2** 32.23N 64.40W
St George, Canada **97 G3** 45.08N 66.50W
St George, USA **96 B2** 37.05N 113.40W
St George, parish, Barbados **78 C2**
St George, parish, Dominica **75 B2**
St George, parish, Grenada **80 B6**

Sena **116 D3** 17.26S 35.01E
Senanga **116 C3** 16.09S 23.16E
Sendai **122 J6** 38.16N 140.52E
SENEGAL, republic **114 B3**
Sénégal River **114 B3**
Sens **108 D5** 48.12N 3.18E
Seoul **122 C5** 37.30N 127.00E
Sepik River **127 E5**
Sept-Îles **95 L3** 50.13N 66.22W
Seram, island **127 C5**
Sereflikochisar **109 J3** 38.56N 33.31E
Sergiyev Posad **107 K4** 56.20N 38.10E
Serifos, island **109 H3**
Serik **109 J3** 36.55N 31.06E
Seroe Colorado **84 B2** 12.05N 70.00W
Serowe **116 C2** 22.25S 26.44E
Serpa **108 B3** 37.56N 7.36W
Serpent's Mouth, passage **15 G2**
Serpukhov **107 K3** 54.53N 37.25E
Servia **109 H4** 40.11N 22.01E
Sesheke **116 C3** 17.30S 24.30E
Séte **108 D4** 43.25N 3.43E
Sétif **114 D5** 36.11N 5.24E
Settat **114 C5** 33.04N 7.37W
Seul, Lake **94 I3**
Sevastopol **107 J1** 44.36N 33.31E
Seven Mile Beach **65 A1**
Seven Rivers **62 C2** 18.20N 77.55W
Severn River **94 I3**
Severnaya Zemlya, islands **119 I11**
Severodonetsk **109 K5** 48.58N 38.29E
Severodvinsk **102 H4** 64.35N 39.50E
Sevilla de Niefang **114 E2** 1.55N 10.08E
Seville **108 B3** 37.24N 5.59W
Seward **94 D4** 60.05N 149.34W
Seward Peninsula **94 B4**
SEYCHELLES, republic **110 H4**
Seydhisfjordhur **102 C4** 65.16N 14.02W
Seydisehir **109 J3** 37.25N 31.51E
Seyhan River **109 K3**
Seym River **107 J3**
Sfantu Gheorghe **107 I2** 45.51N 25.48E
Sfax **114 E5** 34.45N 10.43E
Shache **124 B4** 38.27N 77.16E
Shackleton Ice Shelf **131 E2**
Shackleton Mountains **131 J4**
Shah Fuladi, mountain **124 A4** 34.39N 67.39E
Shahjahanpur **124 C3** 27.53N 79.55E
Shakhty **109 L5** 47.43N 40.16E
Shaki **114 D2** 8.39N 3.25E
Shala, Lake **115 G2**
Shanghai **118 N7** 31.06N 121.22E
Shannon River **106 B3**
Shark Bay **127 B3**
Sharpe, Lake **96 C3**
Sharya **107 M4** 58.22N 45.20E
Shasta, Mount **96 A3** 41.25N 122.12W
Shawinigan **95 K2** 46.33N 72.45W
Shay Gap **126 C3** 20.30S 120.10E
Shchekino **107 K3** 54.00N 37.34E
Shchors **109 J6** 51.50N 31.59E
Shea **85 B2** 2.54N 59.04W
Sheboygan **97 E3** 43.46N 87.44W
Shebshi Mountains **114 E2**
Sheffield, Jamaica **62 B2** 18.17N 78.19W
Sheffield, UK **106 C3** 53.23N 1.30W
Shendi **115 G3** 16.41N 33.22E
Shenyang **118 N8** 41.50N 123.26E
Shepetovka **107 I3** 50.12N 27.01E
Shepparton **126 E2** 36.23S 145.24E
Sherbourne **78 C3** 13.10N 59.31W
Sherbro Island **114 B2**
Sherbrooke **95 K2** 45.24N 71.54W
Sheridan **96 C3** 44.48N 106.57W
Sherman **97 D2** 33.39N 96.35W
Sherriffs **71 C1** 17.07N 62.33W
s'Hertogenbosch **106 E3** 51.41N 5.19E
Sherwood Content **62 C2** 18.23N 77.39W
Shetland Islands **102 D4**
Shibarghan **124 A4** 36.40N 65.42E
Shibeli River **115 H2**
Shibetsu **122 K9** 44.10N 142.10E
Shibîn el Kôm **109 J2** 30.33N 31.00E
Shikarpur **124 A3** 27.58N 68.42E
Shikoku, island **122 F3**
Shikotsu, Lake **122 J8**
Shillong **124 D3** 25.34N 91.53E
Shimoga **124 B2** 13.56N 75.31E
Shimonoseki **122 E3** 33.59N 130.58E
Shindand **124 A4** 33.16N 62.05E
Shinyanga **116 D4** 3.40S 33.20E
Shiogama **122 J6** 38.19N 141.00E
Shiono, Cape **122 G3** 33.28N 135.47E
Ships Stern, bay **77 D1**
Shipstern Lagoon **86 B4**
Shipyard **86 B3** 17.54N 88.37W
Shirakawa **122 J5** 37.07N 140.11E
Shirane, Mount **122 I5** 36.49N 139.23E
Shiretoko, Cape **122 L9** 44.24N 145.20E
Shiriya, Cape **122 J7** 41.24N 141.30E
Shirley Heights **72 B2** 17.00N 61.45W
Shizunai **122 K8** 42.20N 142.23E
Shizuoka **122 I4** 34.59N 138.24E
Shkodër **109 G4** 42.03N 19.30E
Shkodër Lake **109 G4**
Sholapur **124 B2** 17.43N 75.56E
Shorawak **124 A4** 31.48N 64.16E
Shorey **78 C4** 13.15N 59.34W
Shoshone Mountains **96 B2**
Shoshong **116 C2** 22.59S 26.30E
Shostka **107 J3** 51.53N 33.30E
Shreveport **97 D2** 32.30N 93.46W
Shuangyashan **122 E10** 46.42N 131.20E
Shumen **109 I4** 43.17N 26.55E
Shuqrah **115 H3** 13.23N 45.44E
Shuya **107 L4** 56.49N 41.23E
Sialkot **124 B4** 32.29N 74.35E
Siauliai **107 H4** 55.51N 23.20E
Sibenik **109 G4** 43.45N 15.55E
Siberia, region **119 K10**
Sibiu **109 H5** 45.46N 24.09E
Sibouli **75 B2** 15.17N 61.23W
Sibun, river **86 B3**
Sicily, island **108 F3**
Sidero, Cape **109 I3** 35.19N 26.19E
Sidi-Bel-Abbès **114 C5** 35.15N 0.39W
Sidi Ifni **114 B4** 29.24N 10.12W
Sidi Kacem **108 B2** 34.15N 5.49W
Sidley, Mount **131 P3** 77.00S 126.00W
Sidon **109 K2** 33.32N 35.22E
Siena **108 F4** 43.19N 11.19E
SIERRA LEONE, republic **114 B2**
Sierra Madre, mountains **88 B3**
Sierra Morena, mountains **108 B3**
Sierra Nevada, mountains, Spain **108 C3**
Sierra Nevada, mountains, USA **96 B2**
Sierra Vista **96 B2** 31.34N 110.21W
Sighet **109 H5** 47.56N 23.53E
Sighisoara **109 H5** 46.12N 24.48E
Sigmaringen **106 E2** 48.05N 9.13E
Signal Hill **72 B4** 17.01N 61.48W
Signy, ant. base **131 L3** 60.54S 45.56W
Siguiri **114 C3** 11.28N 9.07W
Sikar **124 B3** 27.33N 75.12E
Sikasso **114 C3** 11.18N 5.38W
Sikeston **97 E2** 36.52N 89.33W
Sikhote Mountains **122 H9**
Silet **114 D4** 22.40N 4.34E
Siliana **108 E3** 36.05N 9.23E
Silifke **109 J3** 36.22N 33.57E
Siliguri **124 C3** 26.42N 88.30E
Silistra **109 I4** 44.06N 27.17E
Silk Cays **86 B2**
Silkeborg **106 E4** 56.10N 9.39E
Siloah **62 C2** 18.11N 77.43W
Silute **107 H4** 55.18N 21.30E
Silver Bank **14 F5**
Silver City **96 C2** 32.47N 108.16W
Silver Hill **73 A4** 16.47N 62.10W
Silver Spring **62 B2** 18.19N 78.17W
Simav **109 I3** 39.05N 28.59E
Simbirsk **102 I3** 54.19N 48.22E
Simcoe, Lake **97 F3**
Simeon Rigby Hole **68 A4**
Simferopol **109 J4** 44.57N 34.05E
Simon's Town **116 B1** 34.12S 18.26E
Simpson Desert **127 D3**
Simson Bay **84 D7**
Simson Bay **84 D7** 18.03N 63.06W
Simson Bay Lagoon **84 D7**
Sinai, Mount, Egypt **115 G4** 28.32N 33.59E
Sinai, Mount, Grenada **80 B6** 12.04N 61.41W
Sinai Peninsula **115 G4**
Sincelejo **54 C2** 9.17N 75.23W
Sineku **75 B3** 15.27N 61.35W
Sines **108 B3** 37.58N 8.52W
Sinfra **114 C2** 6.35N 5.56W
Singa **115 G3** 13.11N 33.55E
Singapore **118 L4** 1.20N 103.50E
SINGAPORE, republic **118 L4**
Singida **116 D4** 4.45S 34.45E
Sinop **109 K4** 42.02N 35.09E
Sintra **108 B3** 38.48N 9.22W
Sinuiju **122 B7** 40.04N 124.25E
Sion Hill **78 B3** 13.13N 59.37W
Sioux City **97 D3** 42.30N 96.28W
Sioux Falls **97 D3** 43.34N 96.42W
Siparia **81 B2** 10.09N 61.30W
Siparia, regional corporation **81 B2**
Siping **122 B8** 43.15N 124.25E
Siple, ant. base **131 N3** 75.55S 83.55W
Siple Island **131 P3**
Siracusa **108 G3** 37.04N 15.18E
Siret River **107 I2**
Sir Francis Drake Channel **70 C2**
Siros, island **109 I3**
Sirte **109 G2** 31.10N 16.39E
Sirte Desert **114 E5**
Sirte, Gulf of **115 E5**
Sitka **94 E3** 57.05N 135.20W
Sittee, river **86 B2**
Sittwe **124 D3** 20.09N 92.55E
Sivas **109 K3** 39.44N 37.01E
Sivrihisar **109 J3** 39.29N 31.32E
Siwa **115 F4** 29.12N 25.31E
Siwalik Range **124 C3**
Six Cross Roads **78 D2** 13.06N 59.28W
Six Hill Cay **68 C7**
Six Men's Bay **78 B4**
Six Roads **80 C1** 12.28N 61.28W
Skadovsk **109 J5** 46.07N 32.56E
Skagen **106 F4** 57.44N 10.37E
Skagerrak, passage **106 E4**
Skagway **94 E3** 59.23N 135.20W
Skarzysko-Kamienna **109 H6** 51.07N 20.52E
Skeena River **94 F3**
Skelleftea **107 H5** 64.47N 20.59E
Skien **106 E4** 59.14N 9.37E
Skikda **114 D5** 36.53N 6.54E
Skiros, island **109 H3**
Skive **106 E4** 56.34N 9.02E
Skopje **109 H4** 42.00N 21.28E
Skvira **109 I5** 49.42N 29.40E
Slantsy **107 I4** 59.09N 28.09E
Slave River **94 G4**
Slavonski Brod **109 G5** 45.09N 18.00E
Slavyansk **109 K5** 48.51N 37.36E
Slavyansk-na-Kubani **109 K5** 45.14N 38.08E
Sligo **106 B3** 54.17N 8.28W
Sligoville **63 E2** 18.05N 76.56W
Sliven **109 I4** 42.40N 26.19E
Slonim **109 I6** 53.05N 25.21E
SLOVAKIA, republic **107 G2**
SLOVENIA, republic **108 F5**
Slupsk **107 G3** 54.28N 17.00E
Slutsk **107 I3** 53.02N 27.31E
Small Hope **78 C3** 13.10N 59.30W
Smallwood Reservoir **95 L3**
Smana Cay **59 H4**
Smara **114 B4** 26.44N 11.41W
Smederevo **109 H4** 44.40N 20.57E
Smith Point **59 B1** 26.31N 78.43W
Smolensk **107 J3** 54.49N 32.04E
Smolyan **109 H4** 41.34N 24.42E
Smyley Island **131 M3**
Snake Cays, The **86 B2**
Snake River **96 B3**
Snug Corner **59 H3** 22.30N 73.51W
Snyder **96 C2** 32.43N 100.54W
Sobradinho Reservoir **99 F5**
Sochi **109 K4** 43.35N 39.46E
Society Islands **12 B2**
Socorro, Colombia **89 E1** 6.30N 73.16W
Socorro, USA **96 C2** 34.05N 106.55W
Socotra, island **119 G5**
Soderhamn **107 G5** 61.19N 17.10E
Södertälje **107 G4** 59.11N 17.39E
Sodo **115 G2** 6.49N 37.41E
Sofia **109 H4** 42.40N 23.18E
Sogamoso **89 E1** 5.43N 72.56W
Sohâg **115 G4** 26.33N 31.42E
Söke **109 I3** 37.45N 27.26E
Sokodé **114 D2** 8.59N 1.11E
Sokólka **107 H3** 53.26N 23.30E
Sokoto **114 D3** 13.02N 5.15E
Soligorsk **109 I6** 52.50N 27.32E
SOLOMON ISLANDS, independent state **126 G5**
Solothurn **106 E2** 47.13N 7.32E
Soltau **106 E3** 52.59N 9.50E
Soma **109 I3** 39.10N 27.36E
SOMALIA, democratic republic **115 H2**
Sombor **109 G5** 45.46N 19.09E
Sombrero, island **70 C9**
Somerset **97 E2** 37.05N 84.38W
Somerset East **116 C1** 32.44S 25.35E
Somerset Island, Bermuda **68 A1**
Somerset Island, Canada **94 I5**
Somerset Village **68 A1** 32.17N 64.52W
Sondrio **106 F2** 46.11N 9.52E
Songea **116 D3** 10.42S 35.39E
Songhua Lake **122 C8**
Songhua River **122 D10**
Songjin **122 D7** 40.38N 129.10E
Songnim **122 B6** 38.45N 125.39E
Sonhat **124 C3** 23.28N 82.35E
Sonsonate **88 D2** 13.43N 89.44W
Sopron **109 G5** 47.40N 16.38E
Sora **108 F4** 41.43N 13.37E
Sorel **95 K2** 46.03N 73.06W
Soria **108 C4** 41.46N 2.28W
Sorobon **84 C2** 12.05N 68.30W
Soroki **107 I2** 48.08N 28.12E
Soroti **115 G2** 1.46N 33.40E
Sortaval **107 J5** 61.40N 30.40E
Sosnowiec **109 G6** 50.16N 19.07E
Sosúa **67 E3** 19.44N 70.31W
Soto **84 D3** 12.20N 69.10W
Soubise **80 C7** 12.06N 61.37W
Soufrière, Dominica **75 B1** 15.13N 61.22W
Soufrière, St Lucia **76 A2** 13.51N 61.03W
Soufrière Bay, Dominica **75 B1**
Soufrière Bay, St Lucia **76 A2**
Soufrière, district **76 A2**
Soufrière Hills **73 A3**
Soufrière, mountain, Guadeloupe **74 A4** 16.02N 61.38W
Soufrière, mountain, St Vincent **77 A3** 13.20N 61.11W
Souk Ahras **108 E3** 36.14N 8.00E
Souk el Arba du Rharb **114 C5** 34.43N 6.01W
Sousse **114 E5** 35.50N 10.38E
SOUTH AFRICA, republic **116 C1**
South America, continent **12 E2**
Southampton **106 C3** 50.55N 1.25W
Southampton Island **94 J4**
South Andaman, island **124 D2**
South Andros Island **58 C4**
South Atlantic Ocean **12 G2**
South Australian Basin **13 K1**
South Australia, state **126 D3**
South Bend **97 E3** 41.40N 86.15W
South Bimini, island **58 B6**
South Bluff **68 A3** 21.45N 72.21W
South Caicos, island **68 D7**
South Canal, passage **66 B2**
South Carolina, state **97 E2**
South China Sea **119 M5**
South Dakota, state **96 C3**
South East Cape **127 E1** 43.38S 146.48E
South-East Pacific Basin **12 D1**
Southend-on-Sea **108 D6** 51.33N 0.43E
Southern Alps **127 G1**
Southern Bush Bay **68 C7**
Southern Indian Lake **94 I3**
Southern Long Cay **86 C3**
Southern Sierra Madre, mountains **88 B2**
Southfield **62 C1** 17.52N 77.40W
South Friars Bay **71 B2**
South Georgia, island **99 G1**
South Hill **73 B2** 18.11N 63.05W
South Island **127 H1**
SOUTH KOREA, republic **122 D5**
South Magnetic Pole **131 B3** 65.85S 139.05E
South Negril Point **62 B2** 18.15N 78.22W
South Olivees, river **71 B2**
South Orkney Islands **131 L2**
South Pacific Ocean **46 D1**
South Platte River **96 C2**
South Point **78 C1** 13.02N 59.31W
South Pole **131 E4** 90.00S
South Rivers **77 B2** 13.14N 61.08W
South Sandwich Islands **131 K2**
South Saskatchewan River **94 G3**
South Soufrière Hills **73 A3**
South Sound **65 A1**
South Sound **70 D2** 18.29N 64.23W
South Town **65 B2** 19.38N 80.06W
South Union **77 B2** 13.12N 61.08W
South Wells **68 E3** 21.26N 71.09W
South West Cape **13 L1** 43.32S 146.03E
South-West Pacific Basin **12 B1**
South West Point, Grenada **80 B1** 12.26N 61.30W
South West Point, Jamaica **62 B2** 18.12N 78.15W
Sovetsk **107 H4** 55.02N 21.50E
Soya, Cape **122 K9** 45.33N 141.58E
SPAIN, kingdom **108 C3**
Spaldings **62 D2** 18.09N 77.27W
Spanish Point, Antigua and Barbuda **72 B1** 17.33N 61.44W
Spanish Point, Bermuda **68 B1** 32.17N 64.49W
Spanish Point, Montserrat **73 B3** 16.44N 62.09W
Spanish Town, British Virgin Islands **70 D2** 18.28N 64.26W
Spanish Town, Jamaica **63 E1** 17.59N 76.59W
Spanish Water, bay **84 E3**
Spanish Wells **58 E6** 25.30N 76.45W
Sparks **94 G1** 39.34N 119.45W
Spárti **109 H3** 37.05N 22.25E
Spartivento, Cape, southern Italy **109 G3** 37.56N 16.04E
Spartivento, Cape, Sardinia **108 E3** 38.53N 8.52E
Spassk-Dalniy **122 F9** 44.37N 132.37E
Spatha, Cape **109 H3** 35.42N 23.44E
Speightstown **78 B3** 13.14N 59.38W
Spenard **94 D4** 61.05N 150.00W
Spencer **97 D3** 43.08N 95.08W
Spencer, Cape **126 D2** 35.18S 136.53E
Spencer Gulf **127 D2**
Speyer **108 E5** 49.18N 8.26E
Speyside **81 D7** 11.15N 60.30W
Spittal **106 F2** 46.48N 13.30E
Split **109 G4** 43.31N 16.28E
Spokane **96 B3** 47.40N 117.25W
Spoleto **108 F4** 42.44N 12.44E
Spot Bay **65 C2** 19.43N 79.43W
Spring Bay **77 E2**
Springbok **116 B2** 29.43S 17.55E
Springdale **97 D2** 36.10N 94.09W
Springerville **96 C2** 34.09N 109.18W
Spring Estate **77 E2** 13.03N 61.11W
Springfield, Illinois **97 E2** 39.49N 89.39W
Springfield, Jamaica **62 C2** 18.24N 77.48W
Springfield, Massachusetts **97 F3** 42.07N 72.35W
Springfield, Missouri **97 D2** 37.11N 93.19W
Springfield, Oregon **96 A3** 44.01N 123.02W
Spring Garden **85 B4** 7.00N 58.30W
Spring Hall **78 B4** 13.18N 59.36W
Springhill **97 D2** 33.00N 93.29W
Spring Point **59 H3** 22.26N 73.56W
Springs **116 C2** 26.15S 28.26E
Spring Village, Jamaica **63 D1** 17.57N 77.04W
Spring Village, St Vincent **77 A2** 13.15N 61.14W
Spur Tree **62 C1** 17.59N 77.33W
Squillace, Gulf of **109 G3**
SRI LANKA, independent state **124 C1**
Srinagar **124 B4** 34.08N 74.50E
Stafford **106 C3** 52.48N 2.07W
Stafford Creek **58 D5** 24.42N 77.55W
Stake Bank, bay **68 D7**
Stake Bay **65 C2** 19.44N 79.49W
Stanger **116 D2** 29.20S 31.18E
Staniel Cay **58 E5**
Stanley **98 E1** 51.45S 57.56W
Stanley Falls **116 C5** 0.18N 25.30E
Stann Creek, district **86 B2**
Stanovoy Range **119 N9**
Stanthorpe **126 F3** 28.40S 151.56E
Stapleton **71 B2** 17.19N 62.44W
Staraya Russa **107 J4** 58.00N 31.22E
Stara Zagora **109 I4** 42.25N 25.37E
Stargard Szczecinski **107 G3** 53.21N 15.01E
Starogard Gdański **109 G6** 53.58N 18.30E
Starokonstantinov **107 I2** 49.48N 27.10E
Starve Gulf Bay **62 C1**
Staryy Oskol **107 K3** 51.20N 37.50E
Statesboro **97 E2** 32.28N 81.47W
Stavanger **106 E4** 58.58N 5.45E
Stavropol **109 L4** 45.03N 41.59E
Steep Point **127 B3** 26.08S 113.10E
Stefanie, Lake **115 G2**
Steinbach **94 I2** 49.32N 96.40W
Steinkjer **106 F5** 64.00N 11.30E
Stella Maris **58 F4** 23.32N 75.15W
Stellenbosch **116 B1** 33.56S 18.51E
Stephenville, Canada **95 M2** 48.33N 58.34W
Stephenville, USA **96 D2** 32.12N 98.13W
Stepney, Mount **78 C4** 13.16N 59.35W
Sterling **96 C3** 40.38N 103.14W
Stewart Island **127 G1**
Stewart Town **62 D2** 18.23N 77.27W
Steyr **106 F2** 48.04N 14.25E
Stip **109 H4** 41.44N 22.12E
Stirling **106 C4** 56.07N 3.57W
Stjørdal **106 F5** 63.27N 10.57E
Stockholm **107 G4** 59.20N 18.05E
Stockton **96 A2** 37.59N 121.20W
Stockton-on-Tees **106 C3** 54.34N 1.19W
Stoke-on-Trent **106 C3** 53.00N 2.10W
Stolin **109 I6** 51.52N 26.51E
Stoney Ground **73 B2** 18.12N 63.02W
Stony Hill **63 E2** 18.06N 76.47W
Stralsund **106 F3** 54.18N 13.06E
Strängnäs **107 G4** 59.22N 17.02E
Stranraer **106 C3** 54.54N 5.02W
Strasbourg **108 E5** 48.35N 7.45E
Streatham **73 A3** 16.44N 62.10W
Stroude Land **78 D2** 13.07N 59.27W
Struma River **109 H4**
Stry **109 H5** 49.16N 23.51E
Stuart **58 A8** 27.12N 80.16W
Stubbs **77 B1** 13.09N 61.09W
Stubbs Bay **77 B1**
Stubbs Cove **68 D4**
Sturt Plain **127 C4**
Sturt Stony Desert **127 E3**
Stutterheim **116 C1** 32.35S 27.26E
Stuttgart **106 E2** 48.47N 9.12E
Subotica **109 G5** 46.04N 19.41E
Suceava **109 I5** 47.37N 26.18E
Sucia Bay **69 A1**
Sucre **98 D5** 19.05S 65.15W
Sud, department **66 B2**
SUDAN, democratic republic **115 F3**
Sudbury **95 J2** 46.30N 81.01W
Sudd, region **115 F2**
Sud-Est, department **66 C2**
Sudetic Mountains **107 G3**
Suez **115 G4** 29.59N 32.33E
Suez Canal **109 J2**
Suez, Gulf of **109 J1**
Suffisant Dorp **84 E3** 12.12N 68.57W
Sugar Bay **73 A3**
Sugar Loaf, island **80 C8**
Suheli Par Island **124 B2**
Suihua **122 C10** 46.40N 127.00E
Sukhumi **109 L4** 43.01N 41.01E
Sukkur **124 A3** 27.42N 68.54E
Sula Islands **127 C5**
Sulaiman Range **124 A3**
Sulawesi, island **119 N3**
Sulechów **107 G3** 52.05N 15.37E
Sumatra, island **119 L4**
Sumba, island **127 C5**
Sumbawa, island **127 B5**
Sumbe **116 B3** 11.13S 13.50E
Sumy **107 J3** 50.55N 34.49E
Sunchon **122 C4** 34.56N 127.28E
Sundargarh **124 C3** 22.04N 84.08E
Sundsvall **107 G5** 62.22N 17.20E
Sungurlu **109 J4** 40.10N 34.23E
Sunyani **114 C2** 7.21N 2.20W
Suo Sea **122 F3**
Superior **97 D3** 46.42N 92.05W

Acknowledgements

The publishers acknowledge the important role played by the Editorial Adviser Neil Sealey for his advice on atlas content and for his help with proof checking.

Thanks are also due to the following companies and individuals for their professional contributions and valuable advice during the production of this atlas: MAPgraphics Pty Ltd (cartography, computer graphics, page layout and index); Gary Fielder, A.C. Design (cover and title page design); Paul Lennon (artwork on pages 10 and 16) and Macmillan Education Australia (for the use of copyright material on pages 4, 5, 12, 13, 18, 19, 20, 24, 25, 28-37, 44-53, 88-116, 118-131).

Special acknowledgement is also made for the assistance and information provided by the following individuals, ministries, government departments and commercial companies: Anne Marie Cooper, Economic/Commercial Assistant, American Embassy, Nassau, Bahamas; Athena Lightbourne, Climate Officer, Dept. of Meteorology, Nassau, Bahamas; Canadian High Commission, London, UK; CARICOM; Commonwealth Secretariat, London, UK; Dept. of Statistics, Ministry of Tourism, Nassau, Bahamas; Indian High Commission, London, UK; Japanese Embassy, London, UK; Librarian, Dept. of Statistics, Nassau, Bahamas; National Oceanic and Atmospheric Administration, US; US Census Bureau; US Geological Survey; World Bank; World Conservation Monitoring Centre, Cambridge, UK.

Photographs

The publishers wish to acknowledge, with thanks, the following photographic sources:

Telegraph Colour Library for the front cover, back cover and title page image; J. Allan Cash Ltd (24TL, 24BC, 28BC); Ecoscene/Sally Morgan (132); Nick Gillard (88); Robert Harding Picture Library (24BL, 29BL); Robert Harding Picture Library/Paul van Riel (119BL); Hutchison/James Henderson (11); Hutchison/Nick Haslam (108); Hutchison/Philip Wolmuth (38); Panos Pictures/Trygve Bølstad (37); Science Photo Library/Bernhard Edmaier (24BR); Science Photo Library/Deplanne, Jerrican (95); Science Photo Library/Earth Satellite Corporation (115, 119BR); Science Photo Library/Geoff Tompkinson (29BC); Science Photo Library/NASA/Goddard Space Flight Center (21); Science Photo Library/Rudiger Lehnen (27); Still Pictures/J.J. Alcalay (106); Still Pictures/Jim Wark (95); Still Pictures/Julia Baine (89); Still Pictures/Michael Gunther (95); Still Pictures/Norbert Wu (17); Tony Stone Images/Doug Armand (127BR); Tony Stone Images/Robert Frerck (24TC); Tony Stone Images/Michael Harris (118BL); Tony Stone Images/Mark E Leman (29BR); Tony Stone Images/Keith MacGregor (118BR); Tony Stone Images/Alan R Moller (24TR); Tony Stone Images/Darryl Torckler (127BL); Tony Stone Images/Ted Wood (28BL); Tony Stone Worldwide/Ian Murphy (28BR); Travel Ink/Geoff Clive (15); Travel Ink/Roy Westlake (43).

Satellite images on page 6/7 courtesy of National Space Science Data Center/NASA Goddard Space Flight Center.

The publishers have made every effort to trace copyright holders but if they have inadvertently overlooked any, they will be pleased to make the necessary arrangements at the first opportunity.